MW00770178

Organizational Behavior Management Approaches for Intellectual and Developmental Disabilities

Comprised of chapters written by notable experts in the field, *Organizational Behavior Management Approaches for Intellectual and Developmental Disabilities* provides an up-to-date, comprehensive assessment of OBM-IDD.

This edited volume not only provides an overview of the area of OBM-IDD, it also summarizes the extant literature, offers research-to-practice recommendations, and includes operational strategies for building successful service settings. *Organizational Behavior Management Approaches for Intellectual and Developmental Disabilities* synthesizes the published literature and directs practice and research in the areas of assessment and evaluation, training, supervision, and performance improvement, systems interventions, and organizational development. By providing the most contemporary and effective OBM practices derived from evidence-based research findings and recommendations from experienced scientist-practitioners, this book is an integral aid for professionals looking to improve different aspects of service delivery.

The book is intended principally for professionals within educational, human services, and behavioral healthcare settings serving persons with IDD comprised of psychologists, educators, program administrators, organizational consultants, behavior analysts, and evaluation specialists. In particular, the book should appeal to practicing behavior analysts who hold the Behavior Analyst Certification Board (BACB) credential and are seeking professional development within OBM as well as academic instructors and researchers, graduate students, and trainees completing doctoral internships and post-doctoral fellowships.

James K. Luiselli, EdD, ABPP, BCBA-D, is Director of Clinical Development and Research, Melmark New England, USA, and Adjunct Faculty, School Psychology Program, William James College, USA.

Rita M. Gardner, MP.H, LABA, BCBA, is President and Chief Executive Officer, Melmark, Inc.

Frank L. Bird, MEd, BCBA, LABA, is Vice President and Chief Clinical Officer, Melmark, Inc.

Helena Maguire, MS, LABA, BCBA, is Executive Director, Melmark New England.

Organizational Behavior Management Approaches for Intellectual and Developmental Disabilities

Edited by James K. Luiselli,
Rita M. Gardner, Frank L. Bird, and
Helena Maguire

Routledge
Taylor & Francis Group

NEW YORK AND LONDON

First published 2022
by Routledge
605 Third Avenue, New York, NY 10158

and by Routledge
2 Park Square, Milton Park, Abingdon, Oxon, OX14 4RN

Routledge is an imprint of the Taylor & Francis Group, an informa business

Library of Congress Cataloging-in-Publication Data
Names: Luiselli, James K., editor. | Gardner, Rita M, editor. |
Bird, Frank L, editor. | Maguire, Helena, editor.
Title: Organizational behavior management approaches for intellectual and developmental disabilities/edited by James K. Luiselli, Rita M. Gardner, Frank L. Bird, and Helena Maguire.
Description: New York, NY: Routledge, 2021. |
Includes bibliographical references and index. |
Identifiers: LCCN 2021008392 (print) | LCCN 2021008393 (ebook) |
ISBN 9780367342913 (hardback) | ISBN 9780367342920 (paperback) |
ISBN 9780429324840 (ebook)
Subjects: LCSH: People with mental disabilities–Employment. |
Developmentally disabled–Employment. | Organizational behavior.
Classification: LCC HV3005 .O73 2021 (print) |
LCC HV3005 (ebook) | DDC 362.2068–dc23
LC record available at https://lccn.loc.gov/2021008392
LC ebook record available at https://lccn.loc.gov/2021008393

ISBN: 978-0-367-34291-3 (hbk)
ISBN: 978-0-367-34292-0 (pbk)
ISBN: 978-0-429-32484-0 (ebk)

Typeset in Goudy
by Deanta Global Publishing Services, Chennai, India

Contents

Contributors

Editors

James K. Luiselli, EdD, ABPP, BCBA-D, is a licensed psychologist, diplomat in cognitive and behavioral psychology (ABPP), and Board Certified Behavior Analyst-Doctoral (BCBA-D). He is Director of Clinical Development and Research at Melmark New England, US, and Adjunct Faculty within the School Psychology Program at William James College, Massachusetts, US. He has served previously as Director of Training of pre-doctoral internship and post-doctoral fellowship programs and Director of Continuing Education at human services organizations. He has published 19 books, 50 book chapters, and more than 280 peer-reviewed journal articles in the areas of applied behavior analysis, organizational behavior management, performance improvement, professional training, and clinical practice.

Rita M. Gardner, MPH, BCBA, LABA, is President and Chief Executive Officer of Melmark, Inc., US, and founder of Melmark New England and Melmark Carolinas. She has devoted almost 40 years to non-profit management in the field of community-based services for individuals with autism spectrum disorders, acquired brain injuries, neurological disabilities, and severe behavior disorders including design, development, and operation of more than 100 community-based programs for children and adults. Among many areas of expertise, her leadership focuses on child advocacy, clinical practice, health service administration, legal issues, public policy, and fundraising. She speaks frequently at local, regional, and national conferences and is a frequent contributor to service, policy, and research publications.

Frank L. Bird, MEd, BCBA, is Vice President and Chief Clinical Officer at Melmark, Inc., US, and founder of Melmark New England and Melmark Carolinas. He is responsible for developing and overseeing clinical policies, procedures, integrity, and resources across program settings. He has extensive experience in community-based human service delivery systems, having developed more than 80 programs in support of children and adults with intellectual and developmental disabilities, neurodevelopmental disorders, acquired brain injury, and mental illness. He has published research within the areas of personnel management, staff training, systems analysis, and intervention for challenging behaviors, as well as presenting more than 250 papers and workshops at local, regional, and national conferences.

Helena Maguire, MS, BCBA, LABA, is Executive Director of Melmark New England, US, a service division of Melmark, Inc., where she oversees implementation of school, residential and adult day programs, home-based consultation services, professional development, and graduate training. Her leadership operations extend to other organizational priorities such as policy development, quality assurance, risk management, regulatory compliance, and fiscal integrity. Ms Maguire is also the primary liaison to advocacy groups and legislative resources in Massachusetts, speaks regularly at state, regional, and national conferences on organizational behavior management, staff training, supervision, and curriculum design, is an Adjunct Professor at Endicott College, and has published several book chapters and peer-reviewed journal articles

Chapter Authors

Abigail L. Blackman is a doctoral student in the Performance Management Laboratory at the University of Kansas, US, under the supervision of Dr Florence DiGennaro Reed. After receiving her bachelor's degree in Psychology from Binghamton University, US, she went on to pursue her master's degree in Applied Behavior Analysis and Organizational Behavior Management at Florida Institute of Technology, US. During her graduate training she gained experience consulting with a human service agency and conducting translational and applied research. Presently, she is interested in identifying training and supervision practices that impact employee retention and the influence of contextual variables on trained behavior.

Daniel Cymbal is a doctoral candidate in the Behavior Analysis program at the Florida Institute of Technology, US. His primary interests center around the implementation of Organizational Behavior Management (OBM) in human service settings. He has contributed to multiple peer-reviewed journal articles and book chapters, as well as serving as a reviewer for various behavior-analytic journals. In addition to scholarship, he provides behavior analysis services to consumers as a Board-Certified Behavior Analyst (BCBA), consults with ABA organizations seeking to incorporate OBM principles, and currently teaches a practicum course at Florida Institute of Technology.

Ms Trang Doan is a research assistant at the Faison Center, Virginia, US. She holds a master's degree in Professional Behavior Analysis and a bachelor's degree in public policy analysis. Fluent in both English and Vietnamese, she has diverse experience in the fields of research, consulting, and teaching. She has previously worked to provide behavioral and educational services to teenagers diagnosed with Autism Spectrum Disorder.

Jessica L. Doucette, BCBA, LBA (MS, Behavior Analysis, University of North Texas, 2007) is the Director of Education Services at the James C. Hormel School at Virginia Institute of Autism, US. She has over 20 years of experience in the field of Behavior Analysis, with the last 14 years committed to providing evidence-based treatment to individuals with developmental disabilities. In her career, she has focused on the development and direction of strong teams through the use of organizational behavior management. She has provided direct and consultative services across a variety of school, home, and residential settings working with individuals across the life span. Her present interests include organizational leadership, curriculum development and instruction, and the treatment of severe problem behavior. She is passionate about effective leadership, staff training, and supervision to support and motivate staff to achieve the best possible outcomes.

Tyler G. Erath is a doctoral student in the Performance Management Laboratory at the University of Kansas, US, working under the supervision of Dr Florence DiGennaro Reed. He received his bachelor's degree in Psychology and his master's degree in Experimental Psychology from Appalachian State University, US. His research interests include employee health, staff training, and performance management. Tyler has served as a guest reviewer for peer-reviewed journals, a practicum supervisor for undergraduate students interested in OBM, and the instructor of record for an undergraduate course on OBM.

Dr Nicole Gravina is an Assistant Professor of Behavior Analysis in the Department of Psychology at the University of Florida, US. She earned her master's in Industrial-Organizational Psychology and her PhD in Behavior Analysis from Western Michigan University, US. She has published over 40 articles and book chapters and delivered over 100 presentations and workshops. She serves on the editorial boards of *Behavior Analysis in Practice* and *Occupational Health Science*, as an Associate Editor for the *Journal of Organizational Behavior Management*, and as a Trustee for the Cambridge Center for Behavioral Studies. In 2019, Nicole was honored with the APA Early Career Impact Award in Consulting Psychology. Nicole specializes in designing behaviorally-based workplace interventions that improve employee safety, healthcare delivery, and leadership and consulting skills. In addition to her faculty appointment, Nicole has consulted in a variety of industries, including healthcare, human services, manufacturing, public utilities, insurance, and construction.

Matt J. Harbison is a graduate student in the Performance Management Laboratory at the University of Kansas. He received his bachelor's degree in Applied Behavioral Science from the University of Kansas with a focus in Organizational Behavior Management. During both his graduate and under-graduate studies, he has consulted for a non-profit human service organization, focusing on performance management techniques such as training and token economies. His current research interests involve rule-governed behavior and instructional control in the workplace.

Dr Amy J. Henley, a Board Certified Behavior Analyst, is an Assistant Professor in the Department of Psychology at Western New England University, US. She received her Bachelor's degree in Psychology from the University of California San Diego, US, and her Masters and PhD in Behavior Analysis from the University of Kansas, US. She was the recipient of awards from the B. F. Skinner Foundation and the Berkshire Association for Behavior Analysis and Therapy for her research examining the application of behavioral economic methodology to evaluate the influence of monetary incentives on employee behavior. She has also published articles and book chapters on a variety of top-ics including instructional control, staff training, feedback, treatment integrity, discounting, and demand.

Dr Elizabeth B. Hughes Fong is a Board Certified Behavior Analyst and licensed Behavior Specialist in Pennsylvania, US. She has published in the area of behavior analysis, culture, and diversity. She serves on the Executive Committee for the American Psychological Association's (APA) Division 35, as the co-chair for the Committee on Technology. She is an ad hoc reviewer for *Behavior Analysis: Research and Practice*, *Behavior Analysis in Practice*, and the National Multicultural Conference and Summit. In addition, she is the founder of the Multicultural Alliance of Behavior Analysts (now called the Culture and Diversity SIG of ABAI), and a member of the Association for Behavior Analysis International (ABAI) Diversity, Equality and Inclusion Board. She was also a Distinguished Scholar with the Cambridge Center for Behavioral Studies, Massachusetts, US.

Einar T. Ingvarsson, BCBA-D, LBA (PhD, University of Kansas, US, 2006) is Director of Training and Research at Virginia Institute of Autism (www.viacenters.org) and Adjunct Faculty in the Curry School of Education and Human Development at University of Virginia. He is former associate editor of the *Journal of Applied Behavior Analysis and The Analysis of Verbal Behavior* and currently serves on the editorial boards of those journals, as well as the *European Journal of Behavior Analysis and Behavioral Interventions*. His research interests fall within the areas of verbal behavior, skill acquisition, and functional assessment and treatment of challenging behavior. He has published 37 articles in peer-reviewed journals. He previously held teaching appointments at Youngstown State University, US, the University of North Texas, US, and Reykjavik University, Iceland.

Ethan S. Long, BCBA-D, LBA (PhD, West Virginia University, US, 2001) is President and CEO of the Virginia Institute of Autism (VIA; www.viacenters.org) and is currently a visiting Assistant Professor of Education at the University of Virginia School of Education and Development. He has authored over 20 peer-reviewed journal articles and book chapters related to Autism Spectrum Disorder, applied behavior analysis, and a variety of developmental and behavioral disorders. Since his arrival at VIA in 2010, he has focused on expanding the highest quality, evidenced-based programs and services to support children, adults, families, and stakeholders struggling with the challenges of autism throughout Virginia. In 2019, Our Health Charlottesville and Shenandoah Valley Magazine named her a local leader in healthcare.

Kathleen E. Marano, PhD, BCBA-D earned her doctoral and master's degrees in Applied Behavior Analysis from Caldwell University. She has experience working with individuals with autism spectrum and related disorders in school-, center-, and home-based settings. She has published several peer-reviewed articles and co-authored book chapters related to her research interests in staff training and behavioral intervention for children with autism spectrum and related disorders. She is on the editorial review board for *Education and Treatment of Children*.

Nicholas Matey earned his master's degree in applied behavior analysis and organizational behavior management (OBM) from Florida Tech in 2017. He is currently a doctoral student at the University of Florida in the behavior analysis program. He has experience using OBM in multiple industries including human services, manufacturing, and healthcare. He has implemented a range of interventions in both research and practice, including behavior-based safety process improvement, leadership development, and performance management. He serves as a Distinguished Scholar for the Cambridge Center of Behavioral Studies. In 2019, he received the OBM Network Chris Anderson research grant for research on feedback.

Dr Azure J. Pellegrino, a Board Certified Behavior Analyst, received a doctorate in disability disciplines from Utah State University, US. She also completed a post-doctoral fellowship at the University of Kansas, US. Azure is currently an adjunct faculty member and behavior analyst for early intensive behavioral intervention services in the Department of Psychology at California State University, Fresno, US. Her research examines behavior acquisition in individuals with intellectual and developmental disabilities and staff training practices. She has published articles in behavior analytic journals, including *Journal of Applied Behavior Analysis* and *Journal of Behavioral Education.*

Joy S. Pollard is the Co-founder and CEO of Clinical Operations at Behavior Change Institute, US. She earned her PhD in Disability Disciplines, with a Specialization in Applied Behavior Analysis at Utah State University, US. She holds a position as Adjunct Lecturer at Stanford University, US, and Co-investigator on several telehealth research projects. She has supervised multi-state telehealth services since 2011 in home, community, residential, day habilitation, and school settings for individuals across the lifespan. Her research and clinical work have focused on leveraging technology to increase access, build capacity, and improve the standards of behavioral healthcare for families in rural and underserved communities. She has served on both state and national committees to advise on best practices in telehealth and applied behavior analysis, is the former President of the New Mexico Association for Behavior Analysis, and is an active member on the New Mexico Public Policy Committee.

Shawn P. Quigley is the Executive Director of Melmark, PA. He earned his doctorate degree in Behavior Analysis at Western Michigan University, US. He completed a post-doctoral psychology fellowship with the University of New Mexico Medical Group where he conducted diagnostic evaluations, supported families and individuals with ASD, and helped build capacity for behavior analytic providers. He has professional experiences in many capacities from direct care to administration across different organizations and states. He has helped develop county level mental health service systems for adults and children; helped develop state regulatory guidelines for autism services; and directed the development of clinical and training practices. These experiences have provided a strong foundation for understanding service development, regulatory requirements, scope of competence issues, resource allocation, and service delivery. He has supported the profession through service on editorial review boards, publishing research, teaching at the university level, and volunteering with regional and national service groups.

Dr Florence D. DiGennaro Reed, a Board Certified Behavior Analyst, received a doctorate in school psychology from Syracuse University, US. She also completed a clinical post-doctoral fellowship at the Institute for Child Development and a pre-doctoral internship in clinical psychology at the May Center for

Education and Neurorehabilitation and the May Center for Child Development. Presently, she is an Associate Professor in and Chairperson of the Department of Applied Behavioral Science at the University of Kansas where she directs the Performance Management Laboratory. Her research examines effective and efficient staff training and performance improvement practices. She has published nearly 95 articles and book chapters and two edited books on a variety of topics including training, performance management, assessment, and intervention. With co-authors Drs Gregory Madden and Derek Reed, she recently published a textbook titled *An Introduction to Behavior Analysis*. Moreover, she has been an Associate Editor for *Journal of Applied Behavior Analysis, Journal of Behavioral Education*, and *Behavior Analysis in Practice*.

Sandra A. Ruby is a doctoral student in the Performance Management Laboratory at the University of Kansas, US. She completed her bachelor's degree in Psychology at California State University, Fresno, US, while managing Dr Steven W. Payne's P.A.W. Lab and working as a Registered Behavior Technician. Under the mentorship of Dr Florence D. DiGennaro Reed, she received her Master of Arts in Behavior Analysis at the University of Kansas. During her graduate studies, she has consulted with a local human service organization serving adults with intellectual and developmental disabilities and has supervised undergraduate practicum students. Her current research interests include efficient staff training practices and technology-based interventions.

Dr Michael C. Strouse has led GoodLife Innovations, Inc., US, and its subsidiaries for more than 25 years. His work encompasses research, development, refinement, and dissemination of evidence-based, nationally-regarded, community service models that consistently produce person-centered care and high quality-of-life outcomes for those served. He is the CEO and developer of iLink Technologies, which is an enterprise solution for providing professional remote support to individuals with a variety of needs. His consultant services include helping private corporations and state governments interested in best-practice and emerging technologies for models supporting semi-independent populations in the community. He earned his PhD in developmental and child psychology and holds a courtesy faculty appointment in the Department of Applied Behavioral Science at the University of Kansas, US. He continues to participate in research, assist with the training of graduate students, and successfully maintains this important, 40-year long partnership.

Peter Sturmey is Professor of Psychology at The Graduate Center, and the Department of Psychology, Queens College, City University of New York, US. He specialized in developmental disabilities, especially in the areas of applied behavior analysis, dual diagnosis, evidence-based practice, and caregiver training. He gained his PhD at the University of Liverpool, UK, and subsequently taught at the University of the South West (Plymouth), UK, and University of Birmingham, UK. He then worked for the Texas Department of Mental Retardation, US, from 1990 to 2000 as Chief Psychologist, first at Abilene, and then at San Antonio State Schools. He has published 28 edited and authored books, over 225 peer-reviewed papers, over 80 book chapters, and made numerous presentations nationally and internationally, including recent presentations in Canada, Brazil, Spain, and Italy. His research focuses on evaluating caregiver training using behavioral skills training.

Dr Amber L. Valentino serves as the Chief Clinical Officer for Trumpet Behavior Health. In this role, she supports clinical services, leads all research and training initiatives, and builds clinical standards for the organization. Her clinical and research interests include the assessment and treatment of verbal behavior, primarily in children with autism. She studies programming to address unique adaptive skill deficits, ways to connect the research to practice gap, and effective supervision. She serves as an Associate Editor for *Behavior Analysis in Practice* and previously served as an Associate Editor for *The Analysis of Verbal Behavior.* She is on the editorial board of the *Journal of Applied Behavior Analysis* (JABA) and serves as a frequent reviewer for several behavior analytic journals. She is an active board member of the California Association for Behavior Analysis (CalABA).

Jason C. Vladescu, PhD, BCBA-D, NSCP, LBA (NY), is a partner at North Jersey Behavioral Health Services, US, and an Associate Professor in the Department of Applied Behavior Analysis at Caldwell University, US. He completed his pre-doctoral internship and post-doctoral fellowship at the University of Nebraska Medical Center's Munroe-Meyer Institute, US. He has published 60+ peer-reviewed articles and several book chapters spanning his research interests in early behavioral intervention for children with autism spectrum and related disorders, increasing the efficiency of academic instruction, staff and caregiver training, equivalence-class formation, and mainstream applications of behavior analysis. He is an associate editor for the *Journal of Applied Behavior Analysis* and is on the editorial board for several behavior analytic journals. He is also the recipient of the APA (Division 25) B. F. Skinner New Applied Researcher Award.

David A. Wilder is a Professor and Chair of the Campus-based Behavior Analysis programs in the School of Behavior Analysis at the Florida Institute of Technology in Melbourne, Florida, US. He has published over 90 peer-reviewed journal articles and has served as an Associate Editor for the *Journal of Applied Behavior Analysis* (JABA) and is the current editor of the *Journal of Organizational Behavior Management* (JOBM). He is also on the editorial boards of *Behavioral Interventions, Education and Treatment of Children, and Behavior*

Modification. He has served as President of the Florida Association for Behavior Analysis (FABA) and the Organizational Behavior Management Network and is a recipient of the outstanding scientific contributions to behavior analysis award from FABA. He has consulted at the individual and organizational level to businesses, schools, private homes, hospitals, group homes, and day treatment centers and is a Board Certified Behavior Analyst-Doctoral (BCBA-D).

Dr Byron Wine is the chief operating officer at the Faison Center, as well as a visiting assistant professor at the University of Virginia, US. He completed an MS. from the Florida Institute of Technology and a PhD from Temple University. He has published over 30 peer-reviewed publications primarily in the area of organizational behavior management. Currently, he serves as an associate editor for the Journal of Organizational Behavior Management, executive director of the Organizational Behavior Management Network, and as a coordinator of OBM for the ABAI program board.

Dr Steve Woolf has been working with individuals and families affected by Autism Spectrum Disorder for over 25 years. He is the President of Butterfly Effects, a nationwide provider of treatment services for children/families affected by Autism Spectrum Disorder (ASD). He regularly communicates with multiple state policymakers at Department of Public Health, Department of Developmental Services, Special Education Directors, and State Legislators on the funding, access, and service quality of Applied Behavior Analysis (ABA) treatment. He has authored publications and regularly presents ABA research at state and national conferences. He is the former president/founder of MassABA, served as an CTABA executive committee member, and served as the ABAI Chapter leadership coordinator. His specialty area is managing large-scale home-based service delivery systems to families affected by ASD. He also served on state committees to define behavior analyst licensure standards and ABA treatment guidelines.

Preface

Organizational Behavior Management Approaches to Intellectual and Developmental Disabilities is intended principally for professionals serving persons with IDD comprised of psychologists, educators, program administrators, organizational consultants, behavior analysts, and evaluation specialists. These and related individuals can use the book to improve many aspects of service delivery by learning the most current and effective OBM practices derived from evidence-based research findings and the recommendations of experienced scientist-practitioners. In particular, the book should appeal to practicing behavior analysts who hold the Behavior Analyst Certification Board (BACB) credential and are seeking professional development within the OBM field. As well, the book can find a home with academic instructors and researchers, graduate students, and trainees completing doctoral internships and post-doctoral fellowships, and be incorporated as a lead or supplementary text in courses and programs devoted to organizational psychology, behavioral psychology, applied behavior analysis, special education, and human services administration.

We are grateful to Routledge/Taylor & Francis for supporting the book and guiding us along the way. Many thanks also to so many of the teachers, mentors, and colleagues who shaped our thinking and inspired us to improve the lives of persons with intellectual and developmental disabilities. Finally, this book and the work we do would not be possible without the presence and loving kindness of our families.

PART I
Introduction

1

Introduction to Organizational Behavior Management in Intellectual and Developmental Disabilities

Rita M. Gardner, Frank L. Bird, Helena Maguire, and James K. Luiselli

Organizational behavior management (OBM) is a sub-discipline of applied behavior analysis (ABA) concerned with the application of learning principles and methods to the performance of employees within business, industry, manufacturing, and similar areas (Wilder et al., 2009; Wine & Pritchard, 2018). An OBM approach concentrates on system-wide assessment and intervention targeting numerous performance measures such as employee productivity, safety, environmental care, attendance, and related on-the-job competencies. Additionally, OBM has been effective in diverse elements of healthcare including patient services, procedural compliance, medication administration, and infection control (Ludwig, 2015).

A third focus of OBM is educating, treating, and supporting persons who have intellectual and developmental disabilities (IDD) within school, human services, and behavioral healthcare settings. The practice of OBM with this population has an early history (Reid, 1998; Sturmey, 1998) and research has expanded in new directions and with implications for service delivery (Luiselli, 2018). However, until the present book, no volume has appeared that reviews the contemporary landscape of OBM in IDD, synthesizes the published literature, and informs practice and research on multiple levels.

In a literature review of OBM interventions in human services settings from 1990 to 2016, Gravina et al. (2018) reported that the published research focused mainly on improving procedural integrity among care providers followed by procedures concerned with safety, client engagement, and staff management. Fewer studies included pre-intervention assessment and addressed managers and supervisors as the target population. We included chapters in this book that considered the main points raised by Gravina et al. (2019) as well as other topics that have emerged within OBM practice and research in IDD, specifically assessment and evaluation, training, supervision and performance management, systems interventions, and organizational development.

A starting point for OBM practitioners and researchers is that human services organizations must integrate systems within a unified framework that stresses clinical operations, benchmark measures, continuous progress monitoring, evidence-based interventions, data-driven performance review, and transparent reporting to stakeholder groups. These interrelated components are dependent upon guiding OBM principles (Daniels & Daniels, 2004) that can be adapted to the unique challenges faced by many human services settings (Dixon & Loukus, 2013). Competent leadership with OBM expertise can design and maintain effective practices while other organizations will require external consultation to achieve desired results. Notably, educational and training specialization in ABA and OBM is a contemporary trend that can benefit IDD human services organizations in identifying competent professionals (Luke et al., 2018).

Assessment and Evaluation. This section of the book considers three areas of assessment that bear on optimal OBM practices within human services organizations. Performance diagnostic assessment focuses on organizational obstacles and barriers that impede service delivery among employees and, in particular, the critical skills and competencies required of direct care providers. Poor training, lack of adequate supervision, competing activities, complex procedures, and environmental design limitations all contribute to performance deficiencies and must be assessed in order to formulate correction plans. The development of standardized instruments such as the *Performance Diagnostic Checklist-Human Services* (*PDC-HS*: Wilder et al., 2020) makes it possible to conduct such assessment and produce indicated interventions which can be formally evaluated.

Many human services organizations use incentives to motivate employee performance including monetary "rewards" and work privileges of early release time, breaks during the day, and access to a special parking space (Wine, 2017). As more research evidence accumulates about the performance-enhancing effects of incentive programs, it is generally recognized that human service organizations should assess employee preferences before designing motivational contingencies. For example, preferences are likely to differ among employees at different levels of an organization, change over time, and have relative value in relation to the available options. These influences make it necessary to conduct preference assessments reliably and at regular intervals. Further considerations are that human services organizations must evaluate the financial costs required to implement and sustain employee incentive programs, ensure that assessment-informed incentives are distributed equitably in the workforce, and verify empirically that incentives function as reinforcement by virtue of improving targeted performance objectives.

Social validity is the third area of assessment emphasized in the book. More than 40 years ago, Wolf (1978) proposed that behavior analysts assess the attitudes and opinions of direct and indirect consumers of services as a subjective outcome measure: do consumers accept and approve the objectives, methods, and results of interventions planned and implemented with them? Through social validity assessment, human services organizations can acquire feedback from employees about the appropriateness of many operations and guidelines, whether procedures should be revised to improve fidelity, the value of gains made with service recipients, and performance goals that might have been overlooked. Comprehensive social validity assessment also extends to external stakeholders involved with organizational practices (e.g., advisory boards, regulatory agencies, third-party payers). The follow-up from social validity assessment should be performance-improvement initiatives by instituting person-specific and systems changes strongly endorsed by consumers and consistent with consensus-based evidence support.

Training, Supervision, and Performance Improvement. Notwithstanding the many training and performance management interventions shown to be effective in human services organizations (DiGennaro Reed et al., 2013; Luiselli, 2018; Reid et al., 2012), the persons responsible for implementation usually have multiple training needs, different levels of expertise, and many performance expectations. How to economize training and performance management with desired outcomes ranks high as an operations priority even when there are adequate numbers of trainers and supervisors. The concerns are magnified within human services organizations that lack the necessary personnel resources.

From a practice perspective, it is desirable to isolate the controlling effects from separate components of antecedent and consequence procedures that typically comprise OBM training and performance management interventions. As one of many examples, antecedent-only interventions through signs, visuals, posted instructions, and similar environmental cues reduce the need for in-person supervision to affect behavior-change, but more research is required to determine the relative effects of variables such as print size, content, location, and static versus variable presentation (Warman et al., 2019). Multi-procedure interventions, also the norm in OBM, should be evaluated to isolate the most time- and effort-efficient combination of methods. Care provider self-management, for example, can be effective as a sole intervention and with the addition of positive reinforcement and performance feedback (Richman et al., 1988; Willis et al., 2020).

Teleconsultation and telesupervision have gained popularity among ABA practitioners (Ferguson et al., 2019; Tomlinson et al., 2018) and can be incorporated efficiently within human services OBM. In illustration, Lerman et al. (2020) described remote coaching approaches to care provider training and performance management of parents who had children with neurodevelopmental disabilities. Schieltz and Wacker (2020) also summarized a telehealth model for teaching care providers how to conduct functional communication training (FCT) in treating child problem behavior. These and other technology advances make it possible for human services organizations to conduct training and supervision virtually while maximizing available resources (see, for example, Newcomb et al., 2019).

A third determinant of training and performance management success is care providers selecting preferred procedures before intervention is introduced. In a study conducted at one of our service settings, Buckley et al. (2020) evaluated an incentive-based OBM intervention with three care providers at a residential school for students with IDD by having them first complete a questionnaire that inquired about their preferences for performance motivators. All of the care providers selected having to complete fewer case management tasks and this preference was incorporated in a negative reinforcement intervention that successfully improved a data recording performance objective. The contribution of pre-intervention assessment of preferences to OBM training and performance management will be strengthened through research that confirms this process yields better outcomes compared to arbitrary and "top-down" selections (Wilder et al., 2018).

Systems Interventions. In this section of the book, we present large-scale interventions that human service organizations should adopt to address several pertinent systems issues. Apropos, employee preference assessment, there are several steps organizations can take to implement incentive-based programs effectively. Beyond the previously cited need to properly identify potential incentives, OBM practitioners must be cognizant about the ability and capacity of employees to demonstrate performance targets. The timing and delivery of behavior-contingent consequences, magnitude of reinforcers, and probabilistic outcomes must also be highlighted. Further, employees will have different opinions about the need for incentive programs, possibly resulting in negative reactions that produce discord and unintended consequences on workplace behavior.

A second topic of interest is the high rate of turnover in human services organizations which can negatively impact program quality, employee morale, strategic planning, and financial resources (Wine et al., 2020). Finding the conditions associated with attrition and systematically applying interventions that address these influences represent OBM priorities. Strouse et al. (2004), for example, were able to reduce employee turnover in a residential program for persons with IDD by resolving problems that were associated with the duration of assigned shifts, weekend work schedules, full-time versus part-time positions, and pay. Reducing turnover begins with strategic hiring and recruitment practices and instituting policies that retain employees for extended tenure.

Most human services organizations for persons with IDD are faced with the challenge of implementing restrictive procedures to safely manage and treat aggression, self-injury, property destruction, pica, elopement, and other high-risk behaviors. Procedures such as response interruption, blocking, contingently applied protective equipment, and physical restraint are often components of behavior support plans that must be clinically justified, implemented with high integrity, shown to be effective, and meet regulatory procedural guidelines (Reed et al., 2013). From an OBM perspective, human services organizations can establish peer review teams, safety committees, and human rights panels whose purpose is to certify acceptable interventions, conduct risk-benefit analyses, ensure mandatory safeguards (e.g., informed consent, written protocols), and monitor outcomes. These operations and functions should be integrated organization-wide and a dominant leadership concern.

We have paid special attention to safety within human services organizations because many persons with IDD are susceptible to injuries from accidents, falls, improper handling of objects, environmental hazards, and physical interactions with care providers (Sherrard et al., 2004; Tyler et al., 2008). Surprisingly, there is limited behavioral research on injury prevention in this population and within congregate-care settings (Gianotti et al., 2020; Luiselli, 2013; Sanders, 2009). Behavior-based safety (BBS) is an evidence-based approach that human services organizations can adopt through pinpointing safety targets, real-time observation of care provider practices, in vivo measurement, goal setting, incentives, and performance feedback (Wilder & Sigurdsson, 2015). Systems-wide application of BBS should be more fully evaluated in human service organizations to equip care providers with injury prevention methods that reduce and eliminate harm to clients and themselves. The importance of safety practices in human services organizations is no more apparent than the health crisis caused by the 2020 COVID-19 pandemic. Grave concerns have been raised about keeping people healthy while maintaining ABA programs with needed precautions and safeguards (Cox et al., 2020; Kornack et al., 2020). Behavioral interventions applied at an organizational level can be implemented effectively to deal with COVID-19 related concerns (Gravina et al., 2020), such as wearing personal protective equipment (PPE) (Casella et al., 2010), cleaning and sanitizing materials (Carr et al., 2013), and washing hands (Jess & Dozier, 2020). Recently, Maguire et al. (2021) described an OBM model towards training and performance management of COVID-19 safety practices by day-school and residential care providers of students with neurodevelopmental and intellectual disabilities. Following the temporary closure of services at the onset of the pandemic, students were gradually re-enrolled preceded by training care providers in critical competencies for: (a) taking and recording temperatures with a digital thermometer; (b) wearing face masks and shields; (c) donning and doffing PPE; (d) washing hands; (e) disinfecting materials; and (f) responding to students who demonstrated high-risk behavior (e.g., aggression and spitting). Supervisors conducted remote and in vivo training using task-analyzed competency checklists, didactic instruction with accompanying visual media, role-playing, directed rehearsal, and positive and corrective feedback. After training, supervisors conducted weekly in vivo observations of care providers to ensure they were displaying learned competencies accurately. These observations included performance feedback and practice routines in cases where 100% competency was not documented. Pre- and post-testing training data and the findings from performance evaluations revealed that care providers acquired and exhibited the high-priority skills necessary for health promotion and risk mitigation amid the COVID-19 pandemic.

Organizational Development. Our final points of emphasis are several areas intended to build and fortify organizational development among service recipients, employees, care providers, families, and other relevant stakeholders. Contemporary standards within behavior analysis, and by extension to OBM, dictate that human services organizations for persons with IDD acknowledge matters of diversity and multiculturalism in delivering services, recruiting and training employees, and demonstrating respect towards marginalized and under-represented populations (Fong et al., 2016). Sensitivity training and education with new and established employees should be pursued by human resources departments and through professional development activities within organizations fully dedicated towards person-first values.

Adhering to ethical principles and guidelines is yet another area of organizational development and integral to scope of competence among ABA and OBM practitioners (Bailey & Burch, 2016; Behavior Analyst Certification Board, 2021). Key domains in this regard include training employees to follow applicable ethics and compliance codes, prevent and identify possible ethical dilemmas, learn ethics problem-solving resolution strategies, and maintain an ethical culture with colleagues, supervisors, and leaders. Brodhead and Higbee (2012) advised that human services organizations establish the position of Ethics Coordinator as a "local expert" who can guide these and related practices. Someone in this position would have an advanced degree, possess considerable ethics knowledge and expertise, advance ethics education within the organization, and participate in workshop and conferences devoted to ethics.

Finally, we encourage human services organizations to promote applied research that can be disseminated to the professional community and, in doing so, translate effective methods and procedures to real-world practitioners. A program of applied research also benefits employees through additional training and providing an avenue for continued professional development. Many human services employees are interested in conducting applied research and having opportunities to disseminate the findings from studies at conferences and in publications (Valentino & Juanico, 2020). It is possible for human services organizations to support research initiatives by forming internal project teams, establishing collaborative relationships with colleges and universities, and applying for grant funding. Research that improves the quality of life of service recipients and care providers should always define the direction of research inquiry and be supported as a meaningful endeavor across all levels of an organization. All of the chapters in this book illustrate the contributions applied research has made and will continue to make to the practice of OBM in IDD.

References

Bailey, J. S., & Burch, M. R. (2016). *Ethics for behavior analysts* (3rd ed.). London: Routledge.

Behavior Analyst Certification Board (2021). *Professional and ethical compliance code for behavior analysts.* Littleton, CO: Author.

Brodhead, M. T., & Higbee, T. S. (2012). Teaching and maintaining ethical behavior in a professional organization. *Behavior Analysis in Practice, 5*(2), 82–88 https://doi.org/10.1007/BF03391827

Buckley, J., Fountain, J., Meuse, S., Whelan, C., Maguire, H., Harper, J. M., & Luiselli, J. K. (2020). Performance improvement of care providers in a child services setting: Effects of an incentive-based negative reinforcement intervention on data recording. *Child & Family Behavior Therapy, 42*, 125–133. https://doi.org/10.1080/07317107.2020.1738733

Carr, J. E., Wilder, D. A., Majdalany, L., Mathisen, D., & Strain, L. A. (2013). An assessment-based solution to a human-service employee performance problem: An initial evaluation of the *performance diagnostic checklist—human services. Behavior Analysis in Practice, 6*, 16–32. https://doi.org/10.1007/BF03391789

Casella, S. E., Wilder, D. A., Neidert, P., Rey, C., Compton, M., & Chong, I. (2010). The effects of response effort on safe performance by therapists at an autism treatment facility. *Journal of Applied Behavior Analysis, 43*, 729–734. https://doi.org/10.1901/jaba.2010.43-729

Cox, D. J., Plavnick, J. B., & Brodhead, M. T. (2020). A proposed process for risk mitigation during the COVID-19 pandemic. *Behavior Analysis in Practice, 13,* 299–305. https://doi.org/10.1007/s40617-020-00430-1

Daniels, A. C., & Daniels, J. E. (2004). *Performance management: Changing behavior that drives organizational effectiveness* (4th ed.). Atlanta, GA: Performance Management Publications.

DiGennaro Reed, F. D., Hirst, J. M., & Howard, V. J. (2013). Empirically supported staff selection, training, and management strategies. In D. D. Reed, F. D. DiGennaro Reed, & J. K. Luiselli (Eds.), *Handbook of crisis intervention and developmental disabilities* (pp. 71–85). New York: Springer.

Dixon, M. R., & Loukus, A. K. (2013). Importance of organizational infrastructure. In D. D. Reed, F. D. DiGennaro Reed, & J. K. Luiselli (Eds.), *Handbook of crisis intervention and developmental disabilities* (pp. 7–26). New York: Springer.

Ferguson, J., Craig, E. A., & Dounavi, K. (2019). Telehealth as a model for providing behavior analytic interventions to individuals with autism spectrum disorder: A systematic review. *Journal of Autism and Developmental Disorders, 49*(2), 582–616. https://doi.org/10.1007/s10803-018-3724-5

Fong, E. H., Catagnus, R. M., Brodhead, M. T., Quigley, S., & Field, S. (2016). Developing the cultural awareness skills of behavior analysts. *Behavior Analysis in Practice, 9*(1), 84–94. https://doi.org/10.1007/s40617-016-0111-6

Gianotti, J., Kahl, T., Harper, J. M., & Luiselli, J. K. (2020). Behavioral safety assessment and intervention among residential care providers of students with intellectual and developmental disabilities. *Journal of Developmental and Physical Disabilities,* 1–10. https://www.researchgate.net/deref/https%3A%2F%2Flink.springer.com%2Farticle %2F10.1007%2Fs10882-020-09773-7

Gravina, N., Nastasi, J. A., Sleiman, A. A., Matey, N., & Simmons, D. E. (2020). Behavioral strategies for reducing disease transmission in the workplace. *Journal of Applied Behavior Analysis, 53*(4), 1–20. https://doi.org/10.1002/jaba.779

Gravina, N., Villacorta, J., Albert, K., Clark, R., Curry, S., & Wilder, D. (2018). A literature review of organizational behavior management interventions in human services settings from 1990 to 2016. *Journal of Organizational Behavior Management, 38,* 191–224. https://doi.org/10.1080/01608061.2018.1454872

Jess, R. L., & Dozier, C. L. (2020). Increasing handwashing in young children: A brief review. *Journal of Applied Behavior Analysis, 53*(3), 1219–1224. https://doi.org/10.1002 /jaba.732

Kornack, J., Williams, A. L., Johnson, K. A., & Mendes, E. M. (2020). Reopening the doors to center-based ABA services: Clinical and safety protocols during COVID-19. *Behavior Analysis in Practice, 13,* 543–549. https://doi.org/10.1007/s40617-020-00462-7.

Lerman, D. C., O'Brien, M. J., Neely, L., Call, N. A., Tsami, L., Schieltz, K. M., Berg, W. K., Graber, J., Huang, P., Kopelman, T., & Cooper-Brown, L. J. (2020). Remote coaching of caregivers via telehealth: Challenges and potential solutions. *Journal of Behavioral Education, 29,* 195–221. https://doi.org/10.1007/s10864-020-09378-2

Ludwig, T. D. (2015). Organizational behavior management: An enabler of applied behavior analysis. In H. Roane, J. E. Ringdahl, & T. Falcomata (Eds.), *Clinical and organizational applications of applied behavior analysis* (pp. 605–625). New York: Elsevier.

Luiselli, J. K. (2013). Descriptive analysis of a staff injury-reduction intervention in a human services setting for children and youth with intellectual and developmental disabilities. *Behavior Modification, 37,* 665–679. https://doi.org/10.1177%2F01454455 13489131

Luiselli, J. K. (2018). Organizational behavior management in human services programs. In B. Wine & J. Pritchard (Eds.), *Organizational behavior management: The essentials* (pp. 340–363). Orlando, FL: Hedgehog.

Luke, M., Carr, J. E., & Wilder, D. A. (2018). On the compatibility of organizational behavior management and BACB certification. *Journal of Organizational Behavior Management, 38*(4), 288–305. https://doi.org/10.1080/01608061.2018.1514347

Maguire, H., Gardner, R. M., Harper, J. M., & Luiselli, J. K. (2021). Behavioral training and performance management of human services organization care providers during the COVID-19 pandemic. Manuscript submitted for publication.

Newcomb, E. T., Camblin, J. G., Jones, F. D., & Wine, B. (2019). On the implementation of a gamified professional development system for direct care staff. *Journal of Organizational Behavior Management, 3–4,* 293–307. https://doi.org/10.1080/016080 61.2019.1632243

Reed, D. D., Luiselli, J. K., Miller, J. R., & Kaplan, B. A. (2013). Therapeutic restraint and protective holding. In D. D. Reed, F. DiGennaro Reed, and J. K. Luiselli. (Eds.), *Handbook of crisis intervention and developmental disabilities* (pp. 107–120). New York: Springer.

Reid, D. H. (1998). *Organizational behavior management in developmental disabilities services: Accomplishments and future directions.* New York: Routledge.

Reid, D. H., Parsons, M. B., & Green, C. W. (2012). *The supervisor's guidebook: Evidence-based strategies for promoting work quality and enjoyment among human service staff.* North Carolina: Habilitative Management Consultants.

Richman, G. S., Riordan, M. R., Reiss, M. L., Pyles, D. A. M., & Bailey, J. S. (1988). The effects of self-monitoring and supervisor feedback on staff performance in a residential setting. *Journal of Applied Behavior Analysis, 21,* 401–409. http://dx .doi .org/10.1901/jaba.1988.21-401.

Sanders, K. (2009). The effects of an action plan, staff training, management support, and monitoring on restraint use and costs of work-related injuries. *Journal of Applied Research in Intellectual Disabilities, 22*, 216–230. https://doi.org/10.1111/j.1468-3148.2008.00491.x

Schieltz, K. M., & Wacker, D. P. (2020). Functional assessment and function-based treatment delivered via telehealth: A brief summary. *Journal of Applied Behavior Analysis, 53*(3), 1242–1258. https://doi.org/10.1002/jaba.742

Sherrard, J., Ozanne-Smith, J., & Staines, C. (2004). Prevention of unintentional injury to people with intellectual disability: A review of the evidence. *Journal of Intellectual Disability Research, 48*(2), 639–645. https://doi.org/10.1111/j.1365-2788.2003.00570.x

Strouse, M. C., Carroll-Hernandez, T. A., Sherman, J. A., & Sheldon, J. B. (2004). Turning over turnover: The evaluation of a staff scheduling system in a community-based program for adults with developmental disabilities. *Journal of Organizational Behavior Management, 23*(2–3), 45–63. doi: 10.1300/J075v23n02_04

Sturmey, P. (1998). Overview of the relationship between organizational behavior management and developmental disabilities. *Journal of Organizational Behavior Management, 18*(2/3), 7–32. https://psycnet.apa.org/doi/10.1300/J075v18n02_02

Tomlinson, S. R. L., Gore, N., & McGill, P. (2018). Training individuals to implement applied behavior analysis procedures via telehealth: A systematic review of the literature. *Journal of Behavioral Education, 27*, 172–222. https://doi.org/10.1007/s10864-018-9292-0

Tyler, C. V., White-Scott, S., Ekvall, S. M., & Abulafia, L. (2008). Environmental health and developmental disabilities: A life span approach. *Family and Community Health, 31*(4), 287–304. doi: 10.1097/01.FCH.0000336092.39066.a0.

Valentino, A. L., & Juanico, J. F. (2020). Overcoming barriers to applied research: A guide for practitioners. *Behavior Analysis in Practice, 13*, 894–904. https://doi.org/10.1007/s40617-020-00479-y

Warman, A. S., Wine, B., Newcomb, E. T., Chen, T., & Morgan, C. A. (2019). An evaluation of static versus variable antecedents on employee performance. *Journal of Organizational Behavior Management, 39*, 257–265. https://doi.org/10.1080/01608061.2019.1666775

Wilder, D. A., & Sigurdsson, S. O. (2015). Applications of behavior analysis to improve safety in organizations and community settings. In H. Roane, J. E. Ringdahl, & T. Falcomata (Eds.), *Clinical and organizational applications of applied behavior analysis* (pp. 583–604). New York: Elsevier.

Wilder, D. A., Austin, J., & Casella, S. (2009). Applying behavior analysis in organizations: Organizational behavior management. *Psychological Services, 6*, 202–211. https://psycnet.apa.org/doi/10.1037/a0015393

Wilder, D. A., Cymbal, D., & Villacorta, J. (2020). The performance diagnostic checklist-human services: A brief review. *Journal of Applied Behavior Analysis, 53,* 1170–1176. https://doi.org/10.1002/jaba.676

Wilder, D. A., Lipschultz, J. L., King, A., Driscoll, S., & Sigurdsson, S. (2018). An analysis of the commonality and type of pre-intervention assessment procedures in the journal of organizational behavior management (2000–2015). *Journal of Organizational Behavior Management, 38,* 5–17. https://psycnet.apa.org/doi/10.1080 /01608061.2017.1325822

Willis, K., Hrdina, J., & Luiselli, J. K. (2020). Performance management and maintenance of data recording by educational care providers. *Behavior Analysis: Research and Practice, 20,* 165.

Wine, B. (2017). Incentive-based performance improvement. In J. K. Luiselli (Ed.), *Applied behavior analysis advanced guidebook* (pp. 117–134). New York: Elsevier.

Wine, B., & Pritchard, J. K. (2018). *Organizational behavior management: The essentials.* Orlando, FL: Hedgehog.

Wine, B., Osborne, M. R., & Newcomb, E. T. (2020). On turnover in human services. *Behavior Analysis in Practice, 13,* 492–501.–. https://doi.org/10.1007/s40617-019-00399-6

Wolf, M. M. (1978). Social validity: The case for subjective measurement or how applied behavior analysis is finding its heart. *Journal of Applied Behavior Analysis, 11,* 203–214. https://dx.doi.org/10.1901%2Fjaba.1978.11-203.

PART II
Assessment and Evaluation

2
Performance Diagnostic Assessment

David A. Wilder and Daniel Cymbal

Performance diagnostic assessment, or performance analysis (PA), is a behavioral approach to the assessment of performance in organizations. PA is the assessment component of performance management (PM), which is itself a sub-discipline of organizational behavior management (OBM). PA includes the up-front, analytic work that occurs before implementing an intervention to improve performance (Chase & Smith, 1994). OBM focuses on the application of behavior analytic principles and procedures to improve performance in business, industry, government, and human service settings, and is a sub-discipline of applied behavior analysis (ABA), which is the application of the principles of behavior to problems of social significance.

In this chapter, we first briefly describe OBM and its sub-disciplines. Next, we describe assessment in the sub-disciplines of OBM, review PA, and highlight the Performance Diagnostic Checklist-Human Services (PDC-HS). The chapter further considers common interventions based on PDC-HS results and recommendations for PA practice and research.

Organizational Behavior Management (OBM)

The discipline of OBM was formally founded in 1977, with the publication of the *Journal of Organizational Behavior Management (JOBM)*. In the decades since, a number of graduate programs have trained students to practice and conduct research in OBM, and the field has become a special interest group (SIG) of the Association for Behavior Analysis, International (ABAI). Consulting firms specializing in OBM have been founded, and these firms now work with *Fortune* 500 clients around the world (see Dickinson, 2001, for a detailed history of OBM). OBM has also been widely applied in human service agencies, including those serving individuals with intellectual and developmental disabilities (IDD).

In recent years, OBM has incorporated a number of sub-disciplines. Behavioral systems analysis (BSA), the first sub-discipline, focuses on the improvement of processes or systems within organizations. Behavioral safety focuses on improving safe performance in organizations. Finally, PM focuses on individual performance in organizations. To better understand PA, it is instructive to review assessment in BSA and behavioral safety first.

Assessment in OBM Sub-disciplines

Behavioral Systems Analysis

Behavioral Systems Analysis (BSA) examines organizations as multifaceted groups that produce a common product. The traditional three-term contingency remains the most basic unit of analysis, but the aggregate interrelated contingencies (i.e., metacontingencies) and the organizational environmental variables that influence them are also investigated (Malott, 2003, pp. 31–38). Pre-intervention assessment using BSA methodology often comprises a multi-level investigation of variables at the organizational, process, and performer levels of a given organization. As such, this broad approach can sometimes subsume other assessment components of OBM sub-disciplines, such as PM.

BSA assessment is conducted at each level of the organization (i.e., organizational, process, and performer), with a focus on identifying how the organization currently functions. Organization-level analysis is recommended first; business outcomes and goals should ultimately inform intervention for all subsequent levels (Diener et al., 2009). A common framework used to analyze organizational performance is the Total Performance System (TPS) which consists of seven components necessary for the system to function and survive, including organizational mission/goals, outputs, receiving systems, processing systems, inputs, and internal/external feedback loops/data (Brethower, 1982). Broadly, the goal of organization-level analysis is to assess what the organization is designed to accomplish, its products, the systems that produce those products, and the way that those systems interact with each other and consumers. Consultants make TPS diagrams that note these components within an organization; absences or deficiencies therein provide areas for intervention (Diener et al., 2009).

In process-level analysis, consultants identify Critical Business Issues (CBIs), a goal derived from problems or opportunities that affect organizational strategy. Identification of CBIs permits an analysis of how organizational processes contribute to or impede them (Rummler & Brache, 1991). Examining organizational departments' interfaces permits a "horizontal" view to examine how the organizational processes impact product, workflow, and, ultimately, the consumer. Processes within organizations describe a group of actions that produce an end product; one common analysis of these processes is conducted using a process map, wherein each step in a process or workflow is diagrammed as it operates currently (i.e., an "is" map) and subsequent inefficiencies or omissions, called "disconnects," can be identified for remediation by making a corresponding corrected diagram (i.e., a "should" map) (Malott, 2003, pp. 91–95; Rummler & Brache, 1991).

The final step in BSA assessment is a performer-level analysis. Organization- and process-level analysis allow the consultant to ensure that the system supports adequate individual performances. Individual performances must then be analyzed in terms of how they function within a process and how they relate to CBIs. Using information from each analysis, critical performances to manage can be identified (Diener et al., 2009). Assessment of these individual performance pinpoints is discussed below in the PA section.

BSA assessment is a complex process, as it accounts for variables that influence organizations across various levels. Assessment could potentially include a combination of TPS diagrams, functional relationship mapping, process mapping, PA, and historical data. As such, there is not a single tool that produces a uniform measurement or intervention recommendation for a given organization, though tools have been developed to make the process more efficient. For example, Diener et al. (2009) developed the Behavioral Systems Analysis Questionnaire (BSAQ), which comprises a series of questions that guide a consultant through each level of an organization. Specifically, the BSAQ is designed to guide assessment of important variables, their impact, and scope of the analysis. Research on assessment in BSA is rare in the empirical literature, comprising only 14% of published studies in the JOBM from 2000 to 2015 (Wilder et al., 2018). While the limited literature is likely due to the inherent complexity of BSA assessment and subsequent intervention, a thoroughgoing investigation of all variables that influence organizational output could potentially yield important data to inform improvement.

Behavioral Safety. Behavioral safety has a longstanding history of success in reducing incident rates and increasing safe behaviors in all kinds of workplaces, including those serving individuals with IDD (Sulzer-Azaroff & Austin, 2000). Safety assessment is an integral component of behavioral safety intervention, as assessment can aid in identifying environmental variables producing unsafe performance (Fante et al., 2007). Moreover, subsequent results can aid in gaining support for intervention (McSween, 2003). A safety assessment does not simply involve checking for safety compliance; rather, it is a thorough examination of history, current supports, management practices, and employee knowledge of procedure. Safety assessments can be conducted as individuals or teams, by those within the company, or by outside consultants. However, the primary goals remain static. Assessment mainly functions to identify and build on existing safety efforts, solicit input from employees, identify at-risk areas and activities, isolate training deficits, find others to help influence intervention design, and ensure managerial support of the intervention (McSween, 2003, pp. 36–40; Myers et al., 2010).

Safety assessments typically begin with a review of historical data. Historical review includes examination of the current rate of incidents (e.g., accidents per year) as well as their severity and type (Martinez-Onstott et al., 2016). Comparison to industry standards may prove useful; relative rates of incidents may indicate how supportive management might be (e.g., if incidents are low relative to other organizations, they may not be as inclined to intervene) and can also demonstrate how much money might be saved through incident prevention. Moreover, historical review can identify individual incidents which may highlight groups or environments at risk (McSween, 2003, p. 40).

After historical review, information about current safety culture and practices (i.e., meetings, trainings, audits, and current environment) is gathered. Interviews with organizational members are used to glean information from employees and managers about how safety is discussed, trained, and managed within the organization. These interviews provide some comparison between how current practices align with research-derived best practice. Interview data can then be verified through direct observation of audits, meetings, and in-situ practices. A consultant can then assess the quality of safety meetings and current auditing processes and pinpoint specific safe and unsafe practices. Through historical review, interview, and observation, findings and recommendations are then synthesized into an intervention plan. The plan may include the people responsible for the implementation, the participants, and the individuals responsible for monitoring. Results can be presented to stakeholders, both to highlight the pinpointed problem(s) and to solicit the support from managers and leadership to participate in the initiative (McSween, 2003, pp. 42–47).

Empirical research on safety assessment exists, but like BSA, is minimal (Wilder et al., 2018). Ludwig (2017) suggests that safety assessment could be further improved with the integration of BSA components to assess the interlocking contingencies that contribute to process safety. Martinez-Onstott et al. (2016) also developed a tool, the Performance Diagnostic Checklist-Safety (PDC-Safety), to assess environmental factors that contribute to unsafe performance. The tool was successfully used to increase the safe performance of a university-based landscaping crew, and PDC-Safety indicated interventions have proved more effective than non-indicated interventions (Cruz et al., in press).

Performance Analysis

The third sub-discipline of OBM is PM. PA focuses on assessment in PM, is akin to functional assessment in clinical areas of ABA, but differs somewhat. Unlike clinical ABA, in which functional assessment is conducted on behavioral excesses, PA is often conducted on behavioral or performance deficits. This makes some forms of PA difficult to conduct, as it is hard to assess behavior that isn't occurring. Three methods of PA exist: experimental, descriptive, and informant. Experimental methods consist of the manipulation of antecedent and consequence environmental variables to identify functional relations between these variables and performance. Descriptive methods consist of direct observation of performance as it is occurring in the work environment. Informant methods consist of interviews, checklists, and surveys.

Like BSA and behavioral safety assessment, empirical research in PA is relatively scant, but it is growing (Wilder et al., 2018). Given the utility of PA, it is somewhat surprising that it is not used more often as a first step in PM. Only in the last 20 years or so has PA appeared in the PM literature. Austin et al. (1999) provide three reasons for the lack of PA in PM, namely that: (1) PM has been successful without PA; (2) much of organizational behavior is rule-governed and assessing the impact of rules is difficult; and (3) PM practitioners are generally interested in increasing, rather than decreasing, performance. Performance to be increased is often not occurring or occurring infrequently, which makes it difficult to observe or manipulate.

Although these are valid reasons, this doesn't mean that PA is useless. First, with additional PA, PM may be even more effective than it already is. Also, rules are not immeasurable and can be manipulated. Finally, environmental stimuli and events affect skill deficits just as they do performance excesses. Many performance problems can be assessed, despite the difficulty involved in doing so.

Experimental methods of PA consist of direct manipulation of environmental variables to assess their effect on performance. Although common in clinical areas of ABA, few examples of experimental methods exist in PA. This is largely due to the impracticalities of manipulating stimuli and events in organizations. That is, it is often too expensive, time-consuming, and disruptive to manipulate stimuli or events which might affect employee performance in actual work settings. In clinical ABA, experimental manipulation is often conducted under relatively controlled conditions, separate from the treatment milieu. Unfortunately, removing employees from the organizational milieu is often impossible, and even when it is possible, the outcomes obtained as a result of the assessment may not generalize to the organizational setting.

Therrien et al. (2005) provide an example of the experimental manipulation of variables to assess employee performance. These authors evaluated customer greeting by employees at a fast-food restaurant. To assess the variables hypothesized to be contributing to low levels of customer greeting, they manipulated a number of antecedent events, including the presence of a manager, and whether employees had a radio on as they worked and used a door chime to indicate when a customer entered the restaurant. The authors systematically manipulated these variables and observed higher levels of customer greeting when the manager was present and the door chime was operational. A subsequent intervention, which consisted of the use of the door chime and the increased presence of a manager, was effective to increase greeting to moderate levels. Finally, the authors added feedback, which improved greeting to even higher levels.

Descriptive methods of PA consist of directly observing performance as well as the antecedent and consequence variables which might be related to the performance in the work environment. Unlike experimental methods, descriptive methods are relatively easy to conduct in organizations. However, they can take some time to complete. Repeated observation is often necessary to identify potential relationships between events and performance, and some variables which contribute to performance deficits might remain unobservable (e.g., training or a lack thereof). Nevertheless, descriptive methods of PA have been shown to be useful to assess employee performance problems.

Pampino et al. (2005) conducted a descriptive assessment of three skills which they hypothesized to be related to poor performance by four construction workers. The results of the assessment identified two skills, product knowledge and computer data entry, as deficient. An intervention, based on assessment results, was then implemented and found to be effective to improve the worker's performance. A social validity measure suggested that the workers were satisfied with the results of the assessment and intervention.

As described above, experimental methods are difficult to conduct in real-world settings and descriptive methods are often time-consuming. Thus, informant methods of PA have become most popular. Informant methods consist of interviews, checklists, or surveys. In some cases, the employees themselves are interviewed about their performance problems. More often, supervisors or managers are asked about their employee's performance. These interviews typically take between 15 and 60 minutes to complete, and in some cases, yield fairly specific information regarding the variables which are likely contributing to the performance deficits. A detailed description of these procedures and the studies which have evaluated them is provided below.

Brief History of Informant Methods in PA

PM consultants have used informant methods to gather information about the variables contributing to employee performance problems for some time. As early as 1970, Mager and Pipe provided a series of questions to ask managers regarding performance issues. The first set of questions centered around determining whether the performance problem is due to a skill deficit or is a result of other management-related issues. If the problem is due to a skill deficiency, Mager and Pipe suggest training, adding a job aid or checklist to the work environment, or assessing whether the employee has the physical and mental capacities to perform the task. If the problem is not due to a skill deficiency, Mager and Pipe suggest asking about the potential rewards and punishers in place for the task (Austin, 2000).

Gilbert (1978) developed a performance assessment model which also involves interviewing managers. He suggests first asking three questions: (1) Have the missions, goals, and responsibilities of the performer/task been adequately described? (2) Are the standards of performance described and are they measurable? and (3) What is the greatest potential for improving performance? After answering these questions, the assessor proceeds to ask questions about information, instruments and equipment, incentives, knowledge, capacity, and motives issues. Based on answers to these questions, the consultant suggests an intervention, which can range from training to the manipulation of consequences (Austin, 2000).

Years later, Kent (1986) proposed a set of diagnostic questions, entitled the "Problem Diagnosis Algorithm." Kent proposed 25 questions, many of which are similar to Gilbert (1978). However, Kent asks some higher-cost questions before some lower-cost questions. This could be problematic because if a manager answers in the affirmative to some higher-cost questions, a consultant might recommend some interventions that will be more costly than some other interventions she might otherwise recommend.

Finally, Bailey and Austin (1996) proposed a brief model based on Mager and Pipe (1970), Gilbert (1978), and Kent (1986). Bailey and Austin arranged the questions in their model based on the likelihood that the question gets at the actual cause of the performance problem, as well as the cost of the proposed intervention. Their model includes questions about the equipment necessary for the performance, as well as possible disincentives for performance.

Modern Informant Methods in PA

More recently, Austin (2000) created the Performance Diagnostic Checklist (PDC), which is now the most frequently used tool in PA (Wilder et al., 2018).

The PDC is designed to identify the variables contributing to inadequate employee performance. It was developed based on research examining the ways in which experts solve performance problems. That is, Austin had experts in the field of PA think aloud as they were asked what questions they would pose when presented with various performance problems in the context of a consult. After compiling the results, Austin arranged the responses into domains, each of which include a specific set of questions.

The PDC includes four domains (*Antecedents and Information, Equipment and Processes, Knowledge and Skills – Training*, and *Consequences*). The tool was designed to be conducted in an interview format. Typically, the consultant or behavior analyst interviews a supervisor or manager about an employee performance problem. The PDC includes no formal scoring mechanism, but consultants are nevertheless instructed to design an intervention which addresses each problematic domain. The PDC has been used in restaurant, retail, and healthcare settings. Austin (2000) suggested that the PDC was a starting point for assessment tools and that future research should expand upon this tool.

In the first empirical evaluation of the PDC, Shier et al. (2003) used a package intervention to increase compliance with cleaning tasks at a grocery store. The PDC was used to assess and determine intervention components, and indicated problems related to *Antecedents and Information* as well as *Consequences*. Task clarification and feedback were implemented, resulting in performance increases in all departments.

Doll et al. (2007) devised an intervention to target store maintenance and cleaning in a ski shop. The PDC was one of two performance analyses conducted. Though researchers did not identify the deficient domains indicated by the PDC, they concluded that both antecedents and consequences were needed to occasion and maintain the desired performance. Cleaning behaviors improved following implementation of a package intervention consisting of task clarification and graphed and task-specific feedback.

Gravina et al. (2008) used the PDC to inform an intervention to increase morning preparation tasks at a physical therapy clinic. A package intervention was devised from PDC results, with a component from each indicated domain: task clarification, equipment manipulations, and feedback corresponding to *Antecedents and Information, Equipment and Processes*, and *Consequences*, respectively. Percentage of completed tasks increased and maintained following intervention.

As noted above, much of PA and PM work has been conducted in human service settings serving individuals with IDD. Thus, a tool similar to the PDC, but which more adequately captures the unique settings and contingencies involved in organizations which serve individuals with IDD, was necessary. Accordingly, Carr et al. (2013) created the Performance Diagnostic Checklist-Human Services (PDC-HS) to assess employee performance problems specifically occurring in human service settings such as schools, clinics, group homes, and residential treatment facilities. Like the PDC, the PDC-HS includes four domains that are similar, but not identical to, the PDC: *Training; Task Clarification and Prompting; Resources, Materials, and Processes*; and *Performance Consequences, Effort, and Competition*. Unlike the original PDC, the PDC-HS includes some direct observation components as well as a scoring, planning, and suggested intervention section. The direct observation components have the observer identify the location of any materials necessary for task completion as well as watch the employee perform the targeted tasks (Wilder, Cymbal, & Villacorta, in press).

In the first study describing the PDC-HS, Carr and colleagues (2013) assessed direct staff member's inadequate cleaning of therapy rooms at a center-based autism program. The PDC-HS suggested a lack of training and consequences were responsible for inadequate performance. An intervention consisting of training and graphed feedback was then implemented and compared to a non-indicated intervention (increased availability of cleaning materials). Results showed that completion of the cleaning tasks in the treatment rooms did not improve until the PDC-HS indicated intervention was implemented. These data suggest that PDC-HS indicated interventions may be more effective than arbitrarily selected interventions. In addition, the PDC-HS may assist behavior analysts and consultants to prescribe effective assessment-based interventions (Wilder et al., in press).

Ditzian et al. (2015) replicated and extended Carr et al. (2013) by targeting a novel performance. The setting for this study was a clinic which served individuals with autism and the target performance was client elopement from treatment rooms. This behavior was both disruptive and dangerous. The researchers used the PDC-HS to identify the variables responsible for inadequate securing of therapy room doors by staff members. The assessment results suggested that staff members' performance was due to a lack of appropriate consequences. The researchers then evaluated an indicated intervention (i.e., graphed and verbal feedback) as well as a non-indicated intervention (i.e., a written prompt), as was done in Carr et al. (2013). The indicated intervention was effective to improve performance, but the non-indicated intervention was not (Wilder, Cymbal, & Villacorta, in press).

Bowe and Sellers (2017) applied the PDC-HS to yet another target performance. These researchers used the PDC-HS to identify and address the variables contributing to paraprofessionals' inaccurate implementation of error correction during discrete trial teaching. The PDC-HS suggested that staff training was insufficient. A PDC-HS indicated intervention (training) was then evaluated, followed by a non-indicated intervention (task clarification and a vocal prompt). For all four participants, the mastery criteria were met immediately following the implementation of the training, but it was not met when the non-indicated intervention was implemented (Wilder, Cymbal, & Villacorta, in press).

In an unusual application, Smith and Wilder (2018) demonstrated that individuals with IDD can learn to use the PDC-HS. These researchers evaluated the tool at a retail facility managed by individuals with IDD. The managers who completed the PDC-HS and implemented the intervention had intellectual disabilities and supervised other employees with disabilities. The managers used the PDC-HS to assess and increase accurate pricing by supervisees with disabilities. With just minor assistance, managers with IDD were able to use the PDC-HS and implement an intervention to improve the performance of their staff members (Wilder, Cymbal, & Villacorta, in press).

Wilder et al. (2018) used the PDC-HS to address poor natural environment training (NET) implementation by therapists at a center serving children with autism. The PDC-HS identified *Task Clarification and Prompting* as well as the *Resources, Materials, and Processes* domains as problematic. They then implemented an intervention to address these deficits. As with previous research, some non-indicated interventions were also implemented but only the PDC-HS indicated interventions were effective (Wilder et al., in press). This study extended the number of PDC-HS domains investigated; previous research had mostly identified only two domains (*Training* and *Performance Consequences, Effort, and Competition*) as problematic.

Another study, by Wilder et al. (2019), evaluated the validity and reliability of the PDC-HS with participants who used the tool to score videos simulating a performance problem. Each of three videos depicted a performance problem that was due to a different problematic domain. In general, participants scored the videos accurately. Upon follow-up two to four weeks later, participants also correctly identified the domain responsible for the performance problem, thus suggesting that the PDC-HS may be a valid and reliable tool. Further, the authors examined accuracy across three training levels in ABA (i.e., one course in ABA, 2–4 courses in ABA, and 5 or more courses in ABA). The results showed that even those with only a single course in ABA accurately identified an appropriate intervention (Wilder et al., in press).

Most recently, Merritt et al. (2009) used the PDC-HS to assess tardiness by four direct-care staff members at a school serving children with autism. The results of the PDC-HS revealed that *Training; Task Clarification and Prompting; and Performance Consequences, Effort, and Competition* were problematic. The intervention consisted of task clarification, a problem-solving discussion, tokens, weekly graphed feedback, and effectively decreased tardiness. This study was particularly noteworthy because the researchers interviewed the employees with performance problems themselves, as opposed to interviewing their supervisors or managers (Wilder et al., in press).

PA and PM Interventions

Historically, PM interventions have been arbitrarily selected and have included multiple components. Indeed, it is not uncommon to see three or more intervention components implemented at once. Although often effective, multi-component interventions make it difficult to determine which components are essential. One advantage of PA is that a specific, focused intervention is suggested by the outcome of assessment. Thus, the use of PA should decrease dependence on multi-component interventions.

PM interventions have typically been organized based on whether or not they consist of antecedent- or consequence-based procedures. Antecedent-based interventions have included intervention components which are implemented before the target performance, or pinpoint, occurs. Consequence-based procedures include intervention components which are implemented after the pinpoint. Recently, however, this manner of organizing PM interventions may be giving way to assessment-based organization that involves categorization based on the variables contributing to the performance problem. If the pinpoint is a result of a lack of training, the most appropriate intervention is to train the employee. Training can be done via written instructions (Graff & Karsten, 2012), behavioral skills training (BST: Sarokoff & Sturmey, 2004), video modeling (Catania et al., 2009), or pyramidal training (Pence et al., 2012). Training may be brief, or may take some time, depending on the complexity of the tasks and the number of employees in need of training.

If the employee has been trained to perform the task, but needs clarification regarding the conditions under which she is supposed to perform, or needs a prompt to perform the task, then task clarification and prompting may be necessary. Task clarification involves clearly describing the task and the conditions under which it should occur (Cunningham & Austin, 2007). Often, a task analysis is created and shared with the employee. Prompting may take a variety of forms, including a vocal prompt (Barker et al., 2004), or a tactile prompt (Petscher & Bailey, 2006); vocal prompts are often delivered immediately before the target performance should occur. Written prompts, when used, are often placed in a salient location.

If the pinpointed performance is not occurring due to inadequate equipment or convoluted processes, intervention should focus on repairing or replacing the equipment, or addressing the problematic processes. In some cases, the tools necessary to complete the task are not available or inconveniently located and intervention should focus on decreasing the effort involved in accessing the tools or materials needed to perform the task (Casella et al., 2010). In other cases, the equipment may not be adequately arranged to evoke ideal performance. Finally, as described above, the OBM sub-discipline of BSA focuses on identification and amelioration of disconnects in this process; a process map should be used to identify and intervene on this process.

If the pinpointed performance lacks appropriate consequences, intervention should focus on adding these consequences. For example, in many organizations, feedback on performance is only delivered annually or semi-annually. However, to achieve maximum performance, feedback may be necessary weekly, or even daily (Pampino et al., 2003). Feedback may be most effective when it is task-specific and delivered by a supervisor (Alvero et al., 2001). In some cases, the delivery of other consequences, such as bonuses, may be appropriate.

Practice Recommendations

Performance problems among employees serving individuals with intellectual and developmental disabilities can have adverse effects on client outcomes. Before addressing these problems, managers, supervisors, and clinicians should take the time to conduct a performance analysis. This involves defining the problem performance, and then conducting an experimental, descriptive, or informant-based assessment of the problem. The PDC-HS is an easy-to-use informant-based tool that can provide an assessment-based solution.

When using the PDC-HS, clinicians should first identify and define (i.e., pinpoint) the problematic performance. Next, a system for measuring the problematic performance should be developed. Baseline data on the problematic performance should then be collected. Using the PDC-HS, interviews with at least two managers or supervisors who are familiar with the problematic performance and the employee(s) exhibiting the performance should be conducted. Based on PDC-HS results, an intervention designed to improve the performance should then be implemented. The intervention may consist of more than one component, particularly if PDC-HS results identify more than one domain as problematic. Data collection should continue during intervention implementation. If the intervention is ineffective, an alternative PDC-HS-based intervention should be evaluated. The interventions described in the section above are common choices and should be considered first. Once an effective intervention has been identified, steps should be taken to ensure the intervention maintains.

Research Directions

Future research on PA should progress along a number of lines. First, additional research on descriptive methods of PA is needed. Although sometimes difficult to conduct, descriptive methods of PA have the potential to provide a more objective counterpart to existing informant methods. Specifically, future research could examine scatterplot methods to identify times when performance is likely to be most problematic. Future research might also examine the use of structured antecedent-behavior-consequence procedures to assess performance problems.

Another potentially fruitful line of future research is to assess the variables contributing to exemplary performance. Most of PA has focused on problematic performance. Nevertheless, identification of the variables contributing to exemplary performance might prove instructive. Once identified, it might be possible to reproduce some or all of these variables to enhance performance among many employees.

A third area for future research involves the PDC-HS itself. Additional research on the reliability and validity of the tool is needed. To date, no studies have compared PDC-HS outcomes across various supervisors. Future research on the extent to which multiple supervisors agree when assessing a performance problem exhibited by the same employee is needed. Also, previous research on the reliability and validity of the tool has been conducted using videos. Although this is a very practical approach to assessing reliability, future research using actual employees who exhibit performance problems is also needed (Wilder et al., in press).

Future research might also compare PDC-HS outcomes with outcomes derived from other methods of PA. As described above, other methods of PA can be difficult to implement, but research comparing the PDC-HS to other methods would be useful. As an example, the outcomes of descriptive methods might be compared to PDC-HS outcomes. Experimental methods, when possible to conduct, could also be compared to PDC-HS outcomes. In clinical ABA, informant-based tools such as the Functional Analysis Screening Tool (FAST) have been subjected to these comparisons (Iwata et al., 2013); although it might be more difficult to do so in PA, it is possible (Wilder et al., in press).

Future PDC-HS research on formal methods of identifying which domains are most in need of intervention is also needed. Currently, the domains with the highest score are targeted for intervention, but in some cases, more than one domain scores highly, making it difficult to determine the most appropriate intervention. Similarly, research examining the relationship between domain score and intervention effectiveness might allow for more accurate identification of effective interventions (Wilder et al., in press).

Finally, it would be beneficial to conduct more research on the use of PDC-HS indicated versus non-indicated interventions. Although non-indicated interventions have so far been ineffective, it is possible that some non-indicated interventions will work. Researchers should investigate the conditions under which non-indicated interventions may be effective (Wilder et al., in press) notwithstanding the advantages of formulating and implementing interventions derived from PDC-HS assessment.

References

Alvero, A. M., Bucklin, B. R., & Austin, J. (2001). An objective review of the effectiveness and essential characteristics of performance feedback in organizational settings. *Journal of Organizational Behavior Management, 21*(1), 3–29. doi: 10.1300/J075v21n01_02.

Austin, J. (2000). Performance analysis and performance diagnostics. In J. Austin, & J. E. Carr, *Handbook of applied behavior analysis* (pp. 321–350). Oakland, CA: Context Press.

Austin, J., Carr, J. E., & Agnew, J. L. (1999). The need for assessment of maintaining variables in OBM. *Journal of Organizational Behavior Management, 19*(2), 59–87. doi: 10.1300/J075v19n02_05.

Bailey, J. S., & Austin, J. (1996). Productivity in the workplace. In M. A. Mattaini, & B. A. Thyer (Eds.), *Finding solutions to social problems: Behavioral strategies for change; Finding solutions to social problems: Behavioral strategies for change* (pp. 179–200, Chapter xii, 427 Pages). Washington, DC: American Psychological Association. doi: 10.1037/10217-007.

Barker, M. R., Bailey, J. S., & Lee, N. (2004). The impact of verbal prompts on child safety-belt use in shopping carts. *Journal of Applied Behavior Analysis, 37*(4), 527–530. http://dx.doi.org.portal.lib.fit.edu/10.1901/jaba.2004.37-527.

Bowe, M., & Sellers, T. P. (2017). Evaluating the performance diagnostic checklist-human services to assess incorrect error-correction procedures by preschool paraprofessionals. *Journal of Applied Behavior Analysis, 51*(1), 166–176. doi:10.1002/jaba.428

Brethower, D. M. (1982). The total performance system. In R. M. O'Brien, A. M. Dickinson, & M. Rosow (Eds.), *Industrial behavior modification: A management handbook* (pp. 350–369). New York: Pergamon Press.

Carr, J. E., Wilder, D. A., Majdalany, L., Mathisen, D., & Strain, L. A. (2013). An assessment-based solution to a human-service employee performance problem. *Behavior Analysis in Practice, 6*(1), 16–32. doi:10.1007/bf03391789.

Casella, S. E., Wilder, D. A., Neidert, P., Rey, C., Compton, M., & Chong, I. (2010). The effects of response effort on safe performance by therapists at an autism treatment facility. *Journal of Applied Behavior Analysis, 43*(4), 729–734. doi: 10.1901/jaba.2010.43-729.

Catania, C. N., Almeida, D., Liu-Constant, B., & DiGennaro Reed, F. D. (2009). Video modeling to train staff to implement discrete-trial instruction. *Journal of Applied Behavior Analysis, 42*(2), 387–392. doi: 10.1901/jaba.2009.42-387.

Chase, P. N., and Smith, J. M. (1994). *Performance analysis: Understanding behavior in organizations.* Morgantown, WV: Envision Development Group, Inc.

Cruz, N. J., Wilder, D. A., Phillabaum, C., Thomas, R., Cusick, M., & Gravina, N. (2019). Further evaluation of the performance diagnostic checklist-safety (PDC-Safety). *Journal of Organizational Behavior Management, 39*(3–4), 266–279, DOI: 10.1080/01608061.2019.1666777

Cunningham, T. R., & Austin, J. (2007). Using goal setting, task clarification, and feedback to increase the use of the hands-free technique by hospital operating room staff. *Journal of Applied Behavior Analysis, 40*(4), 673–677. doi:10.1901/jaba.2007.673-677.

Dickinson, A. M. (2001). The historical roots of organizational behavior management in the private sector. *Journal of Organizational Behavior Management, 20*(3–4), 9–58. doi: 10.1300/J075v20n03_02.

Diener, L. H., McGee, H. M., & Miguel, C. F. (2009). An integrated approach for conducting a behavioral systems analysis. *Journal of Organizational Behavior Management, 29*(2), 108–135. doi: 10.1080/01608060902874534.

Ditzian, K., Wilder, D. A., King, A., & Tanz, J. (2015). An evaluation of the performance diagnostic checklist–Human services to assess an employee performance problem in a center-based autism treatment facility. *Journal of Applied Behavior Analysis, 48*(1), 199–203. doi: 10.1002/jaba.171.

Doll, J., Livesey, J., McHaffie, E., & Ludwig, T. D. (2007). Keeping an uphill edge: Managing cleaning behaviors at a ski shop. *Journal of Organizational Behavior Management, 27*(3), 41–60. doi:10.1300/j075v27n03_04.

Fante, R., Gravina, N., & Austin, J. (2007). A brief pre-intervention analysis and demonstration of the effects of a behavioral safety package on postural behaviors of pharmacy employees. *Journal of Organizational Behavior Management, 27*(2), 15. Retrieved from https://search-proquest-com.portal.lib.fit.edu/docview/199274617?ac countid=27313.

Gilbert, T. F. (1978). *Human competence.* New York: McGraw-Hill.

Graff, R. B., & Karsten, A. M. (2012). Evaluation of a self-instruction package for conducting stimulus preference assessments. *Journal of Applied Behavior Analysis, 45*(1), 69–82. https://doi.org/10.1901/jaba.2012.45-69

Gravina, N., VanWagner, M., & Austin, J. (2008). Increasing physical therapy equipment preparation using task clarification, feedback and environmental manipulations. *Journal of Organizational Behavior Management, 28*(2), 110–122. doi:10.1080/01608060802100931.

Iwata, B. A., DeLeon, I. G., & Roscoe, E. M. (2013). Reliability and validity of the Functional Analysis Screening Tool. *Journal of Applied Behavior Analysis, 46*, 271–284. doi:10.1002/jaba.31.

Kent, R. S. (1986). *25 Steps to getting performance problems off of your desk and out of your life!* New York: Dodd, Mead, and Company.

Ludwig, T. D. (2017). Process safety behavioral systems: Behaviors interlock in complex metacontingencies. *Journal of Organizational Behavior Management, 37*(3–4), 224–239. doi: 10.1080/01608061.2017.1340921.

Mager, R. F., & Pipe, P. (1970). *Analyzing performance problems.* Belmont, CA: Fearon Publishers.

Malott, M. E. (2003). *Paradox of organizational change: Engineering organizations with behavioral systems analysis.* Context Press, Reno, NV.

Martinez-Onstott, B., Wilder, D., & Sigurdsson, S. (2016). Identifying the variables contributing to at-risk performance: Initial evaluation of the performance diagnostic checklist–safety (PDC-Safety). *Journal of Organizational Behavior Management, 36*(1), 80–93. doi:10.1080/01608061.2016.1152209.

McSween, T. E. (2003). *Values-based safety process: Improving your safety culture with behavior-based safety.* Hoboken, NJ: Wiley.

Merritt, T. A., DiGennaro Reed, F. D., & Martinez, C. E. (2019). Using the performance diagnostic checklist: Human services to identify an indicated intervention to decrease employee tardiness. *Journal of Applied Behavior Analysis, 52*(4), 1034–1048. doi:http://dx.doi.org.portal.lib.fit.edu/10.1002/jaba.643.

Myers, W. V., McSween, T. E., Medina, R. E., Rost, K., & Alvero, A. M. (2010). The implementation and maintenance of a behavioral safety process in a petroleum refinery. *Journal of Organizational Behavior Management, 30*(4), 285–307. doi: 10.1080/01608061.2010.499027.

Pampino, R. N. Jr., MacDonald, J. E., Mullin, J. E., & Wilder, D. A. (2003). Weekly feedback vs. daily feedback: An application in retail. *Journal of Organizational Behavior Management, 23*(2–3), 21–43. doi: 10.1300/J075v23n02_03.

Pampino, R. N. Jr., Wilder, D. A., & Binder, C. (2005). The use of functional assessment and frequency building procedures to increase product knowledge and data entry skills among foremen in a construction organization. *Journal of Organizational Behavior Management, 25*:2, 1–36. doi: 10.1300/J075v25n02_01.

Pence, S. T., St. Peter, C. C., & Tetreault, A. S. (2012). Increasing accurate preference assessment implementation through pyramidal training. *Journal of Applied Behavior Analysis, 45*(2), 345–359. http://dx.doi.org.portal.lib.fit.edu/10.1901/jaba.2012.45-345.

Petscher, E. S., & Bailey, J. S. (2006). Effects of training, prompting, and self-monitoring on staff behavior in a classroom for students with disabilities. *Journal of Applied Behavior Analysis, 39*(2), 215–226. doi: 10.1901/jaba.2006.02-05.

Rummler, G. A., & Brache, A. P. (1991). Managing the white space. *Training, 28*(1), 55. Retrieved from https://search-proquest-com.portal.lib.fit.edu/docview/203368334?ac countid=27313.

Sarokoff, R. A., & Sturmey, P. (2004). The effects of behavioral skills training on staff implementation of discrete-trial teaching. *Journal of Applied Behavior Analysis, 37*(4), 535–538. doi: 10.1901/jaba.2004.37-535.

Shier, L., Rae, C., & Austin, J. (2003). Using task clarification, checklists and performance feedback to improve the appearance of a grocery Store. *Performance Improvement Quarterly, 16*(2), 26–40. doi:10.1111/j.1937-8327.2003.tb00277.x.

Smith, M., & Wilder, D. A. (2018). The use of the performance diagnostic checklist-human services to assess and improve the job performance of individuals with intellectual disabilities. *Behavior Analysis in Practice, 11*(2), 148–153. doi:10.1007/s40617-018-0213-4.

Sulzer-Azaroff, B., & Austin, J. (2000). Does BBS work? *Professional Safety, 45*(7), 19–24. Retrieved from https://search-proquest-com.portal.lib.fit.edu/docview/200386901?ac countid=27313.

Therrien, K., Wilder, D. A., Rodriguez, M., & Wine, B. (2005). Preintervention analysis and improvement of customer greeting in a restaurant. *Journal of Applied Behavior Analysis, 38*, 411–415. doi:10.1901/jaba.2005.89-04.

Wilder, D. A., Cymbal, D., & Villacorta, J. (in press). The performance diagnostic checklist – Human Services: A brief review. *Journal of Applied Behavior Analysis* 53(2), 1170–1176. doi: 10.1002/jaba.676.

Wilder, D. A., Lipschultz, J., & Gehrman, C. (2018). An evaluation of the performance diagnostic checklist: Human services (PDC–HS) across domains. *Behavior Analysis in Practice, 11*(2), 129–138. doi:10.1007/s40617-018-0243-y.

Wilder, D. A., Lipschultz, J., Gehrman, C., Ertel, H., & Hodges, A. (2019). A preliminary assessment of the validity and reliability of the performance diagnostic checklist-human services. *Journal of Organizational Behavior Management, 39*(3–4), 194–212. doi: 10.1080/01608061.2019.1666772.

Wilder, D. A., Lipschultz, J., King, A., Driscoll, S., & Sigurdsson, S. (2018). An analysis of the commonality and type of pre-intervention assessment procedures in the journal of organizational behavior management (2000–2015). *Journal of Organizational Behavior Management, 38*(1), 5–17.

3
Assessing Employee Preferences for Incentives

Byron Wine and Trang Doan

In the modern, post-industrial society, most employees are remunerated for their work via paychecks presented at regular intervals. Receiving paychecks at regular intervals removes employees from the direct contingencies of their work. For example, compare the biweekly paycheck of an accountant in a large firm to the pay of a more directly connected job such as a farmer. Assuming the farmer owns her own farm, she is naturally incentivized to rise early and work hard without direct supervision because if she fails to do so she will not raise a crop and will make no money. Aside from some instances of entrepreneurship and the rare occurrence of a well-designed pay-for-performance system (the discussion of both are beyond the scope of this chapter), the naturally occurring consequences of work often do not support high-quality work-related behavior. It is small wonder then that employees may not always engage in an appropriate amount, or quality, of work. Since the pay system is not optimally designed, contingencies must be created by the management to augment the lack of naturally occurring contingencies.

In the paycheck-laden work environment employees are incentivized to show up and engage in some behavior so that they are not terminated. Anything above and beyond the minimum performance is largely under the control of the contingencies management can generate. Management has several options available to them when designing systems to impact employee performance. Perhaps the most intuitive of these options is to design a system whereby extra incentives, either money or other items with value, are delivered.

The delivery of rewards, above and beyond salary and benefits, is often used to motivate employees. A report generated by the Incentive Federation Incorporated (2016) evaluated the degree to which various incentive systems such as award points, gift cards, travel, and merchandise were common in a cross-section of US-based organizations. The report suggested up to 84% of organizations used at least one type of incentive system and the money spent on such programs topped $90 million dollars. These measures reflect increases, both in percentage and actual money spent from 2013 to 2015, up from 74% and $77 billion in 2013, respectively.

Given the amount of money spent on incentive programs, one would expect a fairly robust analysis of the effects on employee performance before and after incentives are implemented in business settings. Surprisingly, in a meta-analysis performed by Condly et al. (2003) of 600 reviewed studies, only 45 collected information about performance before incentives were implemented. Of the 45 included in the analysis there was an overall average effect of a 22% gain in performance, suggesting that incentives are, in general, effective at changing employee behavior.

Most of the research concerned with implementing and assessing employee preferences for incentives has been conducted within industrial, business, and manufacturing settings. However, the assessment principles, concepts, and procedures apply similarly to human services organizations (HSOs) serving persons who have intellectual and developmental disabilities (IDD). In this chapter, we review several areas of research that have contributed to the design of assessment methods, selecting and delivering rewards, identifying variables impacting the effectiveness of incentive-based systems, and implementing programs to improve performance of HSO employees.

Selecting and Delivering Rewards

Ensuring the delivery of highly preferred items may not immediately seem to be of the utmost importance in employee performance programs. After all, receiving any item in addition to standard pay could, at least conceptually, be considered better than a standard pay condition. Wine and Axelrod (2014) evaluated the effects of a progressively thinning chance of earning a highly preferred item relative to a less-preferred item. That is, within each session the percent chance of earning a highly preferred reward was decreased systematically until the participant declined to continue. Conceptually, the study was designed to mimic a reward error where a non-preferred item was delivered for completing work. Results demonstrated that four of the five participants did not reliably complete work when there was less than a 100% chance of earning a highly preferred item. Although preliminary, this study suggests that it is important to identify preferred items for employees and not simply rely on the idea that "something is better than nothing." It may even be that delivering low-preference items to employees for completing work is detrimental to performance. Follow-up interviews with the participants suggested that the even the smallest percent chance (25%) of earning a low-preference item was unappealing.

Many may assume that a generalized conditioned reinforcer (i.e., money) could always be used in incentive programs to circumvent the chance of delivering a low-preference item. However, there are several potential shortcomings involved in relying on monetary incentives. First, using money over time across a number of employees can lead to exorbitant costs that cannot be borne by the organization—incentive systems can include many items or programs that have little cost to an organization (e.g., access to preferred work duties). Second, providing money may be seen in some settings as impersonal and potentially even counterproductive. For example, if employees in an organization become aware of record-breaking profits, a small monetary incentive may actually be viewed as insulting, whereas something management took time to assess and obtain especially for the employee may be viewed as more valuable. Moreover, there is some evidence to suggest that money may not always be the most valuable option to employees.

Wine et al. (2013) evaluated preference in employees across two groups of items. In this study, the participants worked in residential facilities for adults with autism spectrum disorder (ASD) and other intellectual disabilities. The participants were responsible for implementing behavior intervention plans and assist in daily living skills. In the first set of items, $10 cash was compared to eight other items of various value: accessing candy, leaving work 40 minutes early, skipping pre-shift meetings, taking an extra 20-minute break during a shift, picking one's work location for a day, picking one's assigned duties for the day, taking clients on an outing, and choosing a preferred parking spot for a day. The second group of items consisted of $10 cash and eight other items all worth $10: movie rental gift card, music gift card, convenience store gift card, donut shop gift card, sweets of the participant's choice, fast-food gift card, lottery tickets, and electronics gift card. Assessments indicated that while money was consistently rated highly by nearly all employees, on several occasions, items other than the cash were rated as first choice.

In Wine et al. (2013) it could be assumed that some of the items and activities from the first group were popular because they could not be obtained otherwise (e.g., an employee could not purchase the ability to leave early from work). Items ranked more highly than cash in the second group are somewhat confusing at first glance because cash could be used to purchase any of the other items. However, examining how money actually functions may shed some light on the employee preference designations. It seems at least possible that a $10 music gift card can only be used to obtain something rewarding, while perhaps the $10 in cash was viewed as a small amount of money that would likely have to be used for something utilitarian in nature (e.g., gasoline). Taken together, money is a powerful reward for employees and is the reason many continue to show up to work. Managers would do well though to consider alternatives to cash in some situations. For example, using a preferred parking spot as a reward for top team members would be cheaper and potentially more meaningful to some employees.

Given that some items may be occasionally considered as rewards in lieu of money, managers might be able to predict what their employees will find rewarding. After all, managers often know their employees well, sometimes having worked with them for years. Wilder et al. (2007) evaluated the degree to which managers could predict what their employees preferred. Participants were employed as representatives in a customer service organization, administrative assistants at a university, service associates at a warehouse, or food service workers. Managers first rank ordered, from most to least, a list of items they thought each of their employees would prefer in an incentive plan. Then, the employees rank ordered the same list based on their own preferences. The mean correlation between the two lists was a modest .11. Managers were able to identify the most valuable item for approximately half of the employees but were much less adept at predicting relative preference for the remaining items. Wilder et al. (2011) replicated Wilder et al. (2007) with a larger sample (100 employees and 15 managers) in one of 13 settings. Participants in this study came from a wide range of employment settings, including human services, hospitals, universities, restaurants, movie theaters, and department stores. The researchers found that the mean correlation was .25, and revealed that managers were able to predict the most valuable item on only 36% of occasions. This line of research suggests that managers should not rely on their personal knowledge and judgement of what their employees would like to earn. Managers should instead use a formal preference assessment when determining what items to incorporate into an incentive plan.

Wilder et al. (2006) was the first formal treatment of preference assessment in the OBM literature. Preceding this publication, practitioners relied upon popular press recommendations to identify meaningful rewards. For example, Daniels (1989) recommended not simply asking employees what they would like to work for, because it is too easy for them to forget. Rather, they should rate specific items according to preference. Daniels recommended a survey method of assessment that required employees to rate a list of items based upon how much work they were willing to complete to obtain the item. The most common scale was: 0 = none at all, 1 = a little, 2 = some work, 3 = much work, and 4 = very much work. In this method, an item that received a rating of "3" or "4" was considered to be high-preference. Wilder et al. (2006) compared this procedure to that of a forced choice procedure found in the clinical literature (Fisher et al. 1992). The verbal forced choice procedure required participants to select from one of two stated potential reinforcers based upon preference. Each item was paired with every other item and items selected on 75% or greater opportunities were considered high-preference.

A reinforcer assessment was conducted after both preference assessment procedures were completed across identical sets of items. Participants, office assistants at a university, completed a simulated office task (filing papers) and the items from the assessment were made available contingent upon completing work. The reinforcer evaluation suggested that the survey assessment correctly identified more items that functioned as rewards and incorrectly classified high-preference items as low-preference less often.

In a follow-up investigation, Waldvogel and Dixon (2008) evaluated preferences in four staff members of a community-based residential setting for adults with acquired brain injury. Waldvogel and Dixon compared a ranking assessment that required participants to order potential items in terms of preference, to a multiple stimulus without replacement (MSWO) procedure often found to be effective in identifying preferences in clinical populations (DeLeon & Iwata 1996). The three most preferred and the three least preferred items from the ranking assessment were included in the MSWO. The MSWO was conducted by allowing participants to choose an item, then shuffling the remaining items, and having them select again. In this way, the MSWO created a hierarchy of items. For one out of four participants the preference results were identical between assessments, but there were significant differences in preference designation for the other three participants, suggesting significant variations in high-preference item identification between the two assessments.

Finally, Wine et al. (2014) compared the MSWO and ranking assessment evaluated in Waldvogel and Dixon (2008) to the survey procedure found to be effective in Wilder et al. (2006). The MSWO took the most time to conduct and was least preferred by the participants after a social validity measure was conducted. While both the ranking procedure and the survey were effective at identifying preferences, the survey identified several more rewards that the ranking procedure missed—likely the survey was more effective because it evaluates each item separately instead of forcing a rank distribution. In summary, the research suggests that the survey procedure is the preference assessment of choice for use with employees, as illustrated in Figure 3.1.

After using the survey to identify preferences for employees, management must remember that preferences are not static. Wine et al. (2012) found that when consecutive monthly preference assessments for an identical list of items were compared to an initial preference assessment, preferences in employees varied considerably, and the same results were never observed twice. The implications of shifting preferences in terms of an incentive program will be discussed later, but it is recommended that preference assessments are delivered at regular time intervals to account for shifts in preference. For example, Wine et al. (2014) measured changes in preference of administrative assistants or technical specialists

Name: Date:

For each of the listed items please select a score, based upon the following scale, indicating how much work you would be willing to complete to receive the item:

0 = none at all, 1 = a little, 2 = some work, 3 = much work, and 4 = very much work

Item 1

0   1   2   3   4

Item 2

0   1   2   3   4

Item 3

0   1   2   3   4

Item 4

0   1   2   3   4

Item 5

0   1   2   3   4

FIGURE 3.1 Sample preference assessment survey

in a university setting. The intervals evaluated preference at four weeks, three weeks, two weeks, and one week. Only the one-week interval contained no shifts from high-preference to low-preference. A reasonable recommendation for managers, therefore, is to evaluate preferences in employees weekly for as long as incentive systems are in place.

Variables Impacting Reward Effectiveness

Conducting preference assessments is only the first step in developing a comprehensive incentive system. While the specifics of developing one of the many variants of incentive systems will be covered in another chapter of this text, we will discuss some basic concepts related to delivering rewards and how preference assessments impact certain variables. When considering effectiveness of a system that provides contingent rewards, there are several influential variables, namely momentary preference for an item, delay in delivery, probability that the reward will be delivered once earned, and magnitude of the reward. Of these variables, we have discussed preference in detail.

In applied settings, including HSOs, delivery of items to employees is usually delayed. Throughout this chapter we have mostly avoided using the term "reinforcer" as opposed to "reward" because it seems unlikely that a manager would be present to deliver an item the exact moment the employee successfully completes a task. In OBM, research delays vary by study. For example, Slowiak et al. (2006) describe earned items as being delivered twice per week. Other studies describe interventions such as lotteries that pay out up to a month after earning entry (e.g., Pampino et al., 2004). Of related interest, Malott et al. (1993) reviewed studies involving typically developed adult populations published in the *Journal of Organizational Behavior Management* and the *Journal of Applied Behavior Analysis* between 1980 and 1989. All of the studies reviewed that used consequences designed to increase behavior contained delays that were too long for the contingencies to be considered direct-acting.

To date, only one study has systematically evaluated delay. Wine et al. (2019) first conducted a reinforcer assessment of highly preferred items in a filing task completed by individuals working in a school serving children diagnosed with ASD. The participants were responsible for implementing acquisition plans based on individual education plans and behavior plans designed to decrease problem behavior. The reinforcer assessment demonstrated that participants were not willing to work for control items and that high-preference items functioned as reinforcers when earned items were delivered as soon as the session terminated. After the reinforcer assessment, the same reinforcers were evaluated in a progressive delay to delivery paradigm in which the participants were told they could earn items that would be delivered after a specified period of time elapsed. The first delay was one day, followed by 2 days, 4 days, 8 days, 16 days, and 32 days. Based on the existing literature, 32 days, or approximately one month, was selected as the longest interval that most employees would likely have to wait to receive an item. For all four participants there was no clear decrement in responding resulting from the various delays. These data suggest that a delay, in and of itself, of up to 32 days does not negatively impact work completed. Although a preliminary analog evaluation, delay to delivery in employees does not appear to have the catastrophic effects seen in other populations (Lattal, 2010).

Another variable, probability of delivery, refers to the likelihood that the actual item earned will be delivered, not the likelihood that another item will be delivered in its place. In a third study within Wine et al. (2019), a 32-day reward delay remained constant while manipulating probabilities of reward delivery. Participants were told before each session that they would receive their rewards in 32 days with 1.0, .5, or .1 probabilities. After employees completed each session, the experimenter determined whether or not they had received the item and informed the participant. Results across two participants suggested that a 1.0 probability produced the greatest increases in responding relative to baseline. A .5 probability resulted in a more modest increase in responding relative to baseline, but a .1 probability did not increase responding above baseline. This series of studies suggests that while delivering earned items immediately may not be necessary, managers should attempt to keep the probability of earned items as close to 1.0 as possible. Restated, failing to deliver items once they are earned will likely have a significant detrimental effect on incentive plans.

The final variable, magnitude of rewards, can be conceptualized as how much an item is worth. For example, a gift card could be programmed to be worth $5, $1,000, or any other value. We are not aware of any formal analyses of what magnitudes of rewards are effective in maintaining responding in employees. However, some clinical work suggests that larger magnitudes are preferred (Trosclair-Lasserre et al., 2008). In the extant literature using tangibles, the worth of the items seems to vary by study. However, attempting to glean guidelines from these studies is confounded because the research was conducted using various implementation strategies over time and so inflation would make definitive calculations difficult. For example, Jessup and Stahelski (1999) implemented a multiple component intervention that included a $25 incentive for approximately 12 weeks of work. Slowiak (2014) also implemented a multiple component intervention that included an incentive condition where participants could earn up to $25 over two and a half weeks. Given inflation, the incentive used in Jessup and Stahelski was worth approximately $38 in 2014. So, the incentive found in Slowiak was worth significantly more at approximately $10 per week ($25 divided by 2.5) compared to Jessup and Stahelski's approximately $3.16 per week ($38 divided by 12 weeks). It is clear that these types of calculations quickly become cumbersome. Moreover, in employee populations it could be that the base pay the employees receive influences the effectiveness of incentives. In the absence of empirically derived guidelines, management will have to use best judgment based upon the funds available to select a magnitude that is both meaningful but affordable.

Conclusion

Incentives are likely to continue to be a popular intervention in the area of performance management. The effective implementation of an incentive system is predicated on management conducting several steps. First, members of management must acknowledge that they likely cannot predict what their employees

will find valuable and so preference assessments are warranted—the most effective of which is the survey assessment. Additionally, preferences change over
time, and so weekly re-assessments of items, if one is not using money, are warranted. Management may elect to avoid the problems associated with delivering
specific items through the use of catalogs, or other methods to allow employees
to choose from a variety of options, when reward criteria are met. In these situations, management may still find occasional preference assessment helpful in
identifying items to populate the catalog.

When examining the likelihood of rewards impacting change, a well-designed
incentive system is required. Within such a system, care should be taken to
ensure that items earned are always delivered—this includes ensuring that
the high-preference item is earned and not another, lower-preference item. An
occasional delay in the delivery of items is likely not detrimental to an incentive
system—as long as the probability remains high and the employees are told
when the items will be delivered. Lastly, empirical evidence regarding magnitude is not available, so management will have to evaluate the values of incentives on a case-by-case basis.

Finally, the extant research literature suggests several implications for assessing employee preferences for incentives within HSOs serving persons with
intellectual and developmental disabilities. HSOs typically rely on many
employees to implement behavior or wellness plans but are not always able
to compete with other industries through compensation. Incentive systems,
through the use of preference assessments, can often contain activities and
privileges that do not cost the organization much, if anything. Lastly, it should
be noted that well-designed incentive systems are not a substitute for other
components of effective management, such as pinpointing, monitoring, goal
setting, and feedback. Incentive systems can be effective as a component of
a well-designed management system and they can be of particular assistance
during high-effort periods. Future research is needed in this area, but HSOs
often contain brief periods where extra effort is required (e.g., intakes and
audits). It could be that the judicious use of highly preferred items contingently delivered during these periods is beneficial for employees both in terms
of increasing effort but in feeling appreciated for the additional hours and
stress that often accompanies these times.

References

Condly, S. J., Clark, R. E., & Stolovitch, H. D. (2003). The effects of incentives on
    workplace performance: A meta-analytic review of research studies. *Performance
    Improvement Quarterly, 16*, 46–63.

Daniels, A. C., (1989). *Performance management: Improving quality productivity through positive reinforcement* (3rd ed., revised). Tucker, GA: Performance Management Publications.

DeLeon, I. G., & Iwata, B. A. (1996). Evaluation of a multiple-stimulus presentation format for assessing reinforcer preferences. *Journal of Applied Behavior Analysis, 29,* 519–533. doi: 10.1901/jaba.1996.29-519.

Fisher, W., Piazza, C. C., Bowman, L. G., Hagopian, L. P., Owens, J. C., & Slevin, I. (1992). A comparison of two approaches for identifying reinforcers for persons with severe and profound disabilities. *Journal of Applied Behavior Analysis, 25,* 491–498. doi: 10.1901/jaba.1992.25-491.

Incentive Federation Incorporated (2016). *Incentive marketplace estimate research study.* Retrieved from http://theirf.org/research/incentive-marketplace-estimate-research -study/1836/.

Jessup, P. A., & Stahelski, A. J. (1999). The effects of a combined goal setting, feedback and incentive intervention on job performance in a manufacturing environment. *Journal of Organizational Behavior Management, 19,* 5–26. doi: 10.1300/ J075v19n03_02.

Lattal, K. A. (2010). Delayed reinforcement of operant behavior. *Journal of the Experimental Analysis of Behavior, 93,* 129–139. doi: 10.1901/jeab.2010.93-129.

Malott, R. W., Shimamune, S., & Malott, M. E. (1993). Rule-governed behavior and organizational behavior management: An analysis of interventions. *Journal of Organizational Behavior Management, 12,* 103–116. doi: 10.1300/J075v12n02_09.

Pampino, J. R. N., Heering, P. W., Wilder, D. A., Barton, C. G., & Burson, L. M. (2004). The use of the performance diagnostic checklist to guide intervention selection in an independently owned coffee shop. *Journal of Organizational Behavior Management 23,* 5–19. doi: 10.1300/J075v23n02_02.

Slowiak, J. M. (2014). "How may I help you?" Improving telephone customer service in a medical clinic setting. *Journal of Organizational Behavior Management, 34,* 39–51. doi: 10.1080/01608061.2013.873382

Slowiak, J. M., Madden, G. J., & Mathews, R. (2006). The effects of a combined task clarification, goal setting, feedback, and performance contingent consequence intervention package on telephone customer service in a medical clinic environment. *Journal of Organizational Behavior Management, 25,* 15–34. doi: 10.1300/J075n25n04_02.

Trosclair-Lasserre, N. M., Lerman, D. C., Call, N. A., Addison, L. R., and Kodak, T. (2008). Reinforcement magnitude: An evaluation of preference and reinforce efficacy. *Journal of Applied Behavior Analysis, 41,* 203–220. Doi: 10.1901/jaba.2008.41-203.

Waldvogel, J. M., & Dixon, M. R. (2008). Exploring the utility of preference assessments in organizational behavior management. *Journal of Organizational Behavior Management, 28*, 76–87. Doi: 10.1080/0160802006831.

Wilder, D. A., Harris, C., Casella, S., Wine, B., & Postma, N. (2011). Further evaluation of the accuracy of managerial prediction of employee preference. *Journal of Organizational Behavior Management, 31*, 130–139. Doi: 10.1080/-1608061.2011.569202.

Wilder, D. A., Rost, K., & McMahon M. (2007). The accuracy of managerial prediction of employee preference: A brief report. *Journal of Organizational Behavior Management, 27*, 1–14. Doi: 10.1300/J075v27n02_01.

Wilder, D. A., Therrien, K., & Wine, B. (2006). A comparison between survey and verbal choice methods of identifying potential reinforcers among employees. *Journal of Organizational Behavior Management, 25*, 1–13. Doi: 10.1300/J075v25n04_01.

Wine, B. & Axelrod, S. (2014). The effects of progressively thinning high-preference item delivery on responding in employees, *Journal of Organizational Behavior Management, 34*, 291–299. Doi: 10.1080/01608061.2014.973629.

Wine, B., Chen, T., & Brewer, A. (2019). An examination of reward probability and delivery delays on employee performance. *Journal of Organizational Behavior Management*. Doi: 10.1080/01608061.2019.1666776.

Wine, B., Gilroy, S., & Hantula, D. A. (2012). Temporal (in)stability of employee preference for rewards. *Journal of Organizational Behavior Management, 32*, 58–64. Doi: 10.1080/01608061.2012.646854.

Wine, B., Gugliemella C., & Axelrod, S. (2013). An examination of generalized-conditioned reinforcers in stimulus preference assessments. *Journal of Organizational Behavior Management, 33*, 244–251. DOI: 10.1080/01608061.2013.843433.

Wine, B., Kelley III, D. P. & Wilder, D. A. (2014). An initial assessment of effective preference assessment intervals among employees. *Journal of Organizational Behavior Management, 34*, 188–195. DOI: 10.1080/01608061.2014.944747.

Wine, B., Reis, M., & Hantula, D. A. (2014). An evaluation of preference assessment methodology in organizational behavior management. *Journal of Organizational Behavior Management, 34*, 7–15. Doi: 10.1080/01608061.2013.873379.

4
Social Validity Assessment

James K. Luiselli

Montrose Wolf introduced social validity to the professional community in a seminal article published in the *Journal of Applied Behavior Analysis*. The year was 1978. His rationale for explaining social validity and how it should be assessed emanated from fundamental applied behavior analysis (ABA) concepts of practicing with social responsibility and producing socially meaningful outcomes (Baer et al., 1968). Specifically, Wolf (1978) proposed that "It seems that if we aspire to social importance, then we must develop systems that allow our consumers to provide us feedback about how our applications relate to their values, to their reinforcers" (p. 213). Further, subjective measurement represented "an attempt to assess the dimensions of complex reinforcers in socially acceptable and practical ways" (p. 213). Consumer values, feedback, and recommendations about services and outcomes would eventually become common nomenclature among ABA practitioners serving persons with intellectual and developmental disabilities (IDD).

In defining social validity, Wolf (1978) suggested that assessment should be directed at three levels. First, what is the social significance of intervention goals, are they justified, and how should measurement be conducted? Second, do service recipients consider intervention procedures to be socially appropriate? And third, what is the social importance of intervention effects, both immediate and long-term? At the time of Wolf (1978), these questions were rarely posed in behavioral practice and research, formal social validity assessment guidelines had not been developed, and more than a few behavior analysts were skeptical about including subjective measurement within the natural science empiricism of ABA.

Gradually, the concepts and principles of social validity found greater traction and application within the ABA professional community. For example, Finney (1991) noted that "Wolf's (1978) paper on social validity changed most behavior analysts' views about how to judge the importance of research findings" (p. 245). That is, judgments about the effectiveness of interventions could not and should not be based solely on whether target behaviors and skills improved. Rather, did the researchers also measure the attitudes and opinions of service recipients about their approval of and satisfaction with the intervention procedures? Such information would be vital for determining whether those procedures should continue to be implemented, recommended, or abandoned.

Similarly, Van Houten (1979), Fawcett (1991), and Hawkins (1991) emphasized the contribution of social validity assessment toward identifying norm-referenced intervention objectives, specific procedures that reasonably fit with proposed goals, and broad indicators of post-intervention effectiveness. Among several research recommendations, Schwartz and Baer (1991) stressed assessing social validity (a) before, during, and following intervention, and (b) with both direct and indirect consumers of services. Most critically, social validity assessment must be accurate by not assessing the opinions of the wrong consumers, incorrectly assessing the opinions of the proper consumers, or correctly assessing the opinions of the proper consumers but not responding to the acquired feedback. Finally, there should be concern about *social invalidity*, or "the behaviors of consumers who not only disapprove of some component in the ongoing program but are going to do something about their disapproval" (p. 190).

Relative to organizational behavior management (OBM) within human services organizations (HSOs), social validity assessment aligns closely with organizational support theory (OST: Eisenberger & Stinglhamber, 2011) and perceived organizational support (POS: Rhodes & Eisenberger, 2002). In particular, POS stipulates that "Employees develop a general perception concerning the extent to which the organization values their contributions and cares about their wellbeing" (Kurtessis et al., 2015). When POS is high, employees report less occupational stress (Shaw et al., 2013), perform more competently (Rhodes & Eisenberger, 2002), and have greater job satisfaction (Eisenberger et al., 1997). Some of the factors positively influencing POS appear to be discretionary organizational practices such as providing desirable environmental conditions, equitable treatment of employees, supervisor support, fairness, and effective leadership (Eisenberger et al., 2016). In effect, organizations function optimally when leaders strategically solicit, review, and respond with noticeable desired outcomes to the assessed occupational priorities of employees.

The need for and contribution of social validity assessment within human services organizations was articulated by Gravina et al. (2018), who cautioned that "human service organizations often come under scrutiny for a variety of reasons including inefficient use of resources, poor quality of service delivery, poor record keeping, client and worker safety concerns, and in rare cases, abuse and neglect" (p. 1). It makes sense that the acceptance, satisfaction, and approval of interventions, corrective actions, and policy decisions to rectify these and related performance deficiencies should be assessed with service recipients, consumers, and stakeholders. And yet, in reviewing OBM research in human services organizations published in three peer-reviewed journals from 1990 to 2016 (*Journal of Applied Behavior Analysis, Journal of Organizational Behavior Management, Behavior Analysis in Practice*), Gravina et al. (2018) found that social validity measures of "quality of engagement/interaction between the staff and target client/consumers or staff members' job satisfaction" were represented in only 11.4%–28.6% of articles. This finding is consistent with 12% of articles reporting social validity assessment that Ferguson et al. (2018) documented in the *Journal of Applied Behavior Analysis* for the period of 1999 to 2016. It would appear that notwithstanding the integral role social validity assessment plays in program evaluation, both ABA and the sub-specialty of OBM (Luke et al., 2018) have yet to fully embrace its contribution to service and research.

This chapter addresses social validity assessment as a vital component of OBM within human services organizations serving persons with intellectual and developmental disabilities (IDD). I begin by describing a framework that is designed to measure social validity among several consumer groups and performance indicators. Next, the chapter reviews social validity assessment research pertinent to human services organization priorities such as training and supervision, procedural fidelity, instituting incentive-based systems, and soliciting program recommendations from employees. The concluding section of the chapter outlines guidelines for integrating and supporting social validity assessment at a systems level and within OBM research.

OBM Framework for Social Validity Assessment

The mission statement of a human service organization will define many purposes of social validity assessment that pertain to the values that drive the organization's operation, goals to be achieved by service recipients, acceptable methods, and outcomes produced. In keeping with the concepts outlined by Wolf (1978) and emerging practice and research trends (Commons & Lane, 2017), assessment should approach social validity of human services organization objectives, procedures, and results, ideally conducted before, during, and following intervention.

Consumer Groups

Direct service recipients represent the primary consumer group for social validity assessment. While acknowledging the cognitive and communication limitations of many persons who have intellectual and developmental disabilities (IDD), human services organizations should elicit their feedback whenever possible. For example, Cunningham et al. (2003) included adults with IDD when assessing social validity of physical restraint procedures as rated by undergraduate students and residential care providers. Using verbal cues and modified language to support functional communication, the adults were asked, "How would you feel if you saw this happening?" and "How would you feel if this happened to you?" after viewing three physical restraint procedures being implemented in video recordings. They were also prompted to rate acceptability of each procedure. The assessment found that the responses by the adults with IDD closely matched the ratings recorded by the students and care providers as to the most acceptable methods of physical restraint.

The parents and guardians of service recipients can also be considered primary consumers for social validity assessment. Referencing physical restraint procedures again, Luiselli et al. (2017) queried the parents-guardians (N = 27) of adults who had IDD and attended a community-based day and residential habilitation setting. Conducted during telephone interviews, the parents-guardians responded to a 12-item questionnaire (Table 4.1) that posed statements about the rationale-justification, training, implementation, and effectiveness of physical restraint with their daughters and sons, rating each statement on a Likert scale (1: strongly disagree, 2: disagree, 3: neither disagree or agree, 4: agree, 5: strongly agree). The assessment revealed that most of the parents-guardians agreed that physical restraint should only be used if less restrictive procedures have failed and can be adapted to ensure safety during application. By endorsing conventionally accepted practice standards for physical restraint (Reed et al., 2013), these responses represented a good measure of social validation. Other findings indicated that parents-guardians would benefit from more information about the therapeutic purposes of physical restraint, procedural guidelines that care providers must follow, and the format for training at the habilitation setting. These are critical areas that human services organizations should consider when employing physical restraint as a clinically justified method of crisis intervention and behavior support.

Third, care providers who implement intervention procedures with service recipients should be assessed as direct consumers, namely teachers, therapists, behavior analysts, vocational instructors, residential staff, and the like. Judgments by care providers would pertain to how they are trained, supervised, and supported in their job responsibilities. Like Cunningham et al. (2003) with service recipients and Luiselli et al. (2017) with parents-guardians, Luiselli et al. (2015) surveyed care providers (N = 25) of adults with IDD about their opinions of physical restraint as one component of behavioral intervention implemented at a community-based habilitation setting. The results confirmed uniformly high

TABLE 4.1 Domains and statements comprising a parent-guardian social validity questionnaire concerned with physical restraint

Domain	Statements
Rationale-Justification	Physical restraint is sometimes needed to ensure safety of my family members
	Physical restraint should only be used if less intensive intervention procedures have failed
	Physical restraint is an acceptable procedure for behavior support
Training	The training that staff receive allows them to implement physical restraint safely
	The training that staff receive teaches them methods to avoid using physical restraint
	The training that staff receive teaches them to use physical restraint as one component of a behavior support plan
	I am confident that staff who implement physical restraint are properly trained to do so
Implementation	Staff are able to implement physical restraint without harming the person being restrained
	Staff are able to implement physical restraint without harming themselves
	If needed, physical restraint can be adapted to ensure safety and minimal-to-no risk
Effectiveness	Physical restraint is an effective intervention procedure
	Physical restraint makes it possible for individuals to progress and achieve a better quality of life

From: Luiselli, J. K., Sperry, J. M., Draper, C., & Richards, C. (2017). Parent-guardian evaluation of physical restraint among adults with intellectual disability: A social validity assessment. *Advances in Neurodevelopmental Disorders, 1,* 73–78.

acceptance ratings by the care providers but also more equivocal impressions of physical restraint as a method of behavior support and contributing to a better quality of life for the adults served. The implication from these findings was that the care providers were comfortable and confident applying physical restraint and more generally that "the strength of social validity assessment is enabling program administrators and supervisors to develop and sustain the most effective, safe, justified, and humane implementation policies and practices" (p. 174).

There are a considerable number of indirect consumers that human services organizations should address through social validity assessment, such as (a) referral and funding sources (e.g., public schools, state agencies), (b) neighbors, (c) extended community members, (d) transportation drivers, and (e) advisory boards. These groups do not typically engage with direct consumers but observe and experience interactions sufficient to form opinions about how human services organizations operate and care for service recipients. Both Wolf (1978) and later commentators were explicit that social validity assessment should apply to this broad sample of consumers whose feedback can be used to sustain acceptable practices, effect meaningful change, and enhance viability of programs in the community (Schwartz & Baer, 1991).

Dimensions of Social Validity Assessment

The common dimensions of social validity assessment are consumer acceptance and approval of the services they received, implemented, and witnessed being applied for and by other individuals. Think of assessment conducted with students at a private special education school who rate a classroom-wide incentive program applied with them. Assessment of social validity should also extend to the teachers implementing the program, parents of the students, and city and town administrators responsible for private school placement. In lay language, acceptance and approval translates to a measure of consumer satisfaction. Consumer choice of services and procedures is also incorporated within social validity assessment of ABA practices. That is, service recipients can be taught to select and care providers observed implementing intervention procedures as empirical indicators of preference and approval (Davis et al., 2000; Gabor et al., 2016; Hanley, 2010).

As noted previously, social validity assessment is relevant before, during, and following intervention. Many assessment indicators apply equally at these time points. For example, consumers could be asked before and after intervention whether behavior change objectives are or were (a) reasonable, (b) norm-referenced, (c) non-stigmatizing, and (d) achievable. During intervention, social validity assessment would concentrate on factors associated with procedural efficiency, practicality, and fidelity. Effectiveness during and following intervention considers obvious outcome measures (e.g., reduced frequency of challenging behaviors, increased percentage of acquired learning objectives) but also absence of negative side effects, evidence of generalization and maintenance, and improved quality of life. A multidimensional approach toward social validity assessment will yield the most comprehensive evaluation of HSO objectives, practices, and outcomes affecting the largest number of direct and indirect consumers.

Assessment Methodology

Social validity assessment is usually conducted by having consumers complete a questionnaire, survey, or rating form. These documents contain either declarative statements (e.g., "The computer-based instructional program was effective.") or queries (e.g., "Do you think the supervision strategy was easy to implement?"). Among other factors, discussed below, the response options available to consumers depend on how items are worded and presented.

First, the social validity assessment document should be as comprehensive as possible in order to capture information most vital to the human services organization. However, consumers may react negatively to a lengthy and complex questionnaire or survey by "tuning out" and responding to items inaccurately and indiscriminately. Although there are no absolute rules or guidelines for preparing a social validity assessment document, a reasonable benchmark is to include no more than 5–10 items that can be presented in no more than 1–2 pages. Of course, there may be situations in which more items are needed to properly assess the breadth of service delivery and relevant dimensions of social validity. In such cases, the alternative is to design several shorter-item documents that can be administered separately over an acceptable period of time; for example, one questionnaire each week for three weeks.

Schwartz and Baer (1991) advised that a social validity assessment document "use scales that invite a workably wide variation in consumers' responses" (p. 198). Likert scales, as depicted earlier, are the conventional metric distributed across a five-to-seven-point continuum such as 1: strongly disagree, 2: disagree, 3: neither disagree or agree, 4: agree, 5: strongly agree; or 1: poor, 2: fair, 3: no opinion, 4: good, 5: excellent. Fewer points could be acceptable, however, depending on the objectives of social validity assessment and information content. In this regard, simple binary ratings of "yes" and "no" or "agree" and "disagree" may be sufficient.

Other document construction guidelines proposed by Schwartz and Baer (1991) were (a) ensuring discriminability among ratings, (b) designating the period of time being assessed, (c) addressing the most highly regarded indices of social validity, and (d) being "as specific as possible, because increased specificity may increase the usefulness of information collected from social validity questionnaires" (p. 198). These and the previously referenced guidelines make it clear that the overriding concerns of HSOs conducting social validity assessment should be to facilitate comprehension of requested information and to simplify the process of recording ratings among consumers.

Some social validity documents encourage consumers to add narrative responses beyond their numerical scale ratings. Figure 4.1 illustrates a questionnaire that was intended to assess the opinions of care providers who implemented a student-specific behavior support plan. For any "strongly disagree" or "disagree" ratings, the care providers were requested to briefly explain their responses. This

| Child-Adult: |
| Setting: |
| Respondent Name (or anonymous): |
| Date: |

Instructions: Please record your opinions about the behavior support plan (BSP) you implemented with the child-adult during September-December 2018 to treat aggression by checking one rating for each statement.

Statements	Ratings				
	1: Strongly Disagree	2: Disagree	3: No Opinion	4: Agree	5: Strongly Agree
The BSP was easy to learn and I understood all of the procedures					
If you selected Rating #1 or #2, please explain:					
The BSP procedures were easy to implement					
If you selected Rating #1 or #2, please explain:					
The BSP properly addressed intervention objectives					
If you selected Rating #1 or #2, please explain:					
I was trained effectively to implement the BSP					
If you selected Rating #1 or #2, please explain:					
The child-adult responded positively to the BSP					
If you selected Rating #1 or #2, please explain:					
I would recommend the BSP for other children-adults					
If you selected Rating #1 or #2, please explain:					
Additional Comments					

FIGURE 4.1 Intervention social validity assessment form

information is valuable because it can inform decisions about how future behavior support plans should be written, the types of procedures in those plans, and the methods used to train care providers. Many social validity assessment documents will also have a "general comments" section available to consumers. As qualitative measures, narrative entries can be assigned category classifications that reflect the most common themes and issues raised by consumers (Rothschild et al., 2019).

The methodology for conducting social validity assessment also considers procedures for distributing and collecting documents. Distribution priorities are encompassing the largest number of consumers and achieving 100% return rate. Further, the process of distributing and completing social validity documents should promote independent responding by consumers. One approach is to gather consumers in groups headed by an assigned leader who explains and distributes a social validity assessment document to them at the same time. This format guarantees that consumers do not confer with each other and all completed documents are returned. Such an arrangement may be less than desirable due to possible reactivity among consumers in the presence of the group leader. Procedures to avoid reactivity would be telling consumers that they should complete the social validity assessment anonymously and using relatively unfamiliar persons to explain, pass out, and collect documents.

In some situations, the human services organization will not be able to assemble groups of consumers centrally and at the same time. Hardcopy social validity assessment documents can be delivered or mailed to consumers, requesting that they return the completed documents to a specific location (e.g., deposit box in a school office) or mailing address by a deadline date. The disadvantages of this method are that some consumers may not respond independently or return documents as instructed. Performing assessment through email-delivered and internet-based electronic surveys is one alternative to hardcopy distribution, but, similarly, consumers are able to confer with each other and return rate may be less than 100%.

Another methodological consideration is establishing a protocol to summarize the data obtained from social validity assessment so that action plans can be proposed in response to consumer feedback. Management of the data can be arranged by averaging the numerical ratings for each item in the document and rank ordering from highest to lowest acceptance and approval. Categorized qualitative measures can also be organized similarly. With these data in hand, administrators, supervisors, program directors, and other responsible personnel can evaluate the basis and accuracy of low-ranking items relative to the needs and performance objectives of the human services organization. Optimally, the consumers who were assessed can be further consulted and invited to participate in project teams aimed at performance improvement that was informed through social validity assessment.

Social Validity Assessment Research Examples

Social validity assessment has been conducted in several areas of research within human services organizations, although not extensively. Notably, the studies reviewed in this section incorporated assessment methodologies that were practical, addressed recognized performance improvement objectives, and have good generality across multiple settings serving persons with IDD.

Training, Supervision, and Service Delivery

Miller et al. (2014) evaluated a performance improvement intervention with educators (N = 3) conducting discrete trial instruction with students at a special education school. Intervention was implemented to increase fidelity of instruction through (a) verbal and graphic feedback from a supervisor, (b) correction, and (c) performance-contingent access to a weekly gift certificate. When intervention concluded, the educators completed a three-item Likert scale survey about "how helpful they found the study, how interested they would be in receiving future feedback, and how satisfied they were with the study overall" (p. 35). The survey also featured open-ended questions to further assess positive and negative perception of the multi-component intervention. The survey results revealed that the educators were receptive to and interested in continued use of the performance improvement procedures. Another outcome from the social validity assessment was recognition that feedback from the supervisor identified performance weaknesses and correction plans.

Luiselli et al. (2010) reported a study that evaluated the effects of a training program to teach ABA knowledge competencies to care providers (N = 35) of adults with IDD. The care providers participated in small group sessions with a lead trainer who delivered three successive instructional modules (measurement, behavior support, skill acquisition) through slide presentations, video clips, demonstration, and practice activities. Upon completion of each module, the care providers filled out a six-item social validity questionnaire according to a five-point Likert scale (1: strongly disagree, 2: disagree, 3: neither disagree or agree, 4: agree, 5: strongly agree). Table 4.2 shows the questionnaire items and average ratings for all of the modules across five training groups. These findings were interpreted as the care providers strongly endorsing the content, methods, and benefits of the training program, noting, however, that care providers in one of the groups were more equivocal in their ratings of trainer communication and session duration. Possible outcomes from a social validity assessment of this type would be documenting implementation fidelity to ensure uniform and comprehensible communication among trainers within reasonable session time.

Noting such challenges as limited resources, employee attrition, and need for exemplary service integrity facing HSOs, Gravina and Austin (2018) conducted social validity assessment with senior therapists (N = 13) involved in consultant-delivered workshop sessions at a human services organization serving individuals with autism spectrum disorder (ASD). During four, full-day workshops over five months, the consultant trained the senior therapists to design and implement OBM performance improvement projects with their staff. Relative to social validity, six of the senior therapists who were available at a 2.5-year post-training follow-up reported that the training they received was "interactive,

TABLE 4.2 Social validity ratings of care providers participating in ABA training (1: strongly disagree, 2: disagree, 3: no opinion, 4: agree, 5: strongly agree)

Statements	Groups and Average Rating				
	A	B	C	D	E
I learned something new from this training	4.4	4.7	4.8	4.6	4
The information provided in the training is important for me to know	4.8	5	4.8	5	4.7
The trainer communicated content clearly	5	5	5	4.4	3.8
The material and media clips were useful	4.4	4.7	4.8	4.4	4
There was sufficient time to cover the training information	5	5	5	4.4.	3.8
The training will be of value at my new job	4.8	5	4.8	4.6	4.2

From: Luiselli, J. K., Bass, J. D., & Whitcomb, S. A. (2010). Teaching applied behavior analysis knowledge competencies to direct-care service providers: Outcome assessment and social validation of a training program. *Behavior Modification, 34*, 403–414.

engaging, personalized, and relevant," and would continue to use some of the procedures they had learned during the workshops. The social validity assessment also found that the senior therapists judged the consultation model too time-consuming, suggested further training was needed, and perhaps most informative, "desired more organizational support for continuing the performance management process" (p. 10). This latter result illustrates the value and contribution of social validity assessment within HSOs, specifically employee endorsement of organizational-led initiatives to improve workforce performance that produces valued outcomes.

At Melmark New England, a human services organization for children and adults with IDD, we have approached social validity assessment as a routine strategy to evaluate acceptance and approval of training, supervision, and service procedures with care providers and other consumers. In Gerald et al. (2019), classroom instructors (N = 9) implemented a self-monitoring intervention to improve scheduled data recording and rated several dimensions of the intervention concerned with effectiveness, application, and recommendation to other care providers. Shlesinger et al. (2019) reported implementation integrity of a computer-assisted sleep monitoring system by residential care providers (N = 20) and their social validity ratings of how easy it was to understand, learn, and apply the system. The consumers in Duhanyan et al (2020) were parents of four students who participated in a multi-year health and wellness intervention to reduce weight and body mass index (BMI). The parents responded to an online survey with their impressions about the health needs of their children, importance of maintaining desirable weight, and positive effects of the residential intervention. As noted previously and emphasized throughout this chapter, the systematic social validation illustrated in these studies enables human services organizations to pinpoint relative strengths and weaknesses of training, supervision, and service delivery, making it possible to revise and create OBM projects that have consumer support.

Consumer Preferences

Reed et al. (2012) proposed that "The assessment and improvement of staff members' subjective valuation of non-preferred work tasks may be one way to increase the quality of staff members' work life" (p. 253). They approached assessment by directly measuring task preference choices of classroom teachers (N = 8) at a human services organization. A subsequent intervention was implemented that reinforced selection of non-preferred tasks by allowing the teachers in one classroom to select their lunch periods and teachers in a second classroom to select students they would work with during the first hour of the school day. The study demonstrated that the intervention was generally effective in shifting preferences of previously non-preferred tasks and the teachers reported overall acceptance on a modified version of the Intervention Rating Scale-15 (Martens et al., 1985). Some of the uniform social validity ratings were (a) "I would suggest the use of this intervention to other classrooms," (b) "If I were lead teacher, I would be willing to use this intervention in my classroom," (c) "The intervention is reasonable for the staff satisfaction problem described," and (d) "Overall, this intervention would be beneficial for staff." This study highlighted the matter of employee preferences related to performance on the job and how to positively influence task choices by evaluating consumer acceptance through social validity assessment.

Pittenger et al. (2014) conducted a social validity assessment of job satisfaction, resources, and support among educational care providers (N = 46) at a residential school for students with IDD. The questionnaire designed for this study included 40 positively and negatively worded statements the care providers endorsed on a four-point Likert scale (1: strongly agree, 2: agree, 3: disagree, 4: strongly disagree) within the categories of *resources* (e.g., "My classroom is organized with easy access to teaching materials" and "Most classroom materials are broken, old, or damaged") *roles and responsibilities* (e.g., I am aware of and understand how my work performance is assessed" and "There is not enough time in the regular workday to do everything that is expected of me"), *sense of support* (e.g., I received sufficient training to perform my job safely" and "I do not feel respected by my supervisors"), and *overall satisfaction* (e.g., "My school provides several staff incentives" and "The incentives and rewards provided by my school do not change how I feel about my job"). Apropos the ultimate goal of social validity assessment, Pittenger et al. (2014) summarized their findings with recommendations to school administrators responsible for organizational change. In the category of resources, there were suggestions to establish a materials and supplies sharing center at the school; create inventory lists to replace old, damaged, and depleted objects in the classrooms; and schedule more frequent observations from supervisors to promote environmental care. School administrators were advised to broaden communication with staff about personnel changes and revisions to the student population. Issues of performance incentives and rewards were an area of need revealed through assessment, leading to recommendations for incentive programs based on identified staff preferences and targeting exemplary attendance and intervention integrity among care providers.

An additional social validity assessment of care provider preferences by Strohmeier et al. (2014) concerned training methods to improve implementation integrity of behavior support plans by special education staff (N = 44) at a human services organization. The staff completed a questionnaire that inquired about their perceived receptivity to performance feedback as a method to promote integrity (very poor, somewhat poor, somewhat well, very well) and how likely integrity would improve by completing online training modules, receiving a financial incentive, and avoiding performance review meetings (very, unlikely, somewhat unlikely, somewhat likely, very likely). The results were that 77% of care providers reported they would respond "very well" to performance feedback and implementation integrity of behavior support plans would "very likely" improve through a performance incentive (52%), meeting avoidance (52%), and online training (32%). Thus, as documented through the *pre-training* social validity assessment of their preferences, a performance feedback training approach would be expected to have the greatest acceptance by care providers at this HSO.

Performance Incentive Systems

Some human services organizations introduce incentive systems to motivate and improve performance of care providers with money, gift certificates, time off, extra privileges, and similar "rewards" delivered contingently (Wine, 2017). These systems are often designed as lottery drawings in which care providers are eligible if they meet certain performance criteria such as properly completing paperwork (Cook & Dixon, 2008), achieving good procedural integrity (Miller et al., 2014), and not missing work (Luiselli et al., 2009). Planning effective incentive-based interventions requires, at the very least, another level of preference assessment—what do care providers identify as desirable performance-contingent objects and activities? Arbitrary selection of incentives by human services organization administrators without empirical support is discouraged because preferences typically vary among care providers, do not remain static, and are not the same for individuals at different levels of the organization.

Some OBM social validity research has evaluated methods to identify incentives, primarily in business settings, but applicable to human services organizations serving persons with IDD as well. Wine et al. (2014) evaluated three assessment methods with care providers (N = 3) at a residential setting including social validity ratings of how well they liked each one. Eight items had been identified as performance incentives before the study (e.g., gift cards for restaurants, movie rentals, coffee, electronics) and the care providers were queried about "what they would like to receive for completing extra work" (p. 9). With the *survey assessment* method, the care providers rated their preference for each incentive item on a five-point scale (0: none at all, 1: a little, 2: a fair amount, 3: much, 4: very much). The *ranking assessment* method required the care providers to order each of the eight incentive items from 1 (most preferred) to 8 (least preferred). The third assessment method, *multi stimulus without replacement* (MSWO), consisted of the care providers selecting index cards with written descriptions of each incentive item from least-to-most preferred.

Wine et al. (2014) found that all three assessment methods identified incentive items for the care providers and these items functioned as reinforcement when later tested on a data recording task. The social validity ratings revealed that the care providers judged the MSWO assessment method as least preferred, most complex, and having poor utility. A key implication from the study is that when conducting social validity assessments of incentives, HSOs should incorporate methods that care providers approve, thereby making it more likely they will provide informative answers to questions about their preferences.

Further, Wine et al. (2014) speculated that "Perhaps the value of preference assessments in OBM lies in detecting and excluding low-preference stimuli from performance improvement interventions rather than identifying differentially effective high-preference stimuli" (p. 15). Asking care providers within human services organizations to rate their acceptance and approval of assessment methods should validate approaches that yield the most valuable information for guiding decisions about performance incentive systems. For example, using a simple open-ended survey administered to residential group home care providers (N = 3), Buckley et al. (2020) documented that having case management tasks temporarily removed was the highest-ranking incentive, later applied successfully in a negative reinforcement performance improvement project to increase previously low occurrence data recording. Similarly, Griffin et al. (2019) incorporated a brief survey and found that "dress down" days, time off from client coverage, and a Visa check card were recorded as performance incentives by Registered Behavior Technicians (N = 8) at two ABA clinics for persons with ASD.

Summary and Conclusions

There are many reasons for human services organizations to incorporate social validity assessment when evaluating service delivery with persons who have IDD, the training and supervision of care providers, and impact within the larger community of stakeholders. Routine, systematic, and consequence-relevant social validity assessment identifies what HSOs "need to know" in order to be most effective with and valued by direct and indirect consumers. The guiding principles of social validity assessment are to acquire feedback from consumers that is accurate, meaningful, and comprehensive. Social validity assessment results, within an OBM framework, must then translate to successful human services organization performance improvement initiatives with individuals, groups, and systems (Luiselli, 2018b).

It would appear that the evolution of social validity assessment within ABA practice has led to procedures that can be reasonably adopted by most human services organizations. The methodologies discussed in this chapter make it possible to design and revise assessment documents that can inform practices and, in doing so, enable human services organizations to demonstrate allegiance with service recipients, care providers, and other consumer groups. The central message here is that human services organizations will build and maintain a satisfied and motivated workforce if administrators, operations managers, and supervisors assess the attitudes and opinions of their consumers concerning provision of services and respond purposefully to identified areas of need.

When conducting social validity assessment, OBM practitioners and researchers need to be aware of the distinction between consumer approval, acceptance, and preference, and the *effectiveness* of interventions, training programs, and performance improvement projects. For example, some care providers may approve a particular instructional strategy with students that is not necessarily the most effective approach for achieving skill acquisition. Or, observations of care providers may demonstrate that they prefer behavior reduction procedures which are easy to implement but have limited evidence support. At the same time, programmatic effectiveness is tied closely to social validity acceptance and approval (Luiselli, 2021) and predicts maintenance of behavioral intervention among practitioners (Kennedy, 2002). Ideally, human services organization administrators, operations managers, supervisors, and related personnel should establish internal processes for studying the relationship between acceptance, approval, and satisfaction ratings of direct and indirect consumers and the most desirable data-based outcome measures affected by the services provided.

Another priority for human services organizations serving persons with IDD is how to approach and conduct social validity assessment within general operations. One consideration is increased training of behavior analysts in OBM (Luke et al., 2018) and OST (Eisenberger & Stinglhamber, 2011) who can advocate for social validity assessment organization-wide in their roles as full-time employees or external consultants. Of course, many human services organizations will have to be educated about the scope and benefits of social validity assessment, including additional implementation guidance and support. This chapter described several human services organization social validity assessment projects that have been published and can be referenced as suitable exemplars for organizational leaders.

However, social validity assessment in OBM (Gravina et al., 2018) and general behavioral (Ferguson et al., 2018) research is lacking. Research informs empirically supported OBM practices (Gravina et al., 2018; Luiselli, 2018a; Wine & Pritchard, 2018) and, accordingly, more studies devoted to social validity will be instructive for human services organizations. Concerning impediments to social validity research, Carr et al. (1999) posited that editorial guidelines in peer-reviewed journals do not specify research criteria for social validity assessment. On this matter, the conclusion by Ferguson et al. (2018) was that "If the assessment of social validity is still important to members of our field, it may be beneficial for editorial boards to include formal recommendations and guidelines for when to include measures of social validity" (p. 8). Establishing journal policies about social validity would also extend to criteria that editorial board members and ad hoc experts should apply when reviewing manuscripts submitted for publication.

Carr et al. (1999) also speculated that social validity assessment in the research literature may be underrepresented because such measurement could be unreliable due to poor psychometric properties of standardized protocols and informal questionnaires and surveys. This situation could be corrected by ensuring that social validity assessments are conducted with co-occurring assessment of inter-rater agreement. Another direction is to compare the data and information from social validity assessment, for example, acceptance and approval of intervention and training procedures with the observed behavior and performance of service recipients and care providers (Hanley, 2010). Social validity in this scenario would be high if the ratings and behavior of direct consumers corresponded.

Finally, Ferguson et al. (2018) commented that the limited appearance of social validity assessment in behavior analytic journals may be the result of poor acceptance by practitioners and researchers. Through surveys administered to the behavior analysis community, individuals could be queried about their social validity assessment practices, methods, and dissemination. These findings could subsequently guide decisions about the curriculum content of ABA graduate training programs, focus of behavior analytic supervision (Valentino, 2021), and field placement experiences that will promote greater understanding and application of social validity assessment among pre-credentialed and early-career professionals. Survey findings could also assist the conference planning committees of agencies such as Association of Behavior Analysis International (ABAI) and Association of Professional Behavior Analysts (APBA) by encouraging symposium, workshop, and invited presentations on the topic of social validity assessment.

References

Baer, D. M., Wolf, M. M., & Risley, T. R. (1968). Some current dimensions of applied behavior analysis. *Journal of Applied Behavior Analysis*, *1*, 91–97. https://doi.org/10.1901/jaba.1968.1-91

Buckley, J., Fountain, J., Meuse, S., Whelan, C., Maguire, H., Harper, J. M., & Luiselli, J. K. (2020). Performance improvement of care providers in a child services setting: Effects of an incentive-based negative reinforcement intervention on data recording. *Child & Family Behavior Therapy*, *42*, 125–133.

Carr, J. E., Austin, J. L., Britton, L. N., Kellum, K. K., & Bailey, J. S. (1999). An assessment of social validity trends in applied behavior analysis. *Behavioral Interventions*, *14*, 223–231. https://doi.org/10.1002/(SICI)1099-078X(199910/12)14:4%3C223::AID-BIN37%3E3.0.CO;2-Y

Common, E. A., & Lane, K. L. (2017). Social validity assessment. In J. K. Luiselli (Ed.), *Applied behavior analysis advanced guidebook: A manual for professional practice* (pp. 73–92). New York: Elsevier/Academic Press. https://doi.org/10.1016/B978-0-12-811122-2.00004-8

Cook, T., & Dixon, M. R. (2008). Performance feedback and probabilistic bonus contingencies among employees in a human services program. *Journal of Organizational Behavior Management*, *25*, 45–63.

Cunningham, J., McDonnell, A., Easton, S., & Sturmey, P. (2003). Social validation data on three methods of physical restraint: Views of consumers, staff, and students. *Research in Developmental Disabilities*, *24*, 307–316. doi: 10.1007/s40617-015-0082-z

Davis, C. A., Reichle, J. E., & Southard, K. L. (2000). High-probability requests and a preferred item as a distractor: Increasing successful transitions in children with behavior problems. *Education and Treatment of Children, 23*, 423–440. https://iris.peabody.vanderbilt.edu/wp-content/...

Duhanyan, K., Shlesinger, A., Bird, F., Harper, J. M., & Luiselli, J. K. (2020). Reuding weight and body mass index (BMI) of adolescent students with autism spectrum disorder: Replication and social validation of a residential health and wellness intervention. *Advances in Neurodevelopmental Disorders, 4*, 168–175. https://doi.org/10.1007/s41252-020-00153-y

Eisenberger, R., Cummings, J., Armeli, S., & Lynch, P. (1997). Perceived organizational support, discretionary treatment, and job satisfaction. *Journal of Applied Psychology, 82*, 812–820. https://psycnet.apa.org/doi/10.1037/0021-9010.82.5.812

Eisenberger, R., & Stinglhamber, F. (2011). *Perceived organizational support: Fostering enthusiastic and productive employees.* Washington, DC: American Psychological Association.

Eisenberger, R., Malone, G. P., & Presson, W. D. (2016). *Optimizing perceived organizational support to enhance employee engagement.* Society for Human Resource Management.

Fawcett, S. B. (1991). Social validity: A note on methodology. *Journal of Applied Behavior Analysis, 24*, 235–239. https://doi.org/10.1901/jaba.1991.24-235

Ferguson, J. L., Cihon, J. H., Leaf, J. B., Van Meter, S. M., McEachin, J., & Leaf, R. (2018). Assessment of social validity trends in the journal of applied behavior analysis. *European Journal of Behavior Analysis, 20*, 146–157. https://doi.org/10.1080/15021149.2018.1534771

Finney, J. W. (1991). On further development of the concept of social validity. *Journal of Applied Behavior Analysis, 24*, 245–249. https://doi.org/10.1901/jaba.1991.24-245

Gabor, A. M., Fritz, J. N., Roath, C. T., Rothe, B. R., & Gourley, D. A. (2016). Caregiver preference for reinforcement-based interventions for problem behavior maintained by positive reinforcement. *Journal of Applied Behavior Analysis, 49*, 215–227. https://doi.org/10.1002/jaba.286

Gerald, D., Keeler, L., Mackey, K., Merrill, R., & Luiselli, J. K. (2019). Application of a self-management intervention to improve data recording of educational care providers. *Behavioral Interventions, 34*, 388–395. https://doi: 10.1080/00168890.2019.1690092

Gravina, N., & Austin, J. (2018). An evaluation of the consultant workshop model in a human service setting. *Journal of Organizational Behavior Management, 38*, 244–257. https://doi.org/10.1080/01608061.2017.1423149

Gravina, N., Villacorta, J., Albert, K., Clark, R., Curry, S., & Wilder, D. (2018). A literature review of organizational behavior management interventions in human service settings from 1990 to 2016. *Journal of Organizational Behavior Management*, 38, 191–224. https://doi: 10.1080/01608061.2018.1454872

Griffin, M., Gravina, N. E., Matey, N., Pritchard, J., & Wine, B. (2019). Using scorecards to improve the performance of behavior technicians in two autism treatment clinics. *Journal of Organizational Behavior Management*, 39, 280–292. https://www.research gate.net/deref/http%3A%2F%2Fdx.doi.org%2F10.1080%2F01608061.2019.1632241

Hanley, G. P. (2010). Toward effective and preferred programming: A case for the objective measurement of social validity with recipients of behavior-change programs. *Behavior Analysis in Practice*, 3, 13–21. https://www.researchgate.net/

Hawkins, R. (1991). Is social validity what we are interested in? Argument for a functional approach. *Journal of Applied Behavior Analysis*, 24, 205–213. https://doi .org/10.1901/jaba.1991.24-205

Kennedy, C. H. (2002). The maintenance of behavior change as an indicator of social validity. *Behavior Modification*, 26, 594–604. https://doi.org/10.1177%2F014544502 236652

Kurtessis, J. N., Eisenberger, R., Ford, M. T., Buffardi, L. C., Stewart, K. A., & Adis, C. S. (2015). Perceived organizational support: A meta-analytic evaluation of organizational support theory. *Journal of Management*, 31, 874–900. https://doi.org /10.1177/0149206315575554

Luiselli, J. K. (2018a). *Conducting behavioral consultation in educational and treatment settings*. San Diego, CA: Elsevier/Academic Press. ISBN: 9780128144459.

Luiselli, J. K. (2018b). Organizational behavior management applications in human services programs. In B. Wine & J. Pritchard (Eds.), *Organizational behavior management: The essentials* (pp. 340–363). Orlando, FL: Hedgehog.

Luiselli, J. K. (2021). Social validity assessment. In J. K. Luiselli (Ed.), *Applied behavior analysis treatment of violence and aggression in persons with neurodevelopmental disabilities*. New York: Springer.

Luiselli, J. K., Bass, J., & Whitcomb, S. (2010). Training knowledge competencies to direct-care service providers: Outcome assessment and social validation of a training program. *Behavior Modification*, 34, 403–414. https://doi.org/10.1177 /0145445510383526

Luiselli, J. K., DiGennaro Reed, F. D., Christian, W. P., Markowski, A., Rue, H. C., St. Amand, C., & Ryan, C. J. (2009). Effects of an informational brochure, lottery-based financial incentive, and public posting on absenteeism of direct-care human services employees. *Behavior Modification*, 33, 175–181. https://doi.org/10.1177 /0145445508320624

Luiselli, J. K., Sperry, J. S., & Draper, C. (2015). Social validity assessment of physical restraint intervention by care-providers of adults with intellectual and developmental disabilities. *Behavior Analysis in Practice*, 8, 170–175. https://doi.org/10.1007/s40617 -015-0082-z

Luiselli, J. K., Sperry, J. S., Draper, C., & Richards, C. (2017). Parent-guardian evaluation of physical restraint among adults with intellectual disability: A social validity assessment. *Advances in Neurodevelopmental Disorders*, 1, 73–78. https://doi.org/10 .1007/s41252-017-0013-9

Luke, M., Carr, J. E., & Wilder, D. A. (2018). On the compatibility of organizational behavior management and BACB certification. *Journal of Organizational Behavior Management*, 38(4), 288–305. https://doi.org/10.1080/01608061.2018.1514347

Martens, B. K., Witt, J. C., Elliott, S. N., & Darveaux, D. (1985). Teacher judegements concerning the acceptability of school-based interventions. *Professional Psychology: Research and Practice*, 16, 191–198. http://dx.doi.org/10.1037/0735-7028.16.2.191

Miller, M. V., Carlson, J., & Sigurdsson, S. O. (2014). Improving treatment integrity in a human service setting using lottery-based incentives. *Journal of Organizational Behavior Management*, 34, 29–38. https://doi.org/10.1080/01608061.2013.873381

Pittenger, A., Barahona, C., Cavalari, R. N. S., Parent, V., Luiselli, J. K., & DuBard, M. (2014). Social validity assessment of job satisfaction, resources, and support among educational service practitioners for students with intellectual and developmental disabilities. *Journal of Physical and Developmental Disabilities*, 26, 737–745. https://do i.org/10.1007/s10882-014-9389-x

Reed, D. D., DiGennaro Reed, F. D., Campisano, N., Lacourse, K., & Azulay, R. L. (2012). Assessing and increasing staff preference for job tasks using concurrent-chains schedules and probabilistic outcomes. *Journal of Organizational Behavior Management*, 32, 253–262. https://doi.org/10.1080/01608061.2012.698121

Reed, D. D., Luiselli, J. K., Miller, J. R., & Kaplan, B. A. (2013). Therapeutic restraint and protective holding. In D. D. Reed, F. DiGennaro Reed, and J. K. Luiselli. (Eds.), *Handbook of Crisis Intervention and Developmental Disabilities* (pp. 107–120). New York: Springer.

Rhodes, L., & Eisenberger, R. (2002). Perceived organizational support: A review of the literature. *Journal of Applied Psychology*, 87, 698–714. https://doi.org/10.1037/0021-9 010.87.4.698

Rothschild, A. W., Ricciardi, J. N., & Luiselli, J. K. (2019). Assessing pain in adults with intellectual disability: A descriptive and qualitative evaluation of ratings and impressions among care-providers. *Journal of Developmental and Physical Disabilities*, 31, 219–230. https://doi.org/10.1007/s10882-019-09663-7

Schwartz, I. S., & Baer, D. M. (1991). Social validity assessments: Is current practice state of the art? *Journal of Applied Behavior Analysis*, 24, 189–204. https://doi.org/10 .1901/jaba.1991.24-189

Shaw, W. S., Reme, S. E., Pransky, G., Woiszwillo, M. J., Steenstra, I. A., & Linton, S. J. (2013). The pain recovery inventory of concerns and expectations: A psychosocial screening instrument to identify intervention needs among patients at elevated risk of back disability. *Journal of Occupational and Environmental Medicine, 55,* 885–894. https://doi.org/10.1007/978-1-4614-6439-6_101918-1

Shlesinger, A., Duhanyan, K., Bird, F., Harper, J. M., & Luiselli, J. K. (2019). Description, implementation integrity, and social validity of a computer-assisted sleep monitoring system among residential care providers of students with autism spectrum disorder. *Journal of Developmental and Physical Disabilities, 32,* 365–374. https://doi.org/10.1007/s10882-019-09698-w

Strohmeier, C., Mule, C., & Luiselli, J. K. (2014). Social validity assessment of training methods to improve treatment integrity of special education service providers. *Behavior Analysis in Practice, 7,* 15–20. https://doi.org/10.1007/s40617-014-0004-5

Valentino, A. L. (2021). Supervision and mentoring. In J. K. Luiselli, R. M. Gardner, F. Bird, & H. Maguire (Eds)., *Organizational Behavior Management (OBM) approaches for intellectual and developmental disabilities.* New York: Routledge.

Van Houten, R. (1979). Social validation: The evolution of standards of competency for target behaviors. *Journal of Applied Behavior Analysis, 12,* 581–591. https://doi.org/10.1901/jaba.1979.12-581

Wine, B. (2017). Incentive-based performance improvement. In J. K. Luiselli (Ed.), *Applied behavior analysis advanced guidebook* (pp. 117–134). San Diego, CA: Elsevier.

Wine, B., & Pritchard, J. K. (2018). *Organizational behavior management: The essentials.* Orlando, FL: Hedgehog.

Wine, B., Reis, M., & Hantula, D. A. (2014). An evaluation of stimulus preference assessment methodology in organizational behavior management. *Journal of Organizational Behavior Management, 34,* 7–15. https://doi.org/10.1080/01608061.2013.873379

Wolf, M. M. (1978). Social validity: The case for subjective measurement or how applied behavior analysis is finding its heart. *Journal of Applied Behavior Analysis, 11,* 203–214. https://doi.org/10.1901/jaba.1978.11-203

PART III
Training, Supervision, and Performance Improvement

5
Behavioral Skills Training

Jason C. Vladescu and Kathleen E. Marano

The importance of effective staff training procedures cannot be overstated. Human service staff[1] are often responsible for implementing a variety of behavior analytic technologies and require training to implement them with high accuracy. High implementation accuracy, also called procedural integrity or fidelity, implies that staff are implementing a technology as designed. Deviations occur when staff emit commission or omission errors. Procedural integrity errors may negatively influence consumer learning by slowing down or preventing skill acquisition (McIntyre et al., 2007). In addition, procedural integrity errors, particularly during programs targeting disruptive behavior, may result in decreased consumer compliance and decreased intervention effectiveness (Fryling et al., 2012). Although a comprehensive review of procedural integrity is beyond the scope of this chapter, recent reviews of the extant literature (Brand et al., 2019; Fryling et al., 2012) concluded that higher procedural integrity is correlated with an increase in the effectiveness of interventions. Further, Van Houten et al. (1988) stated that poor treatment implementation resulting from procedural integrity errors might violate consumers' rights to effective treatment.

Therefore, it is important that trainers use empirically supported procedures to ensure staff learn how to correctly implement behavioral technologies. Along these lines, DiGennaro et al. (2015) administered a survey to determine the most common staff training procedures. Results indicated that didactic approaches (e.g., verbal or written instructions) are most commonly used, despite limited evidence supporting their efficacy (Fixsen et al., 2005). The frequent use of didactic approaches indicates that staff often do not receive best practice training prior to or while working with consumers. Given the potential reduced efficacy of poorly implemented interventions, trainers must conduct training using optimal training techniques. Behavioral skills training (BST) is considered one of the most effective training procedures for teaching staff to implement a variety of behavioral technologies (DiGennaro Reed et al., 2018). In fact, a meta-analysis of practitioner training strategies found that BST was associated with the most consistent improvements in procedural integrity by special education teachers (Brock et al., 2017).

BST consists of four primary components: instructions, modeling, rehearsal, and feedback (Parsons et al., 2012). First, trainers provide a description of the target skill, including the rationale for why learning the skill is important and operational definitions of each step. Trainers can provide these instructions in one or more formats (e.g., spoken, written). Second, staff watch a model perform the target skill correctly. To implement the model component, a trainer can implement the skill directly with a consumer, model the skill via a role-play scenario in which another trainer serves as a confederate consumer, or staff can watch a video model. Third, a trainer watches staff implement the target skill. Fourth, the trainer provides positive and corrective feedback to the staff regarding the components of the target skill performed correctly and incorrectly, and for the latter, how the component should be performed during subsequent implementations. The rehearsal and feedback components are repeated until staff implement the target skill at a predetermined mastery criterion (Parsons et al., 2012). That is, staff are required to *perform* the target skill until a minimum level of *competency* is achieved. BST represents a drastic departure from didactic training approaches because it includes these performance- and competency-based requirements.

Researchers have demonstrated the usefulness of BST for establishing a variety of technologies often used with consumers with intellectual and developmental disabilities, including the completion of activity schedules (Fetherston & Sturmey, 2014), discrete trial instruction (DTI; Lerman et al., 2008; Sarokoff & Sturmey, 2004), incidental teaching (Fetherston & Sturmey, 2014), mand training (Nigro-Bruzzi & Sturmey, 2010), and preference assessment implementation (Lerman et al., 2008; Pence, St. Peter, & Tetreault, 2012). In fact, researchers have employed BST to teach staff to implement BST themselves (Erath et al., 2020; Parsons et al., 2013). In addition to its use as a staff training technique, BST has also proven effective for teaching fire safety skills (Houvouras & Harvey, 2014), appropriate behavior during lockdown drills (Dickson & Vargo, 2017), interview skills (Stocco et al., 2017), installation and use of child passenger safety restraints (Giannakakos et al., 2018; Himle & Wright, 2014), safe tackling skills when playing football (Tai & Miltenberger, 2017), and gun safety skills (Lee et al., 2019). Therefore, BST has strong empirical support for a wide variety of applications.

The purpose of this chapter is to describe how BST is applicable for training human service staff who provide services to consumers with intellectual and developmental disabilities. The chapter will include a detailed review of the components of BST, the research base supporting the efficacy of BST,

TABLE 5.1 Practice recommendations

BST recommendation	Considerations
Instructions	• Use both written and vocal instructions • Avoid technical jargon • Provide detailed data sheets if applicable • Incorporate diagrams when possible
Modeling	• Model the skill in the context where the skill should occur • Model skills with high treatment integrity • Provide multiple examples of implementation of the skill • Consider the use of video models
Rehearsal	• Require staff to meet a mastery criterion (2–2 consecutive sessions) • Consider use of scripts for confederate
Feedback	• Specify how future performance can improve • Use both evaluative and objective feedback • Provide feedback after every rehearsal during training • Use vocal feedback initially
Conduct ongoing support	• Monitor treatment integrity • Be transparent about when, why, and what behaviors you are monitoring • Conduct more observations initially, then increase time between observations contingent on correct performance • Provide feedback immediately after observations • Use directed rehearsal when needed • Incorporate reinforcement contingencies for staff performance
Reduce barriers to effective staff training	• Consider using videos, telehealth procedures, computer-based instruction, or pyramidal training structures
Troubleshoot problems	• Identify the reason for poor performance • Address performance based on reason for poor performance
Assess social validity	• Assess trainee satisfaction with procedures and outcomes • Consider using IRP-15 or a similar rating scale

recommendations for clinical practice, and directions for future consideration. Readers are directed to Table 5.1 for practice recommendations.

Review of Research Literature

As noted, BST consists of four primary components, each of which researchers evaluated alone and in combination with the other components. We provide an overview of the research on each BST component, followed by a review of the research on applications of BST, and the implications of this research.

Instructions: Research Base and Implications

The first component of BST is to provide instructions to staff. These instructions typically include a description of the target skill, including operational definitions and descriptions of the individual steps required to perform that skill (DiGennaro Reed et al., 2018). Conceptually, instructions may provide a description of the correct behavior staff should engage in, as well as the contingencies under which that behavior should be performed, resulting in staff creating rules for the appropriate responses in various situations (Gutierrez et al., 2019). Survey data suggests that instruction delivered in the form of workshops or lectures is the most commonly used staff training procedure (DiGennaro Reed & Henley, 2015). For example, DiGennaro Reed et al. (2010) provided participants with a written protocol that provided information regarding how to implement students' individual behavioral interventions. The experimenters provided participants with written instructions, provided a verbal review of the instructions, answered questions, and then required participants to complete a written post-test consisting of five questions related to the instructions. Following initial training with written and verbal instructions, participants' implementation of behavioral interventions remained at an average of less than half of steps performed correctly. These results, in conjunction with the results of similar studies, suggest that instructions alone may be ineffective for training staff to implement behavioral technologies (Feldman et al., 1989; Hudson, 1982; Krumhus & Malott, 1980). In addition, it is not uncommon for researchers to provide instructions to participants during a baseline phase and observe suboptimal levels of integrity (e.g., Gutierrez et al., 2019; Hansard & Kazemi, 2018; Moore & Fisher, 2007), which adds support to the literature suggesting that instructions alone may not be sufficient to evoke high levels of staff integrity.

Other researchers also evaluated the use of instructions for training parents and staff and found that instructions alone did not produce substantial increases in correct responding, but that modifications to instructions increased their efficacy. For example, Graff and Karsten (2012b) evaluated the influence of enhanced written instructions on staff implementation of stimulus preference assessments. During the initial phase of the study, participants were provided with written instructions alone, which did not result in high procedural integrity. Next, participants were provided with the written instructions and a data sheet, which improved performance for some participants, but did not result in mastery-level responding. Participants were then given enhanced written instructions, which included a detailed data sheet, step-by-step instructions written without technical jargon, and additional diagrams. The enhanced written instructions resulted in accurate implementation of the assessments. Additional studies have demonstrated that instructional packages consisting of enhanced instructions (Berkman et al., 2019; Griffith et al., 2020; Gutierrez et al., 2020; Ramon et al., 2015; Shapiro et al., 2016; Tyner & Fienup, 2016) and self-instructional packages consisting of enhanced written instructions with video models (Hansard & Kazemi, 2018; Luna, Nuhu et al., 2019; Miljkovic et al., 2015) may be effective staff training techniques. Therefore, although basic written instructions alone may prove ineffective, the application of enhanced written instructions (i.e., written instructions supplemented with pictures and diagrams) may increase the efficacy of instructions.

Modeling: Research Base and Implications

The second component of BST is modeling. Modeling consists of staff viewing someone else performing the target skill with perfect treatment integrity. Trainers may provide an in vivo model by performing the target skill themselves while staff watch (e.g., Adams et al., 1980). However, providing an in vivo model may result in the trainer delivering inconsistent performance across demonstrations (DiGennaro Reed et al., 2018). Inconsistent performance is problematic because staff may imitate trainer commission errors or fail to perform an aspect of the target skill due to trainer omission errors. Also, in vivo modeling always requires the presence of a trainer.

An alternative to in vivo models is a video model, in which staff view a video of someone performing the target skill. Although traditional video models involve the presentation of videos only, researchers have added voiceover instruction (e.g., Lipshultz et al., 2015) and on-screen text (e.g., Spiegel et al., 2016) in an attempt to increase the saliency of important features of training videos. Video modeling may be advantageous for several reasons. First, staff can watch a video without the need for a trainer to be present—this may be beneficial because of the lack of qualified trainers relative to the number of staff requiring training (Graff & Karsten, 2012b; Karsten et al., 2015). Second, using a video ensures that the target skill is modeled perfectly and consistently during each presentation, whereas in vivo demonstrations run the risk of trainer errors resulting in inconsistent models. Third, a video may be a more cost-effective option. Although the creation of a video will likely have a relatively higher up-front cost compared to an in vivo model, a video requires little subsequent investment as additional staff experience training involving the video (DiGennaro Reed et al., 2018). Collectively, these advantages make video modeling an attractive alternative to in vivo models when training skills using BST.

In fact, there is substantial research demonstrating the efficacy of training that incorporates videos alone or in combination with other components to train staff and caregivers to implement behavioral technologies, including DTI (Catania et al., 2013; Vladescu et al., 2013), direct teaching procedures (Giannakakos et al., 2015), guided compliance procedures (Spiegel et al., 2016), individualized behavioral programming (DiGennaro Reed et al., 2010), preference assessments (Deliperi et al., 2015; Delli Bovi et al., 2017; Hansard & Kazemi, 2018; Lavie & Sturmey, 2002; Lipschultz et al., 2015; Marano et al., 2019; Nottingham et al., 2017), performance feedback (Shuler & Carroll, 2019), and problem-solving interventions (Collins et al., 2009). Moreover, in a review of various training procedures that do not require face-to-face training, Gerencser et al. (2019) suggested that video models are a particularly good option for training skills (e.g., preference assessments) that are not particularly complex (e.g., preference assessments typically have fewer steps than DTI).

It is also important to consider how modeling may lead to change in staff behavior. Modeling may be effective because it demonstrates the responses staff should emit when in situations similar to those modeled. For example, if staff view a demonstration of DTI implementation, the model will depict the correct way to respond following each possible consumer response. Then, when staff are in similar situations and must respond to the same consumer responses, those stimuli may evoke the appropriate responses. However, it is possible that staff will not attend to relevant components of the modeled performance and will attend to irrelevant components of the model instead (e.g., rather than looking at the placement of stimuli, staff attend to the model's facial expressions). Therefore, requiring an active response component may be beneficial if doing so ensures attending to the relevant components of the modeled performance. For example, Marano et al. (2019) evaluated the influence of having participants conduct behavioral observations and ratings on implementation of a paired-stimulus preference assessment. Participants watched videos depicting both accurate and inaccurate implementation of each step of the preference assessment and were required to answer questions regarding the accuracy of implementation in each video. Following the completion of this training procedure, participants implemented the skill correctly, suggesting that requiring an active response while watching someone else's behavior may be beneficial.

Rehearsal: Research Base and Implications

The third component of BST is rehearsal (i.e., behavioral rehearsal or role-play; Jenkins & DiGennaro Reed, 2016), in which staff are given the opportunity to perform the target skill after experiencing the instruction and modeling components. It is possible that rehearsal following viewing a model improves staff performance of the target skill because it allows staff the opportunity to compare their own performance to that of the model. If the staff's performance is similar to the model's performance, this may reinforce staff's accurate performance and result in correct implementation of the skill again in the future. However, researchers (Jenkins & DiGennaro Reed, 2016; Ward-Horner & Sturmey; 2012) found that rehearsal alone is not sufficient for training staff to implement behavioral technologies at mastery levels.

Rehearsal may be performed in a natural or analog setting (Jenkins & DiGennaro Reed, 2016). When rehearsal is conducted in a natural setting, staff are put in a situation to implement a behavioral technology with a consumer while the trainer observers. For example, Lavie and Sturmey (2002) required participants to practice implementing preference assessments with consumers. When rehearsal is conducted in an analog setting, staff are put in a situation to implement a behavioral technology with a confederate such as the trainer or another staff playing the role of a consumer (Pence et al., 2012). Role-playing the behavioral technology with a confederate may offer some attractive advantages. First, staff may initially make errors when implementing the behavioral technology. By requiring rehearsals with a confederate, actual consumers are not exposed to the implementation of a behavioral technology with low treatment integrity. Second, if the confederates respond according to a script that includes the full range of consumer responses, it is possible to expose staff to a variety of responses they may later experience. This allows training to better program for generalization. When rehearsing the behavioral technology with the actual consumer, it is possible the consumer will not engage in the full range of potential responses, thus limiting the staff's exposure to all possible responses during training, and potentially increasing the likelihood of subsequent errors.

Additional research relevant to the rehearsal component has focused on the number of times staff should rehearse the target skill. Jenkins and DiGennaro Reed (2016) conducted a parametric analysis of rehearsal opportunities within BST by comparing one, three, and ten rehearsals followed by performance feedback on participants' implementation of functional analysis procedures. The results demonstrated that rehearsals, regardless of number, plus feedback increased participants' correct implementation. However, one rehearsal was associated with the most efficient training. That is, the researchers found that requiring staff to perform one rehearsal resulted in the least total rehearsals and the lowest training time to meet the mastery criterion. The results of Jenkins and DiGennaro Reed (2016) suggest that requiring repeated rehearsals may not result in higher treatment integrity following training, although additional replications are warranted to evaluate the generality of this finding.

Feedback: Research Base and Implications

The fourth component of BST is performance feedback. After observing the staff rehearse the target skill, trainers provide feedback to the staff regarding their performance. Feedback involves providing information to staff following a performance that specifies what and how well they are doing, which may lead the staff to adjust their performance in the future (Alvero et al., 2001). Trainers may deliver positive and/or corrective feedback following rehearsals. Positive, or supportive, feedback involves specifying which steps of the target skill were performed correctly (e.g., "You delivered reinforcement immediately after the target response, as specified in the protocol"). Corrective feedback involves describing which steps of the target skill were performed incorrectly and specifying how staff can improve their performance during subsequent opportunities to implement the skill (e.g., "You waited five seconds to deliver reinforcement after the target response. Make sure you deliver reinforcement immediately during future sessions"; Parsons et al., 2012). In a review of the effectiveness and essential characteristics of feedback, Alvero et al. (2001) found that feedback alone is often effective to produce performance improvements, but feedback used in combination with other procedures is most consistently effective. That is, feedback is most effective when it is used as part of a package with other empirically supported training procedures, such as first having staff view a video model and then providing feedback on staff performance after they have watched the video. Researchers have also been active in evaluating a number of variables that may impact the influence of feedback on behavior, including feedback modality, frequency, location, and content.

Trainers can deliver feedback using a variety of modalities, including verbal, written, and visual. Verbal feedback typically involves the face-to-face delivery of feedback. For example, after a trainer watches staff implementing a behavioral technology, the trainer can speak to the staff member in person and provide an evaluation of their performance. Verbal feedback allows for the immediate delivery of feedback and provides an opportunity for the trainer and staff to discuss the performance in person. This is potentially beneficial because the in-person component of verbal feedback allows the trainer to model the skill when describing how to improve performance. However, if the trainer is responsible for training multiple staff in different locations, the ability to provide in-person verbal feedback may be limited. Written feedback is often provided after staff have already reached a predetermined mastery criterion for performance and involves a textual description of staff performance (DiGennaro Reed et al., 2018). For example, a trainer may write an email describing staff performance that includes the components of the skill that were performed correctly and areas for improvement. Finally, visual feedback typically involves graphical depictions of staff implementation of the skill. Written and visual feedback offer some advantages over verbal feedback because they do not require that the trainer and staff be present simultaneously. Also, feedback that is spoken does not produce a lasting outcome on the environment, whereas written and visual feedback do. Therefore, written and visual feedback offer an additional advantage over verbal feedback because staff may refer back to the feedback. Additionally, providing a visual description of staff performance can allow staff to see how their performance has improved or worsened over time, potentially reinforcing or punishing their behavior. The different feedback modalities can be used individually or in conjunction with each other. For example, trainers can provide verbal feedback combined with visual feedback to the trainee during an in-person meeting or can email the trainee written feedback. Although written feedback alone is most commonly used, a combination of written, visual, and verbal feedback has been found to result in the highest levels of consistent effects (Alvero et al., 2001).

The frequency with which feedback is delivered is another variable that trainers must consider when using BST. Trainers can provide feedback immediately after a training session, immediately before the next session, after every session, or after a few sessions. Researchers have evaluated the relative influence of delivering feedback immediately after a rehearsal opportunity to feedback delivered before the subsequent rehearsal opportunity. Conceptually speaking, delivering feedback immediately after performance of the skill may function as reinforcement or punishment of staff performance, whereas feedback that is delivered before the subsequent opportunity to perform the skill could serve a discriminative function for staff behavior. For example, if a trainer delivers corrective feedback immediately after rehearsal indicating that an error was emitted, the feedback delivery may punish such behavior and result in a decreased future frequency of that error. However, feedback delivered prior to subsequent implementation may evoke correct responding by specifying the contingencies necessary for reinforcement. Although Aljadeff-Abergel et al. (2017) found that providing feedback before the subsequent opportunity was more effective for improving performance, other researchers (Bechtel et al., 2015; Wine et al., 2019) found no such substantial difference. Additionally, research is necessary to clarify the conditions under which it is optimal to provide feedback immediately after performance, immediately prior to subsequent performance, or a combination of both.

Relatedly, Kang et al. (2003) evaluated the relative influence of different frequencies of feedback, as well as different pay schedules, on work performance. The researchers devised four conditions: (a) feedback delivered after every session with hourly pay, (b) feedback after every session with incentive pay, (c) feedback delivered after every fourth session with hourly pay, and (d) feedback delivered every fourth session with incentive pay. Under the incentive pay conditions, participants could earn money in addition to their base pay by completing additional tasks. The results showed that feedback after every session was more effective under the incentive pay system. These findings suggest that the effects of feedback frequency may be impacted by the differential consequences for performance.

Trainers may also choose to provide only positive, only corrective, or both positive and corrective feedback to staff. Choi et al. (2018) evaluated the relative effectiveness and impact of positive and negative feedback on staff performance and negative emotional responses (e.g., aggressiveness, resistance, withdrawal). Providing only positive or only negative feedback resulted in higher performance, whereas a combination of positive and negative feedback resulted in lessened negative emotional responses to receiving feedback. These outcomes indicate that if trainers deliver positive and corrective feedback (compared to either alone), staff may be less likely to emit negative emotional responses. However, if the only concern is improved staff performance, providing only positive or only negative feedback may be more effective. In situations where trainers deliver both positive and corrective feedback, the feedback sequence may influence outcomes. Henley and DiGennaro Reed (2015) found that corrective feedback followed by positive feedback (e.g., "You did not deliver reinforcement immediately. Make sure you provide the reinforcer within five seconds. Good job changing your tone of voice when you provided praise!") was more effective than alternative feedback sequences (e.g., positive feedback followed by corrective feedback). However, other researchers (Parkes et al., 2013; Slowiak & Lakowske, 2017) have found no differences between different sequences of positive and corrective feedback. Therefore, trainers may evaluate the influence of feedback sequences on their staff's behavior, and if no differences are noted, may ask staff how they would prefer to receive feedback.

Researchers have also given consideration to the use of objective and evaluative feedback. A trainer provides objective feedback by providing details about staff performance without providing an evaluation of performance. For example, a trainer might say, "You completed three steps correctly." A trainer provides evaluative feedback by providing an appraisal of the individual's performance, such as "You did a great job implementing the preference assessment." Trainers can also use a combination of objective and evaluative feedback when providing performance feedback. Thus, a trainer might say, "You did a great job implementing the preference assessment. You completed three steps correctly. That was more than the previous session." Johnson (2013) conducted a component analysis of the effects of evaluative and objective feedback and found that a combination of both was necessary to optimize the effectiveness of feedback.

It is possible that both objective and evaluative feedback maximize performance because each operates on behavior through different mechanisms. One hypothesis is that evaluative feedback reinforces or punishes desirable or undesirable behavior, respectively (Johnson, 2013), whereas objective feedback specifies how current performance relates to the contingencies necessary to contact reinforcement. In layman's terms, objective feedback can describe staff improvements that are necessary to perform the skill correctly, receive praise, and avoid criticism. Evaluative feedback involves the delivery of praise or criticism that increase or decrease the frequency of behavior. Feedback may be an essential component of BST because of these behavioral functions. For example, if staff receive positive feedback for correctly implementing an error correction procedure, staff may be more likely to implement that step correctly again in the future. Similarly, corrective feedback may serve as a punisher by decreasing the frequency with which the individual makes the same error again in the future. To illustrate, if staff receive corrective feedback for incorrectly implementing an error correction procedure, staff may be less likely to make the same mistakes again. An alternative hypothesis is that evaluative feedback leads staff to develop rules that describe the contingencies for positive and negative evaluations in the future, thereby controlling future performance. For example, a negative evaluation may lead staff to generate a rule such as "I am supposed to deliver reinforcement immediately. If the consumer responds correctly and I do not deliver reinforcement immediately, I will be criticized." Then, staff may engage in correct behavior during subsequent sessions, leading to self-generated verbal statements that may have reinforcing or punishing properties (e.g., "I did that right, so they should praise me next time").

BST Packages: Research Base and Implications

Component Analysis

Researchers have conducted component analyses to evaluate the independent influence of the four BST components of instructions, modeling, rehearsal, and feedback. Ward-Horner and Sturmey (2012) demonstrated that instructions and rehearsal alone were ineffective for training staff to conduct functional analyses, whereas feedback was the most effective component of BST. Moreover, modeling was also effective, although the influence was less robust than that of feedback. Drifke et al. (2017) found that written instructions and modeling improved participant performance, but mastery-level responding was only achieved when participants experienced the full BST package. It may be the case that modeling and feedback are essential components of BST, but training is likely most effective when all components are included.

Skills Trained

BST has been used to train staff to implement a variety of behavioral technologies. One subset of behavioral technologies that BST is often used to train is how to teach consumers new responses. For example, Sarokoff and Sturmey

(2004) taught participants to implement DTI procedures using BST and Drifke et al. (2017) used BST to teach parents to implement a three-step prompting procedure with their children. In these studies, participants were provided with written instructions, shown how to perform the skills, then practiced performing the skills and received feedback. The positive results of both studies demonstrate that BST is applicable for training staff to implement technologies that have the goal of consumer skill acquisition.

Similarly, BST has also often been used to train staff to implement procedures aimed at increasing the communication responses of individuals with intellectual and developmental disabilities such as making requests (Nigro-Bruzzi & Sturmey, 2010). Similarly, Madzharova et al. (2012) used BST to train staff to conduct mand training that targeted peer-to-peer mands in a series of two case studies. In the first case study, a staff member was given written instructions and the experimenter verbally explained how to implement each step of a task analysis. Then, the staff member watched 11 videos depicting correct implementation of each step. Next, the staff member practiced implementing the procedure while the experimenter served as a confederate consumer and provided verbal feedback. In a follow-up case study, only the modeling and feedback components of BST were evaluated. The results of both case studies demonstrated an increase in staff correct teaching responses and independent student mands, suggesting that the BST package and the abbreviated BST package were effective for training staff and increasing the students' communication abilities.

BST has also been employed to train staff to promote activity engagement by teaching staff to use activity schedules. Activity schedules involve the presentation of a sequence of pictorial cues that prompt the completion of complex chains of behavior and are often used to improve the independent play skills of children with autism spectrum disorder (McClannahan & Krantz, 1999). For example, Fetherston and Sturmey (2014) used BST to train human service staff to implement activity schedules. First, experimenters presented participants with a task analysis consisting of definitions of steps, read them aloud, and then answered relevant questions. The participants practiced implementing the activity schedules while the experimenter provided models and feedback. This BST procedure resulted in improved participant implementation of the activity schedules. The literature on training staff to promote activity engagement is important because children with autism spectrum disorder often have deficits in play abilities (McClannahan & Krantz, 1999). Therefore, research has demonstrated that BST is effective for training staff to teach individuals with autism spectrum disorder to complete activity schedules.

There is also substantial research on training staff to implement procedures to identify putative reinforcers. The use of putative reinforcers by human service staff is ubiquitous, with nearly 90% of behavior analysts reporting the use of at least one type of procedure designed to assess preference (Graff & Karsten, 2012a). Multiple studies demonstrated the efficacy of BST for training staff to implement a variety of stimulus preference assessments (Lavie & Sturmey, 2002; Roscoe & Fisher, 2008; Pence et al., 2012).

Delivery Modality

Researchers also evaluated variations of traditional BST packages to train staff to implement behavioral technologies by using different delivery modalities that may require less in vivo training by a designated trainer. Although a number of studies required the presence of a designated trainer during all components of training, there are other delivery modalities that may not require the continued presence of a trainer, namely pyramidal training structure and computer-based training.

In a pyramidal training structure, a "train the trainer" approach is taken, in which a designated trainer provides training to some staff within an organization, and those individuals then train other staff, thereby eliminating the need for the designated trainer to train all staff. Pence et al. (2012) used a pyramidal training structure to train special education teachers to conduct stimulus preference assessments. The special education teachers first learned to conduct three types of preference assessments using BST and then learned how to conduct BST themselves. The teachers subsequently trained other teachers to implement the same preference assessments using BST. Specifically, after learning to conduct the preference assessments themselves, the teachers reviewed and discussed the instructions with other teachers, modeled correct implementation, and provided feedback to the second-tier teachers. Erath et al. (2020) also evaluated pyramidal training to train human service staff to implement BST procedures when training others to implement behavior analytic technologies. The participants learned how to conduct BST in a group-training format, then trained confederate staff to implement behavioral procedures using BST. Results showed that the training procedure effectively increased BST integrity for most participants, results generalized to the training of a different behavioral procedure, and BST integrity maintained during follow-up probes, a similar finding reported by Parsons et al. (2013).

Computer-based training procedures, in which technology is incorporated into training to minimize the need for face-to-face training, are an additional modification to traditional BST that may decrease the amount of training a trainer must provide. For example, Higgins et al. (2017) trained direct-care staff to implement a preference assessment using a web-based telehealth BST training package that included a multimedia presentation using instructions and modeling, feedback from previously recorded sessions, and role-play with feedback. The results demonstrated that staff learned to implement the procedure without any direct in vivo training by the experimenters. The results of Pence et al. (2012), Erath et al. (2020), and Higgins et al. (2017) are particularly noteworthy because staff in rural or remote areas may have limited access to qualified trainers (Higgins et al., 2017). For a comprehensive review efforts to leverage telehealth to train staff to implement behavioral technologies, see Tomlinson et al. (2018). Therefore, it is necessary to empirically evaluate modifications to training procedures that increase their accessibility.

Individual and Group BST

Trainers can provide BST to staff individually or in a group-based format. Individual BST involves a trainer working one-on-one with a staff member to provide individualized training. However, training all staff individually may be time-consuming and the competency component of BST often increases total training time as staff must practice implementing the skill until a predetermined mastery criterion is reached (Parsons et al., 2013). Therefore, some trainers conduct BST in a group setting with multiple staff members present. In a study by Parsons et al. (2013), participants implemented BST individually with an experimenter serving as a confederate staff member who required training. Then, the experimenters provided training for up to four participants simultaneously by reviewing the rationale for using BST, describing the steps of BST, providing written instructions, and modeling how BST should be implemented. The participants practiced implementing BST themselves by working in pairs with other participants, with one participant serving as the trainer and the other serving as a confederate consumer. The experimenters provided feedback to the participants while they practiced implementing BST. The group training format was effective for training staff to implement BST and acceptability measures suggested that a group training method was acceptable to the participants. The results of this study suggest that providing BST in a group setting may be an effective way to reduce the time it takes to train multiple staff to implement the same behavioral technology.

Practice Recommendations

Practice Recommendations: Instructions

When implementing the instruction component of BST, trainers should use a combination of both written and vocal instructions (DiGennaro Reed et al.,

2018; Parsons et al., 2012). The trainer should first provide the staff with a written description or task analysis of all steps necessary to complete the target skill. The trainer should review each step with staff by providing a rationale for why the step is necessary and how to perform the step correctly. We also recommend that trainers avoid using technical jargon when describing each step so that staff understand the instructions clearly. Additionally, when applicable, trainers should provide detailed data sheets (e.g., LeBlanc et al., 2019) and incorporate diagrams with visual depictions (e.g., Graff & Karsten, 2012b) that help describe how the skill should be performed (DiGennaro Reed et al., 2018).

Practice Recommendations: Modeling

When providing an in vivo model, trainers should model the target skill in the context in which the behavior is expected to occur (DiGennaro Reed et al., 2018). Trainers must also ensure they are modeling the skill with high treatment integrity, as models that include errors may result in staff engaging in those same errors (DiGennaro Reed et al., 2018; Miltenberger, 2003). In addition, it is important to provide multiple examples of each step of the target skill and the range of potential staff and consumer responses (Moore & Fisher, 2007; Stokes & Baer, 1977). By providing multiple examples of each step, staff are exposed to a range of potential responses they must perform, which may increase the likelihood that they are able to respond correctly and facilitate high implementation integrity in the context where the target skill should occur.

Trainers should use videos when conducting the modeling component of BST. Videos offer advantages over in vivo models because they may be less likely to include treatment integrity errors, do not require the presence of a trainer, and allow for rewinding if staff want to rewatch the model of a particular step (DiGennaro Reed et al., 2018). Although videos will likely require a greater upfront investment, they may result in reduced long-term training time.

Practice Recommendations: Rehearsal

We recommend that staff rehearse the target skill until they reach a predetermined mastery criterion, as per the recommendation by DiGennaro Reed et al. (2018), that staff rehearse the target skill two or three consecutive times with correct implementation before training is terminated. Moreover, to ensure staff are exposed to the full range of potential consumer responses during rehearsal, the trainer should follow a script when serving as a confederate consumer (e.g., Lipshultz et al., 2015; Marano et al., 2019). The script should include the range of responses consumers may emit. For example, when training staff to implement stimulus preference assessments, the confederate consumer will respond with a typical response during half of the trials (e.g., selecting one item), but will engage in atypical responses during half of the trials (e.g., engaging in problem behavior, selecting two items, not responding).

Practice Recommendations: Feedback

When providing performance feedback, trainers should ensure they specify how performance can be improved in the future and include a combination of both objective and evaluative feedback (DiGennero Reed et al., 2018; Johnson, 2013). For example, when training staff to conduct a stimulus preference assessment, a trainer might say,

> Nice job removing the item the student did not take! Remember that the student should only have access to the toy they selected for ten seconds. You allowed them to play with the toy for more than ten seconds. In the future, make sure you use the timer to make sure they only have ten seconds to play with the toy.

In terms of the schedule to follow when providing feedback during training, Jenkins and DiGennaro Reed (2016) suggest that staff receive feedback after every rehearsal during initial training. Trainers should also ensure feedback is delivered vocally during the early stages of training. Thereafter, trainers can use written and graphic feedback (DiGennaro Reed et al., 2018) and may choose to provide this feedback before staff implement behavioral technologies with consumers (Aljadeff-Abergel et al., 2017). Additionally, trainers may assess staff preference for positive feedback, corrective feedback, or positive and corrective feedback combined.

Practice Recommendations: Reduce Barriers

Despite substantial evidence supporting BST for staff training, there are some potential limitations of this training procedure. BST is resource-intensive because it often relies heavily on the presence of trainers and can be very time-consuming (Karsten et al., 2015). Additionally, there are a limited number of trainers available to provide training relative to the number of staff who require training (Graff & Karsten, 2012b). Therefore, other methods may be necessary to increase the efficiency of BST by increasing the number of people who can be trained and reducing the total direct training time. Video models are an alternative method to in vivo models that increase how many people can be trained simultaneously, while also decreasing trainer involvement (Macurik et al., 2008). Further, telehealth procedures involve video conferencing and teleconferencing and may be useful when it is difficult or impossible to provide direct training in vivo due to travel time, cost, or geographical limitations (Higgins et al., 2017; Knowles et al., 2017; Machalicek et al., 2010). For example, Knowles et al. (2017) used a telehealth training procedure, in which staff viewed training modules online, and asked the experimenter questions via text message, email, or telephone calls. The experimenters observed staff performance during biweekly teleconference calls and then emailed specific written feedback and graphs of trainee performance. This telehealth procedure was effective for training staff and required no in-person training, making it a viable training procedure when in-person training is not accessible. Pyramidal training structures, in which previously trained staff train new staff, is another approach that allows new staff to be trained without requiring additional training by a designated trainer or consultant (Erath et al., 2020; Pence et al., 2012).

Trainers can also use computer-based procedures to supplement video modeling procedures. Computer-based instruction, or interactive computerized training, requires staff to complete computerized training that is typically self-paced and involves a variety of empirically supported training methods, including video models, instructions, and performance feedback. Higbee et al. (2016) required participants to complete modules describing how to implement discrete trial instruction on a computer that included slides, narration, video models, and embedded quizzes. The participants then performed discrete trial instruction in role-play scenarios with the experimenter and received feedback when necessary. Marano et al. (2019) also evaluated a computer-based procedure that required participants to complete stimulus preference assessment training modules. Following this computer-based training, all participants implemented the target procedure at mastery levels. Trainers could use similar computer-based procedures to supplement BST packages when direct training time is limited.

Practice Recommendation: Support After BST and Troubleshooting Problems

After staff demonstrate the target skill at a predetermined mastery criterion, trainers must provide ongoing support to ensure skill maintenance. In the vein of ongoing support, trainers should continue to collect treatment integrity data on staff implementation following initial training. Trainers should be transparent with staff about why they are collecting treatment integrity data and specify when that they share when they will conduct observations and which behaviors they will observe (DiGennaro Reed et al., 2018; Parsons et al., 2012). Such communication facilitates a good relationship between the trainer and the staff. To avoid staff behavior changing as a result of the trainer's presence, the trainer may choose to observe from behind a one-way mirror so the staff members do not see them, or videotape staff performance when the trainer is not physically present. Additionally, trainers should conduct more observations immediately after training ends and then begin to increase the time between subsequent observations contingent on the maintenance of correct staff performance (DiGennaro Reed et al., 2018; Parsons et al., 2012).

When treatment integrity data indicate that staff performance is not maintaining at sufficient levels, the trainer should provide performance feedback immediately following the observation (Goodman et al., 2008). If performance feedback is not sufficient for improving the staff's performance, trainers should use directed rehearsal to retrain steps with errors. Directed rehearsal procedures require staff to practice the steps performed incorrectly during the observation and follow similar procedures to BST training. First, the incorrectly implemented step is described, and then the step is rehearsed three times (Ward et al., 1998). Trainers can also provide ongoing support by reinforcing appropriate staff behavior with praise, providing preferred parking spaces, and meals contingent on correct intervention implementation (DiGennaro Reed et al., 2018). Direct and ongoing assessment of preference may be important to capture shifts in staff preference for tangible items (Wine et al., 2014). Trainers can also use negative reinforcement contingencies, such as allowing staff to skip meetings contingent on correct performance (DiGennaro et al., 2007; DiGennaro Reed et al., 2018; DiGennaro Reed et al., 2013).

If staff are still not performing at optimal levels after these measures are taken, trainers should identify the reasons for nonproficient performance and address the problems accordingly. Trainers can use informant assessments to identify the variables that are negatively affecting staff performance. Notably, the Performance Diagnostic Checklist-Human Services (PDC-HS; Carr et al., 2013) is designed specifically to identify the variables that could be resulting in substandard staff performance in a human-service setting. Conducting the PDC-HS involves interviewing supervisors of staff and directly observing staff performance. After the variables maintaining staff behavior are identified, a function-based intervention is implemented to improve staff performance (Merritt et al., 2019). See Wilder (2019), this volume, for a detailed discussion of the PDC-HS.

Reid, Parsons, and Green (2012) state that the most common reasons for non-proficient staff performance include a lack of skills necessary to perform the skill, insufficient resources or time, incapability of performing duties, and a lack of motivation to complete work tasks in a quality manner. If trainers find that staff lack the skills needed to complete a task correctly, the trainer should determine which training strategy was previously used and then provide effective training. Some staff may lack the resources or time to perform the target skill correctly. For example, if a staff member is learning to teach a consumer to follow an activity schedule, but there are no leisure items available, the staff member cannot perform the skill correctly. Therefore, the trainer can address the problem by ensuring all necessary materials are available. Oftentimes, staff members are physically incapable of performing the job duties, resulting in poor performance (e.g., a staff member with a broken ankle cannot model a gym routine). In these instances, all reasonable attempts must be made to modify the job demands, make accommodations for physical challenges, or find another job within the organization for that staff member to complete (Reid et al., 2012). The most common reason for poor staff performance is a lack of motivation to exert the time and effort to complete the task correctly (Reid et al., 2012). Reid et al. suggest that in cases where the staff lack motivation, the trainer should first provide performance feedback that specifies performance deficits and how staff should correct these deficits in the future. If this is ineffective for changing trainee behavior, then disciplinary action must be taken.

Practice Recommendation: Social Validity

We recommend that trainers assess the social validity of the training procedures and outcomes during and after training using BST (see Luiselli, 2019, this volume). Although it is vital that a training procedure is effective, it is also important that the training is satisfactory and meaningful to training recipients. Parsons et al. (2012) found that staff typically report high social validity of BST, most likely because the training involves a competency component, in which training continues until staff can demonstrate correct implementation of the skill. Additionally, staff have an active involvement in and receive supportive feedback throughout the training, which likely increases the acceptability of the procedures. Trainers may ask staff to complete written surveys regarding the acceptability of the procedures, for example, the Intervention Rating Profile-15 (IRP-15; Martens et al., 1985) that requires a rater to score 15 items on a Likert-type scale. Trainers can use the ratings obtained by the IRP-15 to modify components of the intervention and increase trainee satisfaction.

Appendix A Sample procedural integrity data sheet for teaching communication abilities

Opportunities	1	2	3	4	5	6	7	8	9	Percentage correct	Total
Target response											
Arrange environment with preferred items out of reach											
Wait for the student to initiate for an item											
Block access to the item											
Prompt a mand/request											
Present item contingent on student echoing the mand/request											
Do not provide access to item if student does not echo the mand/request											
Percentage of steps implemented correctly											

Appendix B Sample procedural integrity data sheet for assessing consumer preference

Trial presentation	1	2	3	4	5	6	7	8	9	Percentage correct	Total
Target response											
Choose appropriate SPA to conduct											
Identify correct items to use in SPA											
Present correct items											
Present items in correct location											
Present items spaced evenly apart and within equal proximity to student											
Deliver instruction											
Block attempts to approach more than one item											
Allow 10 s to approach an item											
Provide access to approached item for 10 s											

Trial presentation	1	2	3	4	5	6	7	8	9	Percentage correct	Total
Target response											
Remove non-approached item											
If no item is approached within 10 s, re-present trial											
If no item is approached on re-presentation trial, present next trial											
Record consumer response											
Ignore problem behavior											
Correctly calculate percentage of approaches											
Rank items correctly											
Identify item to use during teaching											
Percentage of steps implemented correctly											

Appendix C Sample procedural integrity data sheet for implementing activity schedules

Opportunities	1	2	3	4	5	6	7	8	9	Percentage correct	Total
Target response											
Deliver instruction, "It's time to do your activity schedule"											
If student does not open book containing schedule, provide appropriate prompt											
If student does not point to the picture, provide appropriate prompt											
If student does not retrieve corresponding items, provide appropriate prompt											
If student does not turn to the next page after the step is completed, provide appropriate prompt											

(Continued)

(Continued)

Opportunities	1	2	3	4	5	6	7	8	9	Percentage correct	Total
Target response											
Deliver praise after each step is completed											
Percentage of steps implemented correctly											

Appendix D Sample procedural integrity data sheet for implementing instruction

Trial presentations	1	2	3	4	5	6	7	8	9	Percentage correct	Total
Target response											
Establish ready behavior											
Wait for ready behavior											
Present stimuli as specified in intervention protocol											
Ensure child attends to all stimuli prior to presenting the instruction											
Present correct instruction											
Provide reinforcement contingent on correct response											
Deliver reinforcement immediately (within 3 s)											
Do not deliver reinforcement for incorrect or no response											
Deliver correct prompt											
Prompt delivered at the prescribed time interval (+/− 2 s)											
Deliver correct error correction procedure											
Record data following each trial											
Remove and/or rearrange stimuli after each trial											
Ignore/block problem behavior											

Trial presentations	1	2	3	4	5	6	7	8	9	Percentage correct	Total
Target response											
Present each target 3 times											
Each position (left, middle, right) used 3 times											
Percentage of steps implemented correctly											

Note

1 We will use the term *staff* to refer to the individuals receiving training, *trainer* to refer to the individual providing training, and *consumer* to refer to the individuals who receive behavioral services implemented by staff.

References

Adams, G. L., Tallon, R. J., & Rimell, P. (1980). A comparison of lecture versus role-playing in the training of the use of positive reinforcement. *Journal of Organizational Behavior Management, 2,* 205–212. doi: 10.1300/J075v02n03_06

Aljadeff-Abergel, E., Peterson, S. M., Hagen, K. K., Wiskirchen, R. R., & Cole, M. L. (2017). Evaluating the temporal location of feedback: Providing feedback following performance vs. prior to performance. *Journal of Organizational Behavior Management, 37*(2), 171–195. doi: 10.1080/01608061.2017.1309332

Alvero, A. M., Bucklin, B. R., & Austin, J. (2001). An objective review of the effectiveness and essential characteristics of performance feedback in organizational settings (1985–1998). *Journal of Organizational Behavior Management, 21,* 3–29. doi: 10.1300/J075v21n01_02

Bechtel, N. T., McGee, H. M., Huitema, B. E., & Dickinson, A. M. (2015). The effects of the temporal placement of feedback on performance. *Psychological Record, 65,* 425–434. doi: 10.1080/01608061.2017.1309332

Berkman, S. J., Roscoe, E. M., & Bourret, J. C. (2019). Comparing self-directed methods for training staff to create graphs using Graphpad Prism. *Journal of Applied Behavior Analysis, 52,* 188–204. doi: 10.1002/jaba.522

Brand, D., Henley, A. J., DiGennaro Reed, F., Gray, E., & Crabbs, B. (2019). A review of published studies involving parametric manipulations of treatment integrity. *Journal of Behavioral Education, 28,* 1–26. doi: 10.1007/s10864-018-09311-8

Brock, M. E., Cannella-Malone, H. I., Seaman, R. L., Andzik, N. R., Schaefer, J. M., Page, E. J., … Dueker, S. A. (2017). Findings across practitioner training studies in special education: A comprehensive review and meta-analysis. *Exceptional Children*, 84, 7–26. doi: 10.1177/0014402917698008

Carr, J. E., Wilder, D. A., Majdalany, L., Mathisen, D., & Strain, L. A. (2013). An assessment-based solution to a human-service employee performance problem: An initial evaluation of the performance diagnostic checklist-human services. *Behavior Analysis in Practice*, 6, 16–32. doi: 10.1007/BF03391789

Catania, C. N., Almeida, D., Liu-Constant, B., & DiGennaro Reed, F. D. (2013). Video modeling to train staff to implement discrete-trial instruction. *Journal of Applied Behavior Analysis*, 42, 387–392. doi: 10.1901/jaba.2009.42-387

Choi, E., Johnson, D. A., Moon, K., & Oah, S. (2018). Effects of positive and negative feedback sequence on work performance and emotional responses. *Journal of Organizational Behavior Management*, 38, 97–115. doi: 10.1080/1608061.2017.1423151

Collins, S., Higbee, T. S., & Salzberg, C. L. (2009). The effects of video modeling on staff implementation of a problem-solving intervention with adults with developmental disabilities. *Journal of Applied Behavior Analysis*, 42, 849–854. doi: 10.1901/jaba.2009.42-849

Deliperi, P., Vladescu, J. C., Reeve, K. F., Reeve, S. R., & DeBar, R. M. (2015). Training staff to implement a paired-stimulus preference assessment using video modeling with voiceover instruction. *Behavioral Interventions*, 30, 314–332. doi: 10.1002/bin.1421

Delli Bovi, G. M., Vladescu, J. C., DeBar, R. M., Carroll, R. A., & Sarokoff, R. A. (2017). Using video modeling with voice-over instruction to train public school staff to implement a preference assessment. *Behavior Analysis in Practice*, 10, 72–76. doi: 10.1007/s40617-016-0135-y

Dickson, M. J., & Vargo, K. K. (2017). Training kindergarten students lockdown drill procedures using behavioral skills training. *Journal of Applied Behavior Analysis*, 50, 407–412. doi: 10.1002/jaba.369

DiGennaro, F. D., Martens, B. K., & Kleinmann, A. E. (2007). A comparison of performance feedback procedures on teachers' treatment implementation integrity and students' inappropriate behavior in special education classrooms. *Journal of Applied Behavior Analysis*, 40, 447–461. doi: 10.1901/jaba.2007.40-447

DiGennaro Reed, F. D., & Henley, A. J. (2015). A survey of staff training and performance management practices: The good, the bad, and the ugly. *Behavior Analysis in Practice*, 8, 16–26. doi: 10.1007/s40617-015-0044-5

DiGennaro Reed, F. D., Blackman, A. L., Erath, T. G., Brand, D., & Novak, M. D. (2018). Guidelines for using behavioral skills training to provide teacher support. *Teaching Exceptional Children*, 50, 373–380. doi: 10.1177/0040059918777241

DiGennaro Reed, F. D., Codding, R., Catania, C. N., & Maguire, H. (2010). Effects of video modeling on treatment integrity of behavioral interventions. *Journal of Applied Behavior Analysis, 43,* 291–295. doi: 10.1901/jaba.2010.43-291

DiGennaro Reed, F. D., Hirst, J. M., & Howard, V. J. (2013). Behavior analytic techniques to promote treatment integrity. In L. Hagermoser Sanetti & T. Kratochwill (Eds.), *A foundation for evidence-based practice in applied psychology* (pp. 203–226). Washington, DC: APA Press.

Drifke, M. A., Tiger, J. H., & Wierzba, B. C. (2017). Using behavioral skills training to teach parents to implement three-step prompting: A component analysis and generalization assessment. *Learning and Motivation, 57,* 1–14. doi: 10.1016/j.lmot.2016.12.001

Erath, T. G., DiGennaro Reed, F. D., Sundermeyer, H. W., Brand, D., Novak, M. D., Harbison, M. J., & Shears, R. (2020). Enhancing the training integrity of human service staff using pyramidal behavioral skills training. *Journal of Applied Behavior Analysis, 53,* 449–464. doi: 10.1002/jaba.608

Feldman, M. A., Case, L., Rincover, A., Towns, F., & Betel, J. (1989). Parent education project III: Increasing affection and responsivity in developmentally handicapped mothers: Component analysis, generalization, and effects on child language. *Journal of Applied Behavior Analysis, 22,* 211–222. doi: 10.1901/jaba.1989.22-211

Fetherston, A. M., & Sturmey, P. (2014). The effects of behavioral skills training on instructor and learner behavior across responses and skill sets. *Research in Developmental Disabilities, 35,* 541–562. doi: 10.1016/j.ridd.2013.11.006

Fixsen, D. L., Naoom, S. F., Blase, K. A., Friedman, R. M., & Wallace, F. (2005). Research on core implementation components. In D. L. Fixsen, S. F. Naoom, K. A. Blase, R. M. Friedman, & F. Wallace (Eds.), *Implementation research: A synthesis of the literature* (pp. 35–55). Tampa, FL: University of South Florida, Louis de la Parte Florida Mental Health Institute, The National Implementation Research Network (FMHI Publication #231).

Fryling, M. J., Wallace, M. D., & Yassine, J. N. (2012). Impact of treatment integrity on intervention effectiveness. *Journal of Applied Behavior Analysis, 45,* 449–453. doi: 10.1901/jaba.2012.45-449

Gerencser, K. R., Akers, J. S., Becerra, L. A., Higbee, T. S., & Sellers, T. P. (2019). A review of asynchronous trainings for the implementation of behavior analytic assessments and interventions. *Journal of Behavioral Education, 29,* 122–152. doi: 10.1007/s10864-019-09332-x

Giannakakos, A. R., Vladescu, J. C., Kisamore, A. N., & Reeve, S. A. (2015). Using video modeling with voiceover instruction plus feedback to train staff to implement direct teaching procedures. *Behavior Analysis in Practice, 4,* 126–134. doi: 10.1007/s40617-015-0097-5

Giannakakos, A. R., Vladescu, J. C., & Simon, R. (2018). Teaching installation and use of child passenger safety restraints. *Journal of Applied Behavior Analysis, 51*, 915–923. doi: 10.1002/jaba.493

Goodman, J. I., Brady, M. P., Duffy, M. L., Scott, J., & Pollard, N. E. (2008). The effects of "bug-in-ear" supervision on special education teachers' delivery of learn units. *Focus on Autism and Other Developmental Disabilities, 23*, 207–216. doi: 10.1177/1088357608324713

Graff, R. B., & Karsten, A. M. (2012a). Assessing preferences of individuals with developmental disabilities: A survey of current practices. *Behavior Analysis in Practice, 5*, 37–48. doi: 10.1007/BF03391822

Graff, R. B., & Karsten, A. M. (2012b). Evaluation of a self-instruction package for conducting stimulus preference assessments. *Journal of Applied Behavior Analysis, 45*, 69–82. doi: 10.1901/jaba.2012.45-69

Griffith, K. R., Price, J. N., & Penrod, B. (2020). The effects of a self-instruction package and group training on trial-based functional analysis administration. *Behavior Analysis in Practice, 13*, 63–80. doi: 10.1007/s40617-019-00388-9

Gutierrez, J., Reeve, S. A., Vladescu, J. C., DeBar, R. M., & Giannakakos, A. R. (2020). Evaluation of manualized instruction to train staff to implement a token economy. *Behavior Analysis in Practice, 13*, 158–168. doi: 10.1007/s40617-019-00386-x

Hansard, C., & Kazemi, E. (2018). Evaluation of video self-instruction for implementing paired-stimulus preference assessments. *Journal of Applied Behavior Analysis, 51*, 675–680. doi: 10.1002/jaba.476

Henley, A. J., & DiGennaro Reed, F. D. (2015). Should you order the feedback sandwich? Efficacy of feedback sequence and timing. *Journal of Organizational Behavior Management, 35*, 321–335. doi: 10.1080/01608061.2015.1093057

Higbee, T., Aporta, A. P., Resende, A., Nogueira, M., Goyos, C., & Pollard, J. S. (2016). Interactive computer training to teach discrete-trial instruction to undergraduates and special educators in Brazil: A replication and extension. *Journal of Applied Behavior Analysis, 49*, 780–793. doi: 10.1002/jaba.329

Higgins, W. J., Luczynski, K. C., Carroll, R. A., Fisher, W. W., & Mudford, O. C. (2017). Evlauation of a telehealth training package to remotely train staff to conduct a preference assessment. *Journal of Applied Behavior Analysis, 50*, 238–251. doi: 10.1002/jaba.370

Himle, M. B., & Wright, K. A. (2014). Behavioral skills training to improve installation and use of child passenger safety restraints. *Journal of Applied Behavior Analysis, 47*, 549–559. doi: 10.1002/jaba.143

Houvouras, A. J., & Harvey, M. T. (2014). Establishing fire safety skills using behavioral skills training. *Journal of Applied Behavior Analysis, 47*, 420–424. doi: 10.1002/jaba.113

Hudson, A. M. (1982). Training parents of developmentally handicapped children: A component analysis. *Behavior Therapy, 13*, 325–333. doi: 10.1016/S0005-7894(82)80041-5

Jenkins, S. R., & DiGennaro Reed, F. D. (2016). A parametric analysis of rehearsal opportunities on procedural integrity. *Journal of Organizational Behavior Management, 36*, 255–281. doi: 10.1080/01608061.2016.1236057

Johnson, D. A. (2013). A component analysis of the impact of evaluative and objective feedback on performance. *Journal of Organizational Behavior Management, 33*, 89–103. doi: 10.1080/01608061.2013.785879

Kang, K., Oah, S., & Dickinson, A. M. (2003). The relative effects of different frequencies of feedback on work performance: A simulation. *Journal of Organizational Behavior Management, 23*, 21–53. doi: 10.1300/J075v23n04_02

Karsten, A. M., Axe, J. B., & Mann, C. C. (2015). Review and discussion of strategies to address low trainer-to-staff ratios. *Behavioral Interventions, 30*, 295–313. doi: 10.1002/bin.1420

Knowles, C., Massar, M., Raulston, T. J., & Machalicek, W. (2017). Telehealth consultation in a self-contained classroom for behavior: A pilot study. *Preventing School Failure, 61*, 28–38. doi: 10.1080/1045988X.2016.1167012

Krumhus, K. M., & Malott, R. W. (1980). The effects of modeling and immediate and delayed feedback in staff training. *Journal of Organizational Behavior Management, 2*, 279–293. doi: 10.1300/J075v02n04_05

Lavie, T., & Sturmey, P. (2002). Training staff to conduct a paired-stimulus preference assessment. *Journal of Applied Behavior Analysis, 35*, 209–211. doi: 10.1901/jaba.2002.35-209

LeBlanc, L. A., Sump, L. A., Leaf, J. A., & Cihon, J. (2019). The effects of standard and enhanced data sheets and brief video training on implementation of conditional discrimination training. *Behavior Analysis in Practice, 13*, 53–62. doi: 10.1007/s40617-019-00338-5

Lee, N., Vladescu, J. C., Reeve, K. R., Peterson, K. M., & Giannakakos, A. R. (2019). Effects of behavioral skills training on the stimulus control of gun safety responding. *Journal of Behavioral Education, 28*, 187–203. doi: 10.1007/s10864-018-9309-8

Lerman, D. C., Tetreault, A., Hovantez, A., Strobel, M., & Garro, J. (2008). Further evaluation of a brief, intensive teacher-training model. *Journal of Applied Behavior Analysis, 41*, 243–248. doi: 10.1901/jaba.2008.41-243

Lipshultz, J. L., Vladescu, J. C., Reeve, K. F., Reeve, S. A., & Dipsey, C. R. (2015). Using video modeling with voiceover instruction to train staff to conduct stimulus preference assessments. *Journal of Developmental and Physical Disabilities, 27*, 505–523. doi: 10.1007/s10882-015-9434-4

Luiselli, J. K. (2019). Social validity assessment. In J. K. Luiselli, R. M. Gardner, F. L. Bird, & H. Maguire (Eds.), *Organizational behavior management approaches for intellectual and developmental disabilities*. London: Routledge.

Luna, O., Nuhu, N. N., Palmier, J., Brestan-Knight, E., & Rapp, J. T. (2019). Using a self-instructional package to train groups to implement reinforcement strategies. *Journal of Behavioral Education, 28*, 389–407. doi: 10.1007/s10864-018-09319-0

Machalicek, W., Rispoli, M., Lang, R., O'Reilly, M. F., Davis, T., Franco, J. H., & Chan, J. M. (2010). Training teachers to assess the challenging behaviors of students with autism using video tele-conferencing. *Education and Training in Autism and Developmental Disabilities, 45*, 203–215.

Macurik, K. M., O'Kane, N. P., Malanga, P., & Reid, D. H. (2008). Video training of support staff in intervention plans for challenging behavior: Comparison with live training. *Behavioral Interventions, 23*, 143–163. doi: 10.1002/bin.261

Madzharova, M. S., Sturmey, P., & Jones, E. A. (2012). Training staff to increase manding in students with autism: Two preliminary case studies. *Behavioral Interventions, 27*, 224–235. doi: 10.1002/bin.1349

Marano, K. E., Vladescu, J. C., Reeve, K. F., & DiGennaro Reed, F. D. (2019). Effect of conducting behavioral observations and ratings on staff implementation of a paired-stimulus preference assessment. *Journal of Applied Behavior Analysis, 53*, 296–304. doi: 10.1002/jaba.584

Martens, B. K., Witt, J. C., Elliott, S. N., & Darveaux, D. (1985). Teacher judgments concerning the acceptability of school-based interventions. *Professional Psychology: Research and Practice, 16*, 191–198. doi: 10.1037/0735-7028.16.2.191

McClannahan, L. E., & Krantz, P. J. (1999). *Activity schedules for children with autism: Teaching independent behavior*. Bethesda, MD: Woodbine House.

McIntyre, L. L., Gresham, F. M., DiGennaro, F. D., & Reed, D. D. (2007). Treatment integrity of school-based interventions with children in the journal of applied behavior analysis 1991-2005. *Journal of Applied Behavior Analysis, 40*, 659–672. doi: 10.1901/jaba.2007.659-672

Merritt, T. A., DiGennaro Reed, F. D., & Martinez, C. E. (2019). Using the performance diagnostic checklist-human services to identify an indicated intervention to decrease employee tardiness. *Journal of Applied Behavior Analysis, 52*, 1034–1048. doi: 10.1002/jaba.643

Miljkovic, M., Kaminski, L., & Wishnowski, L. (2015). Evaluation of video modeling and self-instructional manual to teach students to conduct a preference assessment. *Journal on Developmental Disabilities, 21*, 3–10.

Miltenberger, R. G. (2003). *Behavior modification: Principles and procedures*. Bedmont, CA. Wadsworth.

Moore, J. W., & Fisher, W. W. (2007). The effects of videotape modeling on staff acquisition of functional analysis methodology. *Journal of Applied Behavior Analysis, 40*, 197–202. doi: 10.1901/jaba.2007.24-06

Nigro-Bruzzi, D., & Sturmey, P. (2010). The effects of behavioral skills training on mand training by staff and unprompted vocal mands by children. *Journal of Applied Behavior Analysis, 43*, 757–761. doi: 10.1901/jaba.2010.43-757

Nottingham, C. L., Vladescu, J. C., Giannakakos, A. R., Schnell, L. K., & Lipshultz, J. L. (2017). Using video modeling with voiceover instruction plus feedback to train implementation of stimulus preference assessments. *Learning and Motivation, 58*, 37–47. doi: 10.1016/j.lmot.2017.01.008

Parkes, J., Abercrombie, S., & McCarty, T. (2013). Feedback sandwiches affect perceptions but not performance. *Advances in Health Sciences Education, 18*, 397–407. doi: 10.1007/s10459-012-9377-9

Parsons, M. B., Rollyson, J. H., & Reid, D. H. (2012). Evidence-based staff training: A guide for practitioners. *Behavior Analysis in Practice, 5*, 2–11. doi: 10.1007/BF03391819

Parsons, M. B., Rollyson, J. H., & Reid, D. H. (2013). Teaching practitioners to conduct behavioral skills training: A pyramidal approach for training multiple human service staff. *Behavior Analysis in Practice, 6*, 4–16. doi: 10.1007/BF03391798

Pence, S. T., St. Peter, C. C., & Tetreault, A. S. (2012). Increasing accurate preference assessment implementation through pyramidal training. *Journal of Applied Behavior Analysis, 45*, 345–359. doi: 10.1901/jaba.2012.45-345

Ramon, D., Yu, C. T., Martin, G. L., & Martin, T. (2015). Evaluation of a self-instructional manual to teach multiple-stimulus without replacement preference assessments. *Journal of Behavioral Education, 24*, 289–303. doi: 10.1007/s10864-015-9222-3

Reid, D. H., Parsons, M. P., & Green, C. W. (2012). *The supervisor's guidebook: Evidence-based strategies for promoting work quality and enjoyment among human service staff.* Morganton, NC: Professional Press.

Roscoe, E. M., & Fisher, W. W. (2008). Evaluation of an efficient method for training staff to implement stimulus preference assessments. *Journal of Applied Behavior Analysis, 41*, 249–254. doi: 10.1901/jaba.2008.41-249

Sarokoff, R. A., & Sturmey, P. (2004). The effects of behavioral skills training on staff implementation of discrete-trial teaching. *Journal of Applied Behavior Analysis, 37*, 535–538. doi: 10.1901/jaba.2004.37-535

Shapiro, M., Kazemi, E., Pogosjana, M., Rios, D., & Mendoza, M. (2016). Preference assessment training via self-instruction: A replication and extension. *Journal of Applied Behavior Analysis, 49*, 794–808. doi: 10.1002/jaba.339

Shuler, N., & Carroll, R. A. (2019). Training supervisors to provide performance feedback using video modeling with voiceover instructions. *Behavior Analysis in Practice*, 12, 576–591. doi: 10.1007/s40617-018-00314-5

Slowiak, J. M., & Lakowske, A. M. (2017). The influence of feedback statement sequence and goals on task performance. *Behavior Analysis: Research and Practice*, 17, 357–380. doi: 10.1037.bar/0000084

Spiegel, H. J., Kisamore, A. N., Vladescu, J. C., & Karsten, A. M. (2016). The effects of video modeling with voiceover instruction and on-screen text on parent implementation of guided compliance. *Child and Family Behavior Therapy*, 38, 299–317. doi: 10.1080/07317107.2016.1238690

Stocco, C. S., Thompson, R. H., Hart, J. M., & Soriano, H. L. (2017). Improving the interview skills of college students using behavioral skills training. *Journal of Applied Behavior Analysis*, 50, 495–510. doi: 10.1002/jaba.385

Stokes, T. F., & Baer, D. M. (1977). An implicit technology of generalization. *Journal of Applied Behavior Analysis*, 10, 349–367. doi: 10.1901/jaba.1977.10-349

Tai, S., & Miltenberger, R. G. (2017). Evaluating behavioral skills training to teach safe tackling skills to youth football players. *Journal of Applied Behavior Analysis*, 50, 849–855. doi: 10.1002/jaba.412

Tomlinson, S. R. L., Gore, N., & McGill, P. (2018). Training individuals to implement applied behavior analytic procedures via telehealth: A systematic review of the literature. *Journal of Behavioral Education*, 27, 172–222. doi: 10.1007/s10864-018-9292-0

Tyner, B. C., & Fienup, D. M. (2016). The effects of describing antecedent stimuli and performance criteria in task analysis instruction for graphing. *Journal of Behavioral Education*, 25, 379–392. doi: 10.1007/s10864-015-9242-z

Van Houten, R., Axelrod, S., Bailey, J. S., Favell, J. E., Foxx, R. M., Iwata, B. A., & Lovaas, O. I. (1988). The right to effective behavioral treatment. *Journal of Applied Behavior Analysis*, 21, 381–384. doi: 10.1901/jaba.1988.21-381

Vladescu, J. C., Carroll, R., Paden, A., & Kodak, T. M. (2013). The effects of video modeling with voiceover instruction on accurate implementation of discrete-trial instruction. *Journal of Applied Behavior Analysis*, 45, 419–423. doi: 10.1901/jaba.2012.45-419

Ward, P., Johnson, M., & Konukman, F. (1998). Directed rehearsal and preservice teachers' performance of instructional behavior. *Journal of Behavioral Education*, 8, 369–380. doi: 10.1023/A:1022827415544

Ward-Horner, J., & Sturmey, P. (2012). Component analysis of behavior skills training in functional analysis. *Behavioral Interventions*, 27, 75–92. doi: 10.1002/bin.1339

Wilder, D. (2019). Performance diagnostic assessment. In J. K. Luiselli, R. M. Gardner, F. L. Bird, & H. Maguire (Eds.), *Organizational behavior management approaches for intellectual and developmental disabilities*. London: Routledge.

Wine, B., Kelley, D. P., & Wilder, D. A. (2014). An initial assessment of effective preference assessment intervals among employees. *Journal of Organizational Behavior Management, 34*, 188–195. doi: 10.1080/01608061.2014.944747

Wine, B., Lewis, K., Mewcomb, E. T., Camblin, J. G., Chen, T., Lisfield, J. E., … Morgan, C. A. (2019). The effects of temporal placement of feedback on performance with and without goals. *Journal of Organizational Behavior Management, 65*, 425–434. doi: 10.1007/s40732-015-0117-4

6
Performance Management Interventions

James K. Luiselli

Performance management within applied behavior analysis (ABA) and organizational behavior management (OBM) concerns "on the job" skills and competencies of employees within occupational settings, including human services organizations for persons with intellectual and developmental disabilities (IDD) (DiGennaro Reed et al., 2015; Luiselli, 2018; Wilder, Austin, & Casella, 2009). Notably, human services care providers typically receive pre-service training in multiple areas such as conducting instruction with children and adults, implementing behavior support plans, progress monitoring, recording data, and providing healthy and safe living environments (Dixon & Loukus, 2013). However, the effects of initial training usually do not generalize to natural conditions where children and adults receive education, habilitation, and treatment (Conrad et al., 2016; Shapiro & Kazemi, 2017). Accordingly, post-training performance management is required to ensure that service delivery by care providers is exemplary and in accordance with regulatory guidelines (Reid et al., 2012).

There are several priority performance management objectives within human services organizations. First, care providers and the individuals supervising them should implement evidence-based practices that have a research foundation and adhere to the competency requirements of professional compliance and ethics codes (Behavior Analyst Certification Board, 2021). Further, care providers must deliver services with integrity according to written protocols, program manuals, and prescribed recommendations (DiGennaro Reed & Codding, 2011). Third, performance management should be concerned about social validity, that is, acceptance and approval of organizational goals, methods, and results among care providers and the people they serve (Wolf, 1978; Luiselli, 2021, this volume). In summary, human services organizations for persons with IDD will produce the most valued and desirable outcomes when the performance of care providers is evidence-based, demonstrates the highest level of intervention integrity, and is judged positively.

Unfortunately, many human services organizations face challenges and obstacles that impede the performance of care providers and, in consequence, the delivery of high-quality programs. For example, limited finances and budget restrictions pose hiring difficulties and constrict allocation of funds to general operations and project development. Training resources are often inadequate and insufficient for large numbers of inexperienced care providers. With many competing responsibilities on the job, care providers are easily overburdened, experience stress, feel unsatisfied, and turn over in high volumes (Britton Laws et al., 2014; Ejaz et al., 2008; Firmin et al., 2013). These and related areas are commonly the targets of performance management interventions applied on an individual and systems-wide level.

More recently, function-based assessment instruments such as the Performance Diagnostic Checklist-Human Services (PDC-HS) have been used to identify the sources of performance deficits among care providers and inform interventions that are matched to controlling variables (Wilder et al., 2020). Presented later in the chapter, such pre-intervention assessment can confirm whether poor performance of care providers is the result of skill deficiency (i.e., a person does not know what to do), inadequate motivation (i.e., a person knows what to do but lacks incentive), or inhibitory influences (i.e., a person knows that to do, is motivated to perform, but is constrained by external variables).

Gravina et al. (2018) reviewed OBM interventions in human services settings reported in three peer-reviewed journals (*Journal of Applied Behavior Analysis, Journal of Organizational Behavior Management, Behavior Analysis in Practice*) during the period 1990 through 2016. The most common topics of research articles were intervention integrity, safety, environmental preparation and cleanliness, administration, attendance, and social validity of client engagement and job satisfaction. Frequently implemented interventions included care provider training, antecedent control, feedback, positive reinforcement, observation, systems redesign, and incentives, all of which are featured in performance management. The review also found that very few studies (6.7%–28.6%) had assessed the factors contributing to performance problems before intervening.

This chapter describes performance management intervention research in human services organizations for persons with IDD, primarily special education schools, day treatment centers, residential care facilities, community habilitation settings, and group homes. I review training, antecedent-focused, and consequence-delivered interventions with care providers in the roles of teachers, therapists, paraprofessionals, and related direct service personnel (DSP). The chapter also presents several research-to-practice recommendations based on the most contemporary evidence-based support.

Overview

Almost all performance management interventions within human services organizations include multiple procedures applied as a behavior-change package. In some research, single procedures were introduced one after another until performance improvement was achieved. Other interventions combined several procedures from the beginning and, in a few cases, evaluated the effects of gradually dismantling the package (Kazdin, 2011). Multi-procedure interventions are usually formulated in order to produce the most robust performance outcomes in the shortest period of time without concern about the individual contribution of each procedure. Nonetheless, for the purpose of this chapter, training, antecedent, and consequence interventions are described separately even though the respective procedures are rarely implemented and evaluated in isolation.

Also, performance management interventions are usually implemented by supervisors, trainers, and other administrators responsible for program oversight. Behavior analysts frequently act as performance managers and need to acquire supervision competencies for interacting effectively with care providers (Turner et al., 2016; Sellers et al., 2016). For example, delivering performance management interventions successfully requires observation, rapport building, personnel evaluation, and progress monitoring skills (Reid & Parsons, 2006). As well, the number of care providers requiring supervision and their abilities, work demands, and expectations will govern performance management effectiveness in most human services organizations. Accordingly, the performance management of the individuals conducting performance management must not be overlooked.

Performance Management Interventions

It is beyond the scope of this chapter to thoroughly review all of the performance management interventions that have been evaluated with care providers. Some of these interventions originated from seminal ABA research in IDD (Reid, 1998) and also have wide application in OBM outside of human services organizations (Wine & Pritchard, 2018).

In Vivo Behavioral Skills Training (BST)

Reid (2017) described BST as a multi-step and competency-based approach to care provider training and performance management. First, care providers are given a rationale for why particular skills will be trained, for example, to carry out instruction with children, teach adults adaptive living routines, and implement safety procedures properly. The behaviors necessary to demonstrate skills are defined and sequenced in a written summary that represents a task analysis. During BST, a supervisor or trainer (a) demonstrates the behaviors compromising the skills, (b) observes care providers practicing the behaviors, (c) delivers feedback to care providers through praise and correction, and (d) directs rehearsal until care providers achieve skill competency. There is ample evidence that BST is effective for teaching care providers skills such as conducting discrete trial instruction (Sarokoff & Sturmey, 2004), guided compliance (Miles & Wilder, 2009), functional analysis (Wallace et al., 2004), and preference assessment (Roscoe & Fisher, 2008).

Behavioral skills training can be applied with individual care providers or in small groups to prepare them for work with children and adults in natural settings. As it pertains to performance management, Reid (2017) cautioned that this initial training is not sufficient and that "the trainer must observe each trainee complete the skill that was targeted during the training session in a competent manner during the trainee's regular work routine" (p. 30). If post-training skills are not demonstrated under natural conditions, additional BST can be used to manage performance.

It is also possible to address performance management by conducting BST in vivo without preceding simulated training. In illustration, Gilligan et al. (2007) measured the percentage of steps in a ten-step discrete trial instructional protocol that three classroom care providers displayed correctly with students who had neurodevelopmental disabilities. The care providers read the written protocol before intervention and participated in a question-and-answer session with a trainer. In vivo performance management was delivered within the classroom through observation from the trainer, who gave verbal feedback to the care providers following their discrete trial instruction with students. Feedback consisted of trainer praise contingent on instructional steps that were followed correctly and review, demonstration, and practice if implementation errors occurred. Each performance intervention was brief, lasting five to eight minutes, and increased correct instruction by the care providers from a baseline average of 66% to 97%.

Belisle et al. (2016) is another example of in vivo BST applied as a performance management intervention with three classroom care providers and students at a school for children with autism. The researchers recorded the percentage of steps the care providers implemented correctly according to a standardized language training program (PEAK-DT: Dixon, 2014). Baseline measurement occurred after the care providers read a program excerpt, exchanged information with a trainer, and completed brief quizzes. The in vivo BST consisting of trainer modeling, demonstration, feedback, and rehearsal in the classroom improved baseline performance of each care provider as well as selected language skills in two of the three students. This latter outcome recognizes that competency improvement of care providers through performance management should also be reflected in the skill acquisition of children and adults who receive services.

There are many variations of BST as an approach to performance management. A key factor with valuable practice implications is whether all of the conventional BST components (instructions, modeling, rehearsal, feedback) are necessary to promote competent performance (Drifke et al., 2017; Ward-Horner & Sturmey, 2012). Similarly, research suggests that the amount of time needed to conduct BST can be shortened without compromising skill acquisition (Reid, 2017; Roscoe & Fisher, 2008). Group BST is another performance management option that can economize time with multiple care providers (Parsons et al., 2013).

Antecedent Interventions

The purpose of antecedent interventions is to cue, prompt, and set the occasion for care provider behaviors that are integral to operations within human services organizations. Antecedent interventions can function as discriminative stimuli for and acquire control over these behaviors through pairing with positive reinforcement and other performance management procedures.

Environmental Cuing

Conspicuous environmental stimuli such as signs and visual cues have effectively promoted many desirable behaviors such as recycling materials and depositing trash (Austin et al., 1993), wearing motor vehicle safety belts (Cox et al., 2005), and eliminating bathroom graffiti (Mueller et al., 2000). This method of antecedent intervention has the advantage of being practical and efficient. Other benefits are that the size, content, visual features, and location of environmental stimuli can be easily modified.

In a study relevant to performance management within human services organizations, Rubio and Sigurdsson (2014) evaluated the effects of signs on improperly stored dishes (a health concern) at a hospital unit. The first intervention was posting a humorous sign in the sink area reminding staff to "Put away your dishes." A second intervention included a neutral sign with different graphics. Compared to baseline conditions in a reversal design, both signs decreased the number of improperly stored dishes and the effects were maintained for many months with the neutral sign still present.

Gianotti et al. (2020) found that a humorous sign similar to Rubio and Sigurdsson (2014) increased safe storage of hazardous materials by care providers in one group home and maintained high baseline performance in a second group home at a human services organization for students with IDD. On the other hand, Ditzian et al. (2015) reported that a posted written prompt to secure therapy room doors at an autism treatment center was not effective with therapists until the intervention was combined with graphic feedback from supervisors. Likewise, Mishra et al. (2020) had to combine brief performance monitoring with previously ineffective environmental cuing displayed as a highlighted activity schedule to increase correct data recording by classroom care providers at a special education school. These results support previous research which found that performance enhancement from environmental cuing may require co-occurring interventions (Fritz et al., 2017; Jason & Liotta, 1982).

Task Clarifying Instructions

Graff and Karsten (2012) evaluated the impact of written instructions in training 11 classroom care providers at a special education school to implement preference assessments. One training condition had the care providers read preference assessment instructions that were derived from published research articles. A comparison condition featured enhanced written instructions without technical language that were accompanied by procedural diagrams and a detailed data sheet. Accuracy of conducting preference assessments was low with written instructions alone but improved to competency level in response to enhanced written instructions which appeared to simplify procedural comprehension for the care providers.

In related research, written and verbal task clarifying instructions (DiGennaro Reed et al., 2010) and written action directives (Garrity & Luiselli, 2005; Garrity et al., 2008) have been combined with other procedures in training programs aimed at performance improvement with human services organization care providers. However, studies to date have not evaluated task clarifying instructions as a stand-alone intervention. Certainly, being able to improve and maintain competencies of care providers through periodic verbal and written instructions offers an easy-to-implement and efficient performance management strategy.

Video Modeling

Video modeling is an empirically supported training methodology in which care providers watch video clips and segments of actual or surrogate care providers demonstrating desired skills with children and adults (Nikopoulos et al., 2016). Through video modeling, care providers have learned to implement preference assessment (Rosales et al., 2012), discrete trial instruction (Vladescu et al., 2013), functional analysis (Moore & Fisher, 2007), and differential attention (Taber et al., 2017). Video modeling can be augmented to improve effectiveness in several ways, such as adding narrative voiceover (Lipshultz et al., 2015) and on-screen text (Spiegel et al., 2016).

Like BST, video modeling is used frequently during initial training of care providers to prepare them for service delivery but is also applicable for post-training performance management. For example, if observations revealed that care providers misapplied procedures or did not follow established protocols, video modeling could be introduced as "booster" sessions to improve performance. Among many desirable features, video modeling depicts consistent performance and eliminates variability that can occur with individual and multiple trainers (DiGennaro Reed et al., 2018). Video modeling as a method of performance management can also be adapted to the busy schedules of care providers, delivered in one-to-one and group formats, and if necessary, presented without a supervisor or trainer present. Performance can be enhanced further by having care providers attend to particular elements of video models or respond to questions after viewing (Marano et al., 2019).

Goal Setting

This antecedent intervention establishes performance goals for care providers that produce feedback and/or positive reinforcement if goals are achieved. Gil and Carter (2016) first exposed approximately 200 residential care providers in 13 group homes for persons with IDD to bar graphs depicting their compliance with data recording responsibilities. Graphic feedback moderately improved data recording above baseline levels but additional intervention was required. While graphic feedback continued, supervisors conducted monthly meetings with the care providers and had them set performance goals for the following month that were higher than the current level of data recording. Goal attainment from month to month was illustrated solely in line graphs without consequences if goals had not been achieved. Adding goal setting increased compliance with data recording above 85% on average, although interpretation of these findings is confounded because supervisors also provided verbal feedback during meetings with care providers. However, these findings suggest that goal setting may be a potentially helpful performance management procedure that can be used in isolation or easily integrated with other methods (see, for example, Doerner et al., 1989).

Self-Management

Teaching care providers to self-manage job skills is a cogent approach to performance management when human services organizations do not have sufficient personnel resources to provide consistent supervision and program oversight (DiGennaro Reed & Henley, 2015). Training care providers of persons with IDD in self-management has included *self-monitoring* with supervisor feedback to increase interactions with clients (Burg et al., 1979), *self-recording* with supervisor feedback to increase on-schedule and on-task behaviors (Richman et al., 1988), and *self-recording and self-graphing* with goal setting to increase social initiations towards residents (Doerner et al., 1989). Self-management in these and related studies has usually been selected based on the targeted care provider skills, setting characteristics, and learning objectives of children and adults receiving services.

At Melmark New England, a human services organization for persons with neurodevelopmental and intellectual disabilities, we have conducted research on self-management to support care provider competencies following initial training. In Gerald et al. (2019), the participants were nine classroom care providers required to record student behavior data at the conclusion of instructional activities during the school day. They had been trained in data recording preceding the study and their subsequent performance was evaluated during a baseline phase. The self-management intervention consisted of the care providers carrying a small countdown timer that signaled the conclusion of instructional activities and cued data recording. Other than informal interactions with classroom supervisors, the care providers independently managed procedures, which increased data recording from a baseline average of 70% to an average of 98% in one classroom and from a baseline average of 68% to an average of 98% in a second classroom. Data recording with continued self-management was maintained at 90%–100% in both classrooms one to two months later.

A second study, by Willis et al., (2020), also concerned data recording (completion of student instructional activities) by nine care providers across two classrooms. The care providers recorded data in a baseline phase as they had been trained before the study. Their percentage of correct data recording increased in both classrooms when a supervisor delivered graphic feedback to them via email. Next, the care providers were taught to self-manage the supervision feedback, in effect, to independently monitor and report their compliance with data recording. The self-management intervention maintained the high percentage of data recording achieved with supervisor feedback through six months' follow-up assessment.

The results of Gerald et al. (2019) and Willis et al. (2020) suggest that self-management can be effective with care providers who received training but require additional support to sustain exemplary performance long-term. Note, too, that the care providers in these studies rated the self-management interventions positively, indicating good social validity associated with program maintenance (Kennedy 2002; Luiselli, 2021, this volume)

Consequence Interventions

Different contingencies can be arranged to reinforce the skills and competencies of care providers. These interventions are intended to have a direct effect on performance through positive and negative reinforcement that incorporates social and tangible consequences. The antecedent procedures reviewed previously are often incorporated with consequence-focused methods of performance management.

Performance Feedback

Delivering feedback to care providers is the most widely implemented and empirically supported performance management procedure within human services organizations (Arco, 2008; DiGennaro Reed et al., 2013; Gravina et al., 2018; Luiselli, 2015; Parsons et al., 2012). Figure 6.1 illustrates the typical process of delivering performance feedback. A supervisor begins by observing a care

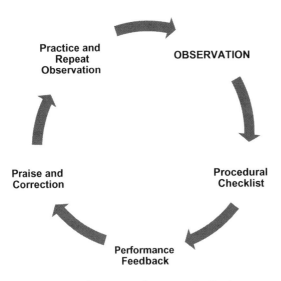

FIGURE 6.1 Delivering performance feedback

provider conducting services with children and adults or engaging in non-service tasks pertinent to the job. The actions of the care provider are recorded on a behaviorally anchored checklist. Upon concluding observation, the supervisor meets with the care provider to present feedback on steps in the checklist that were completed correctly and incorrectly. The care provider practices and rehearses the sequence of steps under direction of the supervisor and with the goal of 100% competency.

The form shown in Figure 6.2 illustrates the type of checklist a supervisor might use when delivering performance feedback to a care provider implementing a student behavior support plan. After observation, the supervisor and care provider review correct and incorrect implementation of the four antecedent steps and the five consequence steps comprising the plan. The supervisor delivers

Date of Observation: Setting: Care Provider:				
Behavior Support Plan Component	**Behavior Support Plan Procedures**	**C (+)**	**IC (-)**	**NA**
ANTECEDENT	States transition cue ("In two minutes….")			
	Sets interval timer			
	When timer sounds, states, "All done, walk to…." next destination			
	Presents transitional object			
CONSEQUENCE	Praises compliance every 30 seconds			
	If aggression occurs, blocks responses and withholds attention			
	If floor-dropping occurs, moves five steps away, waits for independent standing, resumes transition			
	At destination: Requests transition object			
	At destination: Delivers praise and token			
	Records transition data			

Scoring Key

C = Implemented step correctly
IC = Implemented step incorrectly
NA = Not applicable (no opportunity to respond)

Total Performance Score (correct steps/total steps x 100) ☐

FIGURE 6.2 Performance feedback checklist

TABLE 6.1 Care provider skills and competencies addressed in performance management research

Skill/Competency	Study
Data recording	Gil & Carter (2016)
	Flood & Luiselli (2012)
	Willis et al. (2020)
Environmental appearance-safety	Ditzian et al. (2015)
	Schmidt et al. (2013)
Instruction	Gilligan et al. (2007)
	Wilson et al. (1991)
Conducting IOA assessment	Garrity et al. (2008)
Implementation integrity	Codding et al. (2005)
	DiGennaro Reed et al. (2010)
	DiGennaro Reed et al. (2007)

performance feedback accordingly and enters a total performance score as an outcome measure to be evaluated over successive observations.

Although there are many variations of performance feedback, conventional application occurs immediately following observations, with a single care provider, and to a level of full competence, where after the frequency of feedback sessions is reduced. Table 6.1 is a representative sample of care provider skills and competencies addressed in performance feedback research. The performance feedback in many of these studies were implemented concurrently with other procedures and in different forms including *verbal feedback* (Codding et al., 2005; Flood & Luiselli, 2012; Gilligan et al., 2007; 1991), *graphic feedback* (Gil & Carter, 2016), *written feedback* (DiGennaro et al., 2007), *verbal* and *video feedback* (DiGennaro Reed et al., 2010), and combinations of *verbal, graphic,* and *written feedback* (Ditzian et al., 2015; Garrity et al., 2008; Schmidt et al., 2013; Willis et al., 2020). The diversity of performance feedback options is noteworthy for tailoring interventions to the specific management priorities within human services organizations, disparate competencies of care providers, preferences of supervisors, and factors contributing to implementation efficiency, fidelity, and effectiveness.

Performance feedback pinpoints and defines the behaviors that care providers should demonstrate in order to achieve competency. Feedback itself may have reinforcing properties (Alvero et al., 2001) but is most likely effective through pairing with praise, approval, recognition, and other social consequences. Additional reinforcers can be delivered when performance management is presented. Self-management by care providers may also be a source of reinforcement. Beyond the mechanisms responsible for effectiveness, research on the influence of frequency, duration, and content of performance feedback interactions between supervisors and care providers deserves attention.

Performance Incentives

Many human services organizations provide performance incentives to care providers, as reported by DiGennaro Reed and Henley (2015) in a survey of board certified behavior analysts (BCBAs). Incentive contingencies have been arranged to improve staff attendance, completion of assigned tasks, and carrying out service plans through "rewards" such as money (Luiselli et al., 2009), tangible items (Reid & Whitman, 1983), and special privileges (Green et al., 1991; Iwata et al., 1976). Other interventions have relied on negative reinforcement to affect change, for example, improving implementation integrity of educational care providers by allowing them to avoid program review meetings (DiGennaro Reed et al., 2007; DiGennaro Reed et al., 2005) and improving data recording of residential care providers by temporarily removing some of their case management tasks (Buckley et al., 2020).

The potential success of performance incentives rests with pre-intervention assessment of care provider preferences (Wine, 2017; Wine et al., 2014). Put another way, human services organizations must ask care providers to identify objects, activities, privileges, and material goods that could be made available to them as "rewards." Such assessment must be comprehensive in order to collect the diversity of incentive choices (Wine et al., 2013) and should be repeated at scheduled intervals since care provider preferences change over time (Wine et al., 2012). An additional consideration is that offering performance incentives can be expensive and place a financial burden on human services organizations. For this reason, naturally occurring, low-cost, and easily managed incentives may be the best option, namely recognition, flex scheduling, gestures of appreciation, time off, parking privileges, and the like.

To function as positive reinforcement, performance incentives should be tied directly to desirable care provider behaviors either documented through permanent product measures (e.g., environmental cleanliness) or direct observation (e.g., percentage of steps completed correctly). Performance incentives that are not behavior contingent will be ineffective. A possible detriment when incentives are conditioned on group performance is that some underperforming care providers may contact reinforcement. Delayed access to performance incentives and possible negative reactions to rewards from some care providers are other qualifying considerations.

Summary and Recommendations

Performance management is critical for the effective, safe, and ethical operation of human services organizations for persons with IDD. This chapter reviewed performance management interventions that have been researched with regularity and can be recommended for application with care providers in educational, habilitation, and treatment settings. It seems apparent that human services organizations will continue to benefit from ABA and OBM performance management research towards evidence-based and empirically supported practices (Gravina et al., 2018; Luke et al., 2018).

Practice Applications

A first step for human services organizations is recognizing performance management as an administrative and operations priority. Having a clear mission statement, sound fiscal plan, interactive service departments, and system of continuous quality improvement (CQI) sets the foundation for dedicated performance management organization-wide. It then is necessary to describe the roles and scope of responsibility of performance managers, screen and hire able professionals, and ensure that these individuals have direct input to and are heard by organizational leadership.

Referenced previously, behavior analysts, clinicians, supervisors, and organization administrators should assess the conditions responsible for performance problems among care providers before intervening. Descriptive assessment via direct observation and data analysis, and indirect assessment through interviews and rating scales are flexible and semi-structured approaches most commonly employed (Wilder et al., 2018). However, the emergence of more formal assessment instruments such as the PHC-HS facilitates objective evaluation and highlights assessment-derived intervention suggestions in the areas of training, resources, prompting, task clarification, materials, and consequences (Wilder et al., 2020).

Notwithstanding the multi-procedure interventions that have dominated performance management research, there is a need for experimental component analyses that examine both the effects of gradually adding single procedures to a package and systematically removing procedures that were initially combined. Individual procedures also have characteristics that can be evaluated with greater specificity. For example, antecedent-only interventions through signs, visuals, posted instructions, and similar environmental cues reduce the need for in-person supervision to effect behavior change, but more research is required to determine the relative effects of variables such as print size, content, location, and static versus variable presentation (Warman et al., 2019).

Multi-procedure interventions should be evaluated further to isolate the most time-efficient combination of methods. In illustration, care provider self-management can be effective as a sole intervention and with the addition of positive reinforcement and performance feedback (Richman et al., 1988; Willis et al., 2020). By adopting a "less is more" perspective, human services organizations would be seeking to select and implement the most practical performance management interventions, undeniably a goal within busy, demanding, and multidisciplinary settings. In situations where multi-procedure packages are needed to rapidly improve performance, dismantling strategies can document the lowest intensity of intervention required to satisfactorily maintain care provider competencies.

Innovations in telehealth and teleconsultation can also make performance management more practical within human services organizations (Fischer et al., 2019; Luiselli & Fischer, 2016). Videoconferencing, virtual training platforms, and web-based applications enable supervisors and program managers to observe care providers remotely, meet at convenient times, schedule feedback sessions, and display data for review. These synchronous (real-time) formats are especially valuable for increasing the frequency of performance management contacts with care providers. Documenting and electronically storing the interactions via recording software are additionally advantageous.

Other facets of performance management may impact intervention effectiveness but have not been examined extensively. As noted, response effort can be manipulated to promote critical competencies of care providers (Casella et al., 2010; Fritz et al., 2017). Many interventions in human services organizations can be labeled "effortful" because they require practitioners to implement several procedures contemporaneously while also recording data and completing other essential tasks. Reduced response effort surely simplifies implementation demands, improves procedural fidelity, and likely has good social validity with care providers.

Second, the value of delivering verbal performance feedback notwithstanding (Alvero et al., 2001), the behavior of persons *receiving* feedback warrants analysis because "Employee behavior that is receptive to receiving feedback might reinforce feedback delivery and contribute to improved performance in the future" (Ehrlich et al., 2020, p. 2). Ehrlich et al. identified eight behaviors employees should demonstrate when receiving verbal performance feedback (e.g., maintaining eye contact with a supervisor, asking follow-up questions, showing appreciation for feedback) and found that behavioral skills training (BST) effectively increased occurrence of those behaviors by three employees and their completion of tasks that were the basis of feedback sessions.

Several studies reviewed in the chapter assessed social validity of performance management interventions by asking care providers to rate their approval and acceptance of procedures and outcomes (Codding et al., 2005; Graff & Karsten,

2012; Gerald et al., 2019; Mishra et al., 2020; Rubio & Sigurdsson, 2014). Social validation enables supervisors and administrators to tailor the most effective interventions to the preferences of care providers with sensitivity to factors that consistently promote satisfaction in the workforce. Thus, some care providers may be more responsive to individually delivered verbal feedback than written or graphic feedback presented through email or in the presence of co-workers. Similar objectives of social validity assessment would be gathering information about the types of incentives included in a performance management intervention, alternative procedures that should be evaluated, and recommendations of care providers to other personnel.

Pre-intervention social validity assessment can also solicit opinions and suggestions from care providers about performance management interventions they think will be most effective and they would like to experience. For example, Strohmeier et al. (2014) found that 100% of educational care providers (N = 44) at a residential school for students with IDD reported that they would respond somewhat well to very well to performance feedback for improving correct implementation of behavior support plans. Other training and performance management methods the care providers judged positively were avoiding supervisor meetings, receiving a financial incentive, and participating in online training modules. Obtaining preference ratings from care providers should enhance receptivity to performance interventions that are designed from such input.

Finally, what are the best methods for training professionals to conduct performance management with care providers? Behavioral skills training appears to be a promising approach towards this objective (Erath et al., 2019; Parsons et al., 2012) and especially relevant with less experienced clinicians and behavior analysts in the roles of supervisor and program manager. Additional training is possible when human services organizations make continuing education opportunities available by supporting internal workshops, conference attendance, and gaining access to the peer-reviewed literature (Mattson, 2017). In summary, the value of performance management with care providers can only be fully realized if it is delivered by individuals who have requisite expertise, adhere to recognized practice standards, and are recognized at all levels of their organization.

Research Applications

Gravina et al. (2018) advised that in conducting OBM studies to improve performance within human services settings, researchers should (a) target supervisors and managers in addition to "front line" staff, (b) include the full range of competency objectives, (c) precisely define intervention procedures to facilitate replication and generalization, (d) address the conditions associated with performance deficits, and (e) measure the effects of intervention on both care provider and client behavior. In addition to these goals, we should incorporate research methodology that will be sensitive to experimental manipulations, specifically single-case research designs common to ABA and OBM (Kazdin, 2011).

Reversal designs are well suited to evaluate the effects of presenting and removing antecedent interventions and the results of adding and withdrawing components of multi-procedure packages. Multiple baseline designs make it possible to introduce interventions sequentially across behaviors, persons, and settings while assessing possible response and stimulus generalization. With a changing criterion design, intervention effects are measured against gradual procedural changes, usually a behavior-specific benchmark for accessing reinforcers. A fourth research methodology, the alternating treatments design, compares two of more interventions and their relative effectiveness on the training and performance management objectives understudy.

Procedural integrity should be measured during intervention evaluations and research studies. Clear interpretation of intervention outcome is only possible if it is shown that procedures were implemented accurately according to behavior-specific guidelines. Procedural integrity assessments identify implementation errors that can be targeted through additional training and performance management (Hartz et al., 2021). Similar to intervention planning, measuring procedural integrity has the dual purpose of isolating conditions that contribute to poor fidelity. Among human services organization care providers, some of these obstacles are inadequate training, non-specific procedural guidelines, diminished performance motivation, and environmental conditions that set the occasion for misapplication. When poor procedural integrity is recognized as a problem, a valuable research strategy would be to confirm the variables that deter performance using an instrument such as the *Performance Diagnostic Checklist-Human Services* (Wilder et al., 2020), followed by an evaluation of interventions that were indicated by the assessment findings.

Even with controlled experimental evaluations of OBM interventions that have strong procedural integrity and social validity, do positive effects maintain months and years later? Poor maintenance is often the result of rapid staff turnover but frequently occurs when care providers do not receive routine supervision and there are lapses in performance management oversight (DiGennaro Reed & Henley, 2015). Research can benefit human services organizations by including maintenance assessment as a component of evaluation and, ideally, identifying conditions that compromise and support sustainable practices. Stated succinctly, maintenance can be viewed as "generalization over time" and in need of an implicit technology for purposeful planning and application (Stokes & Baer, 1977).

References

Alvero, A. M., Bucklin, B. R., & Austin, J. (2001). An objective review of the effectiveness and essential characteristics of performance feedback in organizational settings (1985–1998). *Journal of Organizational Behavior Management, 21*, 3–29. https://doi .org/ 10.1300/J075v21n01_02

Arco, L. (2008). Feedback for improving staff training and performance in behavioral treatment programs. *Behavioral Interventions, 23*, 39–64. https:// dx.doi.org/10.1002 /bin.247

Austin, J., Hatfield, D. B., Grindle, A. C., & Bailey, J. S. (1993). Increasing recycling in office environments: The effects of specific informative cues. *Journal of Applied Behavior Analysis, 26*(2), 247–253. https://doi.org/10.1901/jaba.1993.26-247

Behavior Analyst Certification Board. (2021). *Professional and ethical compliance code for behavior analysts.* Littleton, CO: Author. Retrieved from http://BACB.com/ethics -code/

Belisle, J., Rowsey, K. E., & Dixon, M. R. (2016). The use of in situ behavioral skills training to improve staff implementation of the PEAK Relational Training System. *Journal of Organizational Behavior Management, 36*, 71–79. https://doi.org/10.1007/s 40614-017-0119-4

Britton Laws, C., Kolomer, S. R., & Gallagher, M. J. (2014). Age of persons supported and factors predicting intended staff turnover: A comparative study. *Inclusion, 2*, 316–328.

Buckley, J., Fountain, J., Meuse, S., Whelan, C., Maguire, H., Harper, J. M., & Luiselli, J. K. (2020). Performance improvement of care providers in a child services setting: Effects of an incentive-based negative reinforcement intervention on data recording. *Child & Family Behavior Therapy, 42*, 125–133. https://www.researchgate.net/deref/ https%3A%2F%2Fwww.tandfonline.com%2Floi%2Fwcfb20

Burg, M. M., Reid, D. H., & Lattimore, J. (1979). Use of a self-recording and supervision program to change institutional staff behavior. *Journal of Applied Behavior Analysis, 12*, 363–375. http://dx.doi .org/10.1901/jaba.1979.12-363

Casella, S. E., Wilder, D. A., Neidert, P., Rey, C., Compton, M., & Chong, I. (2010). The effects of response effort on safe performance by therapists at an autism treatment facility. *Journal of Applied Behavior Analysis, 43*, 729–734. https://doi.org/10.1901/jaba .2010.43-729

Codding, R. S., Feinberg, A. B., Dunn, E. K., & Pace, G. M. (2005). Effects of immediate performance feedback on implementation of behavior support plans. *Journal of Applied Behavior Analysis, 38*, 205–219. https://doi.org/10.1901/jaba.2005.98-04

Conrad, A. L., Johnson, D. A., Morrison, J. D., & Ditzian, K. (2016). Tactics to ensure durability of behavior change following the removal of an intervention specialist: A review of temporal generality within organizational behavior management. *Journal of Organizational Behavior Management, 36*, 210–253. https://doi.org/10.1080/016080 61.2018.1514347

Cox, C. D., Cox, B. S., & Cox, B. J. (2005). Long term benefits of prompts to use safety belts among drivers exiting senior communities. *Journal of Applied Behavior Analysis, 38*(4), 533–536.https://doi.org/10.1901/jaba.2000.33-635

DiGennaro Reed, F. D., Blackman, A. L., Erath, T. G., Brand, D., & Novak, M. D. (2018). Guidelines for using behavioral skills training to provide teacher support. *Teaching Exceptional Children, 50*, 373–380. https://doi.org/10.1177/0040059918777241

DiGennaro Reed, F. D., & Codding, R. S. (2011). Intervention integrity assessment. In J. K. Luiselli (Ed.), *Teaching and behavior support for children and adults with autism spectrum disorder: A practitioner's guide*. New York: Oxford University Press.

DiGennaro Reed, F. D., Codding, R., Catania, C. N., & Maguire, H. (2010). Effects of video modeling on treatment integrity of behavioral interventions. *Journal of Applied Behavior Analysis, 43*, 291–295. https://doi.org/10.1901/jaba.2010.43-291

DiGennaro Reed, F. D., & Henley, A. J. (2015). A survey of staff training and performance management practices: The good, the bad, and the ugly. *Behavior Analysis in Practice, 8*, 16–26. https://doi.org/10.1007/s40617-015-0044-5

DiGennaro Reed, F. D., Hirst, J. M., & Howard, V. J. (2013). Empirically supported staff selection, training, and management strategies. In D. D. Reed, F. D. DiGennaro Reed, & J. K. Luiselli (Eds.), *Handbook of crisis intervention and developmental disabilities* (pp. 71–85). New York: Springer.

DiGennaro, F. D., Martens, B. K., & Kleinmann, A. E. (2007). A comparison of performance feedback procedures on teachers' treatment implementation integrity and students' inappropriate behavior in special education classrooms. *Journal of Applied Behavior Analysis, 40*, 447–461. https://doi.org/10.1901/jaba .2007.40-447

DiGennaro Reed, F. D., Martens, B. K., & McIntyre, L. L. (2005). Increasing treatment integrity through negative reinforcement: Effects on teacher and student behavior. *School Psychology Review, 34*, 220–231. https://doi.org/10.1901/jaba.2007.40-447

Ditzian, K., Wilder, D. A., King, A., & Tanz, J. (2015). An evaluation of the *performance diagnostic checklist—human services* to assess an employee performance problem in a center-based autism treatment facility. *Journal of Applied Behavior Analysis, 48*, 199–203. https://doi.org/10.1007/s40617-018-0243-y

Dixon, M. R. (2014). *The PEAK relational training system: Direct training module*. Carbondale, IL: Shawnee Scientific Press.

Dixon, M. R., & Loukus, A. K. (2013). Importance of organizational infrastructure. In D. D. Reed, F. D. DiGennaro Reed, & J. K. Luiselli (Eds.), *Handbook of crisis intervention and developmental disabilities* (pp. 7–26). New York: Springer.

Doerner, M., Miltenberger, R. G., & Bakken, J. (1989). The effects of staff self-management on positive social interactions in a group home setting. *Behavioral Residential Treatment, 4,* 313–330.

Drifke, M. A., Tiger, J. H., & Wierzba, B. C. (2017). Using behavioral skills training to teach parents to implement three-step prompting: A component analysis and generalization assessment. *Learning and Motivation, 57,* 1–14. doi: 10.1016/j.lmot.2016.12.001

Ehrlch, R. J., Nosik, M. R., Carr, J. M., & Wine, B. (2020). Teaching employees how to receive feedback: A preliminary investigation. *Journal of Organizational Behavior Management, 40,* 19–29. https://doi.org/10.1080/01608061.2020.1746470

Ejaz, F. K., Noelker, L. S., & Menne, H. L. (2008). The impact of stress and support on direct care workers' job satisfaction. *Gerontologist, 48*(Spec No 1), 60–70. https://doi.org/10.1093/geront/48.Supplement_1.60

Erath, T. G., DiGennaro Reed, F. D., Sundermeyer, H. W., Brand, D., Novak, M. D., Harrison, M. J., & Shears, R. (2019). Enhancing the training integrity of human service staff using pyramidal behavioral skills training. *Journal of Applied Behavior Analysis, 53,* 449–464.https://doi.org/10.1002/jaba.608

Firman, M. W., Orient, K. M., Steiner, H., & Firmin, R. L. (2013). Factors affect the employment longevity of staff working with clients possessing intellectual disabilities. *International Journal of Business Anthropology, 4,* 54–65.

Fischer, A. J., Collins, T. A., Dart, E. H., & Radley, K. C. (Eds.) (2019). *Technology Applications in School Psychology Consultation, Supervision, and Training.* London: Routledge.

Flood, W. A., & Luiselli, J. K. (2012). Supervisory intervention: Improving data reporting by direct-care staff at a child services program. *Child & Family Behavior Therapy, 34,* 70–75.

Fritz, J. N., Dupuis, D. L., Wu, W., Neal, A. E., Rettig, L. A., & Lastrapes, R. E. (2017). Evaluating increased effort for item disposal to improve recycling at a university. *Journal of Applied Behavior Analysis, 50*(4), 825–829. https://doi.org/10.1002/jaba.405

Garrity, M. L., & Luiselli, J. K. (2005). Brief report: Effects of an administrative supervisory protocol on preparation of behavior support plans at a child service setting. *International Journal of Behavioral Consultation and Therapy, 1,* 287–291.

Garrity, M. L., Luiselli, J. K., & McCollum, S. A. (2008). Effects of a supervisory intervention on assessment of interobserver agreement (IOA) by educational service providers. *Behavioral Interventions, 23,* 105–112. https://doi.org/10.1002/bin.258

Gerald, D., Keeler, L., Mackey, K., Merrill, R., & Luiselli, J. K. (2019). Application of a self-management intervention to improve data recording of educational care providers. *Behavioral Interventions, 34,* 388–395. https://doi:10.1080/00168890.2019.1690092

Gianotti, J., Kahl, T., Harper, J. M., & Luiselli, J. K. (2020). Behavioral safety assessment and intervention among residential care providers of students with intellectual and developmental disabilities. *Journal of Developmental and Physical Disabilities.* Published online: 13 October 2020.

Gil, P. J., & Carter, S. L. (2016). Graphic feedback, performance feedback, and goal setting increased staff compliance with a data collection task at a large residential facility. *Journal of Organizational Behavior Management, 36,* 56–70. https://doi.org/10.1080/01608061.2016.1152207

Gilligan, K. T., Luiselli, J. K., & Pace, G. M. (2007). Training paraprofessional staff to implement discrete trial instruction: Evaluation of a practical performance feedback intervention. *Behavior Therapist, 30,* 63–66.

Graff, R. B., & Karsten, A. M. (2012). Evaluation of a self-instruction package for conducting stimulus preference assessments. *Journal of Applied Behavior Analysis, 45,* 69–82. https://doi.org/10.1901/jaba.2012.45-69

Gravina, N., Villacorta, J., Albert, K., Clark, R., Curry, S., & Wilder, D. (2018). A literature review of organizational behavior management interventions in human service settings from 1990 to 2016. *Journal of Organizational Behavior Management, 38,* 191–224. https://doi.org/ 10.1080/01608061.2018.1454872

Green, C. W., Reid, D. H., Perkins, L. L., & Gardner, S. M. (1991). Increasing habilitation services for persons with profound handicaps: An application of structural analysis to staff management. *Journal of Applied Behavior Analysis, 24,* 459–471. https://doi.org/10.1901/jaba.1991.24-459

Hartz, R. M., Gould, C., Harper, J. M., & Luiselli, J. K. (2021). Assessing interobserver agreement (IOA) with procedural integrity: Evaluation of training methods among classroom instructors. *Child & Family Behavior Therapy, 43,* 1–12.

Iwata, B. A., Bailey, J. S., Brown, K. M., Foshee, T. J., & Alpern, M. A. (1976). A performance-based lottery to improve residential care and training by institutional staff. *Journal of Applied Behavior Analysis, 9,* 417–431. https://doi.org/10.1901/jaba.1976.9-417

Jason, L. A., & Liotta, R. F. (1982). Reduction of cigarette smoking in a university cafeteria. *Journal of Applied Behavior Analysis, 15*(4), 573–577. https://doi.org/10.1901/jaba.1982.15-573

Kazdin, A. E. (2011). *Single case research design in clinical and applied settings.* New York: Oxford University Press.

Kennedy, C. H. (2002). The maintenance of behavior change as an indicator of social validity. *Behavior Modification, 26,* 594–604.

Lipshultz, J. L., Vladescu, J. C., Reeve, K. F., Reeve, S. A., & Dipsey, C. R. (2015). Using video modeling with voiceover instruction to train staff to conduct stimulus preference assessments. *Journal of Developmental and Physical Disabilities, 27,* 505–523. https://doi.org/ 10.1007/s10882-015-9434-4

Luiselli, J. K. (2015). Performance management and staff preparation. In F. D. DiGennaro & D. D. Reed (Eds.), *Autism service delivery: Bridging the gap between science and practice in autism service delivery.* New York: Springer.

Luiselli, J. K. (2018). Organizational behavior management in human services programs. In B. Wine & J. Pritchard (Eds.), *Organizational behavior management: The essentials* (pp. 340–363). Orlando, FL: Hedgehog.

Luiselli, J. K. (2021). Social validity assessment in human services organizations. In Luiselli, J. K., Gardner, R. M., Bird, F. L., & Maguire, H. (Eds.). *Organizational Behavior Management (OBM) approaches for intellectual and developmental disabilities.* London: Routledge.

Luiselli, J. K., & Fischer, A. J. (Eds.) (2016). *Computer-assisted and web-based innovations in psychology, special education, and health.* New York: Elsevier/Academic Press.

Luiselli, J. K., DiGennaro Reed, F. D., Christian, W. P., Markowski, A., Rue, H. C., St. Amand, C., & Ryan, C. J. (2009). Effects of an informational brochure, lottery-based financial incentive, and public posting on absenteeism of direct-care human services employees. *Behavior Modification, 33,* 175–181. https://doi.org/10.1177 /0145445508320624

Luke, M., Carr, J. E., & Wilder, D. A. (2018). On the compatibility of organizational behavior management and BACB certification. *Journal of Organizational Behavior Management, 38*(4), 288–305. https://doi.org/10.1080/01608061.2018.1514347

Marano, K. E., Vladescu, J. C., Reeve, K. F., & DiGennaro Reed, F. D. (2019). Effect of conducting behavioral observations and ratings on staff implementation of a paired-stimulus preference assessment. *Journal of Applied Behavior Analysis, 53,* 296–304. https://doi.org/10.1002/jaba.584

Mattson, J. G. (2017). Continuing education: Accessing the per-reviewed literature. In J. K. Luiselli (Ed.), *Applied behavior analysis advanced guidebook: A manual for professional practice* (pp. 309–324). New York: Elsevier/Academic Press.

Miles, N. I., & Wilder, D. A. (2009). The effects of behavioral skills training on caregiver implementation of guided compliance. *Journal of Applied Behavior Analysis, 42,* 405–410. https://doi.org/10.1901/jaba.2009.42-405

Mishra, P., Grasso, E., Essien, J., & Luiselli, J. K. (2020). Case demonstration of environmental cuing and brief supervision monitoring as performance management interventions with educational care providers. *Child & Family Behavior Therapy, 42,* 37–47.

Moore, J. W., & Fisher, W. W. (2007). The effects of videotape modeling on staff acquisition of functional analysis methodology. *Journal of Applied Behavior Analysis, 40,* 197–202. https://doi.org/10.1901/jaba.2007.24-06

Mueller, M. M., Moore, J. W., Doggett, R. A., & Tingstrom, D. H. (2000). The effectiveness of contingency-specific and contingency-nonspecific prompts in controlling bathroom graffiti. *Journal of Applied Behavior Analysis*, 33(1), 89–92. https://doi.org/10.1901/jaba.2000.33-89

Nikopoulos, C., Luiselli, J. K., & Fischer, A. J. (2016). Video modeling. In Luiselli, J. K., & Fischer, A. J. (Eds.). *Computer-assisted and web-based innovations in psychology, special education, and health* (pp. 187–210). New York: Elsevier/Academic Press.

Parsons, M. B., Rollyson, J. H., & Reid, D. H. (2012). Evidence-based staff training: A guide for practitioners. *Behavior Analysis in Practice*, 5, 2–11. https://doi.org/ 10.1007/ BF03391819

Parsons, M. B., Rollyson, J. H., & Reid, D. H. (2013). Teaching practitioners to conduct behavioral skills training: A pyramidal approach for training multiple human service staff. *Behavior Analysis in Practice*, 6, 4–16. https://doi.org/10.1007/BF03391798

Reid, D. H. (1998). *Organizational behavior management in developmental disabilities services: Accomplishments and future directions*. New York: Routledge.

Reid, D. H. (2017). Competency-based staff training. In J. K. Luiselli (Ed.), *Applied behavior analysis advanced guidebook: A manual for professional practice* (pp. 21–40). New York: Elsevier/Academic Press.

Reid, D. H., & Parsons, M. B. (2006). *Motivating human service staff: Supervisory strategies for maximizing work effort and work enjoyment* (2nd edition). North Carolina: Habilitative Management Consultants, Inc.

Reid, D. H., & Whitman, T. L. (1983). Behavioral staff management in institutions: A critical review of effectiveness and acceptance. *Analysis and Intervention in Developmental Disabilities*, 3, 131–149. https://doi.org/10.1016/0270-4684(83)900 11-3

Reid, D. H., Parsons, M. B., & Green, C. W. (2012). *The supervisor's guidebook: Evidence-based strategies for promoting work quality and enjoyment among human service staff*. North Carolina: Habilitative Management Consultants.

Richman, G. S., Riordan, M. R., Reiss, M. L., Pyles, D. A. M., & Bailey, J. S. (1988). The effects of self-monitoring and supervisor feedback on staff performance in a residential setting. *Journal of Applied Behavior Analysis*, 21, 401–409. http://dx .doi .org/10.1901/jaba.1988.21-401

Rosales, R., Gongola, L., & Homlitas, C. (2015). An evaluation of video modeling with embedded instructions to teach implementation of stimulus preference assessments. *Journal of Applied Behavior Analysis*, 48, 209–214. https://doi.org/10 .1002/jaba.174

Roscoe, E. M., & Fisher, W. W. (2008). Evaluation of an efficient method for training staff to implement stimulus preference assessments. *Journal of Applied Behavior Analysis*, 41, 249–254. https://doi.org/10.1901/jaba.2008.41-249

Rubio, E. K., & Sigurdsson, S. O. (2014). Sustained effects of a visual prompt on dish storage in a hospital unit. *Journal of Applied Behavior Analysis, 47*(4), 845–849. https://doi.org/ 10.1002/jaba.161

Sarokoff, R. A., & Sturmey, P. (2004). The effects of behavioral skills training on staff implementation of discrete-trial teaching. *Journal of Applied Behavior Analysis, 37,* 535–538. https://doi.org/ 10.1901/jaba.2004.37-535

Schmidt, J. S., Urban, K. D., Luiselli, J. K., White, C., & Harrington, C. (2013). Improving appearance, organization, and safety of special education classrooms: Effects of staff training in a human services setting. *Education and Treatment of Children, 36,* 1–13. https://doi.org/ 10.1353/etc.2013.0012

Sellers, T. P., Valentino, A. L., & LeBlanc, L. A. (2016). Recommended practices for individual supervision of aspiring behavior analysts. *Behavior Analysis in Practice, 9,* 274–286. https://doi.org/10.1007/s40617-016-0110-7

Shapiro, M., & Kazemi, E. (2017). A review of training strategies to teach individuals implementation of behavioral interventions. *Journal of Organizational Behavior Management, 37*(1), 32–62. https://doi.org/10.1080/01608061.2016.1267066

Spiegel, H. J., Kisamore, A. N., Vladescu, J. C., & Karsten, A. M. (2016). The effects of video modeling with voiceover instruction and on-screen text on parent implementation of guided compliance. *Child and Family Behavior Therapy, 38,* 299–317. https://doi.org/ 10.1080/07317107.2016.1238690

Stokes, T. F., & Baer, D. M. (1977). An implicit technology of generalization. *Journal of Applied Behavior Analysis, 10,* 349–367. https://doi.org/10.1901/jaba.1977.10-349

Strohmeier, C., Mule, C., & Luiselli, J. K. (2014). Social validity assessment of training methods to improve treatment integrity of special education service providers. *Behavior Analysis in Practice, 7,* 15–20. https://doi.org/10.1007/s40617-014-0004-5

Taber, T., Lambright, N., & Luiselli, J. K. (2017). Video modeling training effects on quality of social attention delivered by educational care providers. *Behavior Analysis in Practice, 10,* 189–194. https://doi.org/10.1007/s40617-017-0182-z

Turner, L. B., Fischer, A. J., & Luiselli, J. K. (2016). Towards a competency-based, ethical, and socially valid approach to the supervision of applied behavior analytic trainees. *Behavior Analysis in Practice, 9,* 287–298. https://doi.org/10.1007/s40617-016-0121-4

Vladescu, J. C., Carroll, R., Paden, A., & Kodak, T. M. (2013). The effects of video modeling with voiceover instruction on accurate implementation of discrete-trial instruction. *Journal of Applied Behavior Analysis, 45,* 419–423. https://doi.org/10.1901/jaba.2012.45-419

Wallace, M. D., Doney, J. K., Mintz-Resudek, C. M., & Tarbox, R. S. F. (2004). Training educators to implement functional analyses. *Journal of Applied Behavior Analysis, 37,* 89–92. https://doi.org/10.1901/jaba.2004.37-89

Ward-Horner, J., & Sturmey, P. (2012). Component analysis of behavior skills training in functional analysis. *Behavioral Interventions, 27,* 75–92. doi: 10.1002/bin.1339

Warman, A. S., Wine, B., Newcomb, E. T., Chen, T., & Morgan, C. A. (2019). An evaluation of static versus variable antecedents on employee performance. *Journal of Organizational Behavior Management, 39,* 257–265. https://doi.org/10.1080/016080 61.2019.1666775

Wilder, D. A., Austin, J., & Casella, S. (2009). Applying behavior analysis in organizations: Organizational behavior management. *Psychological Services,* 6, 202–211. https://doi.org/ 10.1037/a0015393

Wilder, D. A., Cymbal, D., & Villacorta, J. (2020). The performance diagnostic checklist-human services: A brief review. *Journal of Applied Behavior Analysis,* 53, 1170–1176. https://doi.org/10.1002/jaba.676

Wilder, D. A., Lipschultz, J. L., King, A., Driscoll, S., & Sigurdsson, S. (2018). An analysis of the commonality and type of pre-intervention assessment procedures in the journal of organizational behavior management (2000–2015). *Journal of Organizational Behavior Management, 38,* 5–17.

Willis, K., Hrdina, J., & Luiselli, J. K. (2020). Performance management and maintenance of data recording by educational care providers. *Behavior Analysis: Research and Practice,* 20, 165. https://doi.org/10.1037/bar0000177

Wine, B. (2017). Incentive-based performance improvement. In J. K. Luiselli (Ed.), *Applied behavior analysis advanced guidebook* (pp. 117–134). New York: Elsevier.

Wine, B., & Pritchard, J. K. (2018). *Organizational behavior management: The essentials.* Orlando, FL: Hedgehog.

Wine, B., Gugliemella C., & Axelrod, S. (2013). An examination of generalized-conditioned reinforcers in stimulus preference assessments. *Journal of Organizational Behavior Management, 33,* 244–251. https://doi.org/10.1080/01608061.2013.843433

Wine, B., Gilroy, S., & Hantula, D. A. (2012). Temporal (in)stability of employee preference for rewards. *Journal of Organizational Behavior Management, 32,* 58–64. Doi: 10.1080/01608061.2012.646854.

Wine, B., Reis, M., & Hantula, D. A. (2014). An evaluation of preference assessment methodology in organizational behavior management. *Journal of Organizational Behavior Management, 34,* 7–15. https://doi.org/10.1080/01608061.2013.873379.

Wolf, M. M. (1978). Social validity: The case for subjective measurement or how applied behavior analysis is finding its heart. *Journal of Applied Behavior Analysis, 11,* 203–214. https://doi.org/10.1901/jaba.1978.11-203

7
Self-Monitoring and Treatment Integrity

Jessica L. Doucette, Einar T. Ingvarsson, and Ethan S. Long

The prevalence of autism spectrum disorder (ASD) has increased significantly over the past 20 years. Today, the CDC estimates that 1 in every 68 children in the United States has ASD, but a recent government study found that number could be as high as 1 in every 48 children (Kogan et al., 2018). With more than 2% of children in the United States living with ASD, advocacy organizations, such as Autism Speaks, have had success in raising public awareness and advocating for supports and services for ASD. Their efforts include ensuring health insurance coverage for autism treatments based on the principles of applied behavior analysis (ABA). These efforts have paralleled unprecedented growth in the professional discipline of behavior analysis. The Behavior Analyst Certification Board (BACB) reports that the annual demand for individuals holding BCBA/BCBA-D certification has increased approximately 1,942% from 2010 to 2018, with increases seen in every state (Behavior Analyst Certification Board, 2019). Researchers have noted that the passage of autism insurance reform laws or state licensing laws that influence the professional practice of applied behavior analysis may be a factor in contributing to the growth of BACB certificants (Deochand & Fuqua, 2016).

With increased incidence of ASD and more funding available to support ABA services, comes a greater demand for ABA services. Typical comprehensive ABA treatment programs for ASD involve a tiered service-delivery model in which Board Certified Behavior Analysts (BCBAs) design and supervise treatment programs delivered by registered behavior technicians (RBTs). The use of supervised RBTs is a common practice in ABA treatment for ASD (Behavior Analyst Certification Board, 2019). This tiered-service delivery model is more cost-effective and enables a potentially larger provider and treatment delivery network. However, the tiered-delivery system relies on BCBAs providing regular, ongoing supervision. Researchers have noted many behavior analysts receive little to no instruction and mentoring in supervision practices (LeBlanc & Luiselli, 2016). Therefore, procedures that effectively and efficiently assist BCBAs in providing quality supervision are important to high-quality ABA service provision. This applies to organizations that provide services to individuals with autism, as well as other populations (e.g., those with intellectual disabilities).

Performance-based staff training and supervision is often delivered in the form of behavioral skills training (BST), a set of procedures consisting of instructions, modeling, rehearsal, and feedback (Sturmey, 2008). Multiple studies have shown improvements in treatment integrity as a function of staff training using BST (e.g., Sarokoff & Sturmey, 2004; Shapiro & Kazemi, 2017). One component of BST, performance feedback, is particularly important to improve treatment integrity (e.g., Codding et al., 2005; Quilitch, 1975). Unsurprisingly, insufficient treatment integrity is likely to have deleterious effects on intervention outcomes (Fryling et al., 2012), especially if levels of integrity are low from the beginning of intervention (Pipkin et al., 2010; Stephenson & Hanley, 2010).

High staff turnover is another challenge faced by providers of behavioral services. Kazemi et al. (2015) evaluated predictors of turnover among registered behavior technicians (RBTs) working with individuals with autism spectrum disorder (ASD). They surveyed 96 RBTs from 19 agencies in Southern California, and found that 38% reported that they were highly or somewhat likely to leave their jobs. They found that while satisfaction with pay significantly predicted intent to leave the job, actual hourly pay did not. However, satisfaction with training, supervision, and opportunities for advancement were significant predictors. This survey provides indirect evidence that turnover rates might be reduced through more effective and efficient supervision, thus reducing the costs associated with training new staff (Gravina et al., 2018).

Performance-based staff training and supervision (such as BST) is necessary for high-quality service provision in applied behavior analysis, but BCBAs who are tasked with supervising RBTs (or other direct care staff) may face challenges in implementing sufficient training and supervision for multiple staff, clients, and intervention programs. Supervising BCBAs typically have multiple clinical and administrative duties, including case management, program development, interacting with and training parents and teachers, and various administrative duties. The Behavior Analyst Certification Board (BACB®) requires that RBTs be supervised for at least 5% of the time they spend providing services to clients. However, 5% is a minimum and may not always be enough to ensure that all intervention programs are delivered with sufficient quality, especially given the high turnover that is the reality in many service organizations. Therefore, service providers could benefit from procedures that can contribute to increased treatment integrity without dramatically increasing the need for supervisors directly observing staff behavior (Shapiro & Kazemi, 2017). One such approach is self-monitoring (Korotitsch & Nelson-Gray, 1999).

Overview of Self-Monitoring

Self-monitoring is a direct observation technique in which an individual observes instances of their own behavior and records these occurrences (Cooper et al., 2020; Korotitsch & Nelson-Gray, 1999; Nelson, 1977). Self-monitoring may be used for assessment purposes, either to monitor changes in behavior over time, or to evaluate the effects of intervention compared to baseline. One potential limitation of self-monitoring as a measurement tool is reduced accuracy, because self-recorded data may not correspond with actual occurrences of behavior. While there is no true independent measure of accuracy, a pragmatic approach involves comparing samples of self-monitored data to data collected by independent trained observers (i.e., interobserver agreement). In a review of the literature, Korotitsch & Nelson-Gray (1999) noted that several variables can increase the accuracy of self-monitored data, including verbal commitment or contracts, observer training, reduced concurrent response requirements, and programming reinforcement contingent on accuracy of self-monitored data as opposed to changes in behavior. Reactivity of measurement can also influence the accuracy of data collection. Thus, self-monitored data may be more likely to be accurate when the observers are aware of accuracy checks. Further, observers may be more likely to record their desirable behavior accurately, as opposed to undesirable behavior.

While reactivity of measurement can be a concern, self-monitoring also characteristically results in a different type of reactivity: changes in a measurable dimension of the target behavior as a result of the self-monitoring procedure (Hartmann, 1984; Korotitsch & Nelson-Gray, 1999). According to Korotitsch and Nelson-Gray, several variables can influence the extent to which this type of reactivity may occur. First, the value (or *valence*) of the target behavior can play a role, with desirable behavior more likely to increase and undesirable behavior more likely to decrease when it is self-monitored. Second, the extent to which the individual is motivated to change their behavior (i.e., a motivating operation is in place) can influence the extent of reactivity. Further, reactivity may be more likely if every occurrence of the behavior is recorded (as opposed to a discontinuous schedules of monitoring), if there are relatively few concurrent response requirements (e.g., monitoring one response vs. multiple responses), if the individual records the response prior to completing it, and if self-monitoring is combined with goal setting, feedback, and reinforcement.

Although a threat to unbiased assessment, reactivity can be utilized for treatment and intervention purposes. Thus, the recipients of behavior change programs may be asked to collect self-monitoring data as a component of a behavioral intervention for the primary purpose of changing the target behavior

(Critchfield, 1999; Hartmann, 1984). As an intervention, self-monitoring is often combined with antecedent interventions such as setting a specific goal for behavior change, as well as checklists or other stimuli that set the occasion for the target behavior (e.g., Burg et al., 1979). Self-monitoring may also be combined with consequent components, such as feedback and reinforcement, for reaching behavior-change goals (e.g., Burgio et al., 1990). Examples of the use of self-monitoring in applied behavior analysis include interventions to increase academic responding of children with learning disabilities (Dunlap & Dunlap, 1989; Harris, 1986; Maag et al., 1993), increasing work productivity in adults with intellectual disabilities (Ackerman & Shapiro, 1984), reduction of self-injurious skin picking in a young man with Asperger Syndrome (Tiger et al., 2009), and reducing energy consumption in residential households (Winett et al., 1979). Thus, self-monitoring can be applied to a variety of populations and target behaviors.

One of the strengths of self-monitoring as an intervention is that it enables individuals to play a more active role in their own behavior intervention programs, potentially reducing the time that interventionists need to be present to collect data and implement procedures. Due to the multiple responsibilities and challenges faced by supervisors, self-monitoring has the potential to increase the efficiency and quality of staff supervision and performance management in human service organizations. The remainder of this chapter will focus on the use of self-monitoring in these settings.

Functions of Self-Monitoring

A number of variables might explain the effectiveness of self-monitoring as a behavior change procedure in human service organizations. On the antecedent side, defining and clarifying responses to be self-monitored may serve to more effectively set the occasion for the target behaviors. Checklists and other reminders associated with self-monitoring may come to serve as discriminative stimuli, signaling the availability of reinforcement such as supervisor approval for completing and recording the tasks. On the consequence side, self-monitoring might result in increased contact with reinforcement contingencies for completing job tasks. These reinforcers might involve supervisor praise, peer acknowledgement, monetary and other tangible rewards, or opportunities for career advancement.

Alternatively, self-monitoring might facilitate contact with reinforcers inherent in the job, for example, improved client behavior and skill acquisition as a result of high treatment integrity. Further, being able to complete job tasks with greater fluency may be inherently reinforcing. To the extent that self-monitoring interventions increase access to these reinforcers, staff adherence to the self-monitoring procedures is likely to be maintained. However, if these reinforcers are not in place, supervisors might have to rely on contrived reinforcers to a greater degree.

One possible function of self-monitoring is to allow individuals to engage in more effective self-management (Dunlap & Dunlap, 1989). Skinner's (1953) discussion of self-control is relevant to this notion. Skinner defined self-control as actively manipulating the variables that influence one's own behavior. A simple example from everyday life is leaving a note on the inside of the front door to remind oneself to bring lunch to work in the morning (Clayton, 2006). In human services organizations, employees might engage in self-control by posting schedules in salient spots, arranging materials to better evoke a specific chain of responses, removing distracting materials from workspaces, and programming timed reminders on electronic devices. If a staff member is already motivated to improve their performance, collecting self-monitoring data might set the occasion for engaging in additional self-management (or self-control) responses to improve the quality and efficiency of their work performance.

Research on Self-Monitoring in Human Service Organizations

Self-Monitoring Combined with Other Intervention Components

Several studies have evaluated the use of self-monitoring as a part of treatment packages to improve staff performance in human services organizations. An early example was reported by Burg and colleagues (1979). These authors evaluated the effects of self-monitoring on social interactions between staff and individuals with developmental disabilities who lived in a state residential facility. The staff members were provided with a self-recording card that listed the 15 target residents. They were instructed to attempt to interact with each of 15 target residents at least four times during each shift, and asked to record each interaction on the card. At the end of the shift, supervisors provided feedback for using the card, but not the specific number of interactions recorded. Thus, the treatment package included instructions, a scoring criterion (i.e., interacting with four residents per shift), discriminative stimuli (i.e., the list of residents printed on the card), and external monitoring, in addition to self-monitoring. Number of observed interactions increased as a function of the intervention. Further, aggressive and disruptive behavior decreased, and the cleanliness of the residents and their environment increased, presumably as a secondary effect of increased staff attention. While the self-monitoring procedure seemingly increased the efficiency of the intervention, it is likely that supervisor feedback for using the self-recording cards also played a role.

Kissel et al. (1983) implemented an intervention with four direct care staff members at a state facility for persons with developmental disabilities. The goal was to improve the staff members' ability to teach residents self-care skills such as toothbrushing, handwashing, and combing hair. The treatment package included written instructions, video and live modeling, rehearsal, and video feedback. After the staff members had learned to score both their own and resident behavior to criterion, they were taught how to graph and interpret the data. The treatment package was effective in improving staff performance, with corresponding improvements in residents' self-care skills. Further, the staff skills generalized from an original teaching context to other contexts. Because the treatment package included multiple components, the independent effects of self-monitoring cannot be determined. However, the authors note self-recording may have helped maintain staff performance as supervision was faded.

In another example of a package intervention, Burgio et al. (1990) combined self-monitoring, supervisor monitoring, and performance feedback to increase use of a prompted voiding procedure by ten direct care staff (geriatric assistants) in a nursing home. The assistants and their supervisors (licensed practical nurses) received training on the use of a self-monitoring checklist listing the components of the prompted voiding procedures. The LPNs observed at least two instances of prompted voiding per week, completed their own version of the checklist, and provided praise and corrective feedback to the assistants. Head nurses also provided group feedback every other week, with 80% completion of scheduled prompted voidings per patient considered satisfactory. The intervention package was effective in increasing and maintaining staff performance, with corresponding improvements in client continence. However, a gradual decline in staff performance occurred four to five months later. When feedback on individuals' performance was introduced, performance again reached or exceeded criterion. As in the previous study, self-monitoring may have contributed to improved performance, but its effects cannot be separated from other intervention components, notably individual and group feedback.

Self-Monitoring Combined with Accuracy Feedback

At least two studies have combined self-monitoring with supervisor-delivered accuracy feedback. In this context, accuracy feedback refers to supervisors delivering feedback on the accuracy of the self-recorded data as compared to experimenter-recorded data. Thus, the supervisor feedback was not delivered contingent on improvements in performing the target tasks. The first of these studies was by Petscher and Bailey (2006), who evaluated the effects of didactic training, tactile prompts, accuracy feedback, and self-monitoring on token economy implementation by three educators serving children with special needs. Didactic training did not result in appreciable improvements in performance, but self-monitoring with tactile prompts (a vibrating pager) and accuracy monitoring resulted in clear and immediate improvements in staff accuracy of implementation. Following the removal of the tactile prompts, self-monitoring and accuracy feedback continued to maintain high and stable performance for two of the three participants.

The second study to include accuracy feedback was conducted by Pelletier et al. (2010), who evaluated the effects of video self-monitoring on the procedural fidelity of behavior support plan implementation across three staff members. Following training, participants completed a checklist while watching themselves implement the behavior support plan. Feedback on self-monitoring accuracy was provided by the experimenter if any errors were identified on the procedural fidelity tool. Each staff member was then videotaped working with the student to measure procedural fidelity. Across staff members, video self-monitoring plus feedback resulted in improved procedural fidelity at or above 86%.

Summary

The studies described in the previous paragraphs demonstrated that treatment packages that include self-monitoring and other components (most notably supervisor feedback) can be effective in changing staff performance (Burg et al., 1979; Burgio et al., 1990; Kissel et al., 1983; Pelletier et al., 2010; Petscher & Bailey, 2006). However, these studies did not convincingly demonstrate that self-monitoring was a necessary component of the package intervention. Additionally, it is possible that self-monitoring might sometimes be sufficient without other intervention components such as supervisor feedback. To answer these questions, self-monitoring must be evaluated without other intervention components that include direct supervisor involvement.

Research on Self-Monitoring Without Other Intervention Components

Richman et al. (1988) evaluated the effects of self-monitoring on the on-task behavior and schedule-following of ten direct-care staff members who worked in two separate buildings in an "intermediate care facility" for individuals with intellectual disabilities. The experimenters first determined that a posted schedule and in-service training were not sufficient to improve staff performance to acceptable levels. During the self-monitoring intervention, each staff member copied their schedule from the master schedule onto individual schedule cards when they reported to work. The schedule cards also contained definitions of appropriate on-task behavior. The staff members were instructed to write their initials in the appropriate blank when they had completed each scheduled activity. The staff members turned in their cards at the end of their shifts, but no supervisor feedback was delivered. The self-monitoring intervention resulted in substantial increases in both target behaviors. For example, mean percentage of on-task behavior increased from 36% to 77% in one of the buildings. Because on-task behavior still had room to improve, the experimenters added supervisor feedback, which resulted in further increases in performance.

Suda and Miltenberger (1993) evaluated the effects of self-monitoring, self-evaluation, and self-praise on positive interactions between staff members and clients at a residential program for individuals with intellectual disabilities. An initial intervention consisting of instructions and goal setting did not markedly improve performance above baseline levels. During this intervention, the staff members were instructed each morning to praise clients for on-task behavior and were provided a rationale for the importance of doing so. The staff members were also instructed to write down their daily goals on a card provided by the supervisor. During the self-monitoring intervention, the staff members were trained to use counters to push a button every time they had a positive interaction with a client. Staff then graphed the frequency of interactions and compared it to the goal they had set for themselves that day. Lastly, they were instructed to praise themselves throughout the day for the positive interactions. Staff were told that their graphs would be reviewed weekly by the investigator. Positive interactions increased for all four staff members during the self-monitoring intervention, but only two reached the individualized criterion. The other two reached criterion when daily supervisor feedback was added. While this study included other components in addition to self-recording (i.e., self-evaluation and self-praise), these components can be viewed as compatible with self-monitoring since they do not require additional intervention by supervisors or other staff. Daily supervisor feedback, on the other hand, involves considerable additional efforts by supervisors.

Belfiore et al. (2008) evaluated the effects of video self-monitoring on the accurate implementation of discrete trial instruction (DTI) by four staff members working in a facility for students with ASD. The self-monitoring checklist consisted of (1) delivery of instruction; (2) waiting for student response; (3) response-specific feedback; (4) immediacy of feedback; (5) latency before delivery of next instruction. Staff were provided with 15-minute training to use the checklist. Immediately following each DTI session, each participant watched a video recording of their session and completed the checklist. Self-monitoring resulted in dramatic increases in the percentage of trials in which all steps of the DTI procedure were implemented correctly across all three participants. When the self-monitoring intervention was removed, accurate implementation of DTI maintained for one participant, but a slight reduction in accuracy was observed with the other two.

Plavnick et al. (2010) examined the effects of a self-monitoring checklist on the procedural fidelity of token economy implementation for two students. Measures of each student's academic readiness were also collected to determine if increased treatment integrity as a result of the use of the self-monitoring tool by staff members would also result in the desired changes in students' behavior. The findings suggested that the self-monitoring checklist increased both treatment integrity of staff implementation of the token economy and students' academic readiness behavior. However, some variability was observed in the self-monitoring intervention phase, with treatment integrity ranging from 70% to 100%.

Simonsen et al. (2013) evaluated the effects of three different self-monitoring procedures (tally, count, and rating) on early childhood special education teachers' use of specific praise. The tally method involved recording a mark after each praise statement, the count method involved using a golf counter to count the instances, and in the rating condition, the teachers rated their use of praise by estimating the number per minute on a scale of 0 to 4. All three forms of self-monitoring increased the target behavior, with the exception of rating procedure for one teacher. However, the experimenters recommended self-monitoring using the counter because it was associated with the greatest decreases in students' inappropriate behavior and increases in appropriate behavior. As well, self-monitoring was reported to be the least effortful procedure and the teachers were most likely to recommend it to others.

Mouzakitis et al. (2015) examined the effects of self-monitoring alone and with feedback on the treatment integrity of special education teachers' behavior plan implementation with children with ASD attending an inclusion program. Prior to baseline, the teachers received brief training (review, modeling, and vocal feedback), but this was not sufficient to establish criterion treatment integrity. Before the self-monitoring phase, the teachers were provided a checklist listing the components of the behavior intervention plan and the steps for correct implementation, with a second column to indicate if the step was completed or not. They were then provided with training on how to accurately score their own implementation of the behavior plans until they could do so with 90% accuracy. Subsequently, the teachers used the sheets to monitor their own performance and turned them in at the end of each day. Self-monitoring resulted in improvements in treatment integrity for three of four teachers. Of these three teachers, one reached the performance criterion with self-monitoring alone, while the other two required the addition of supervisor feedback to reach that goal. The fourth teacher also eventually reached the performance criterion with the combination of self-monitoring and performance feedback. Further, generalization to a non-target student was seen with all four teachers. Performance feedback was eventually removed for the three teachers who required it, and criterion treatment integrity maintained for two of these teachers with self-monitoring alone.

Summary

The results of available research suggest that self-monitoring without supervisor feedback can be effective to increase and maintain high levels of treatment integrity (Belfiore et al., 2008; Mouzakitis et al., 2015; Plavnick et al., 2010; Richman et al., 1988; Simonsen et al., 2013; Suda & Miltenberger, 1993). Nevertheless, self-monitoring is not always sufficient to achieve and maintain criterion performance for all staff members (e.g., Mouzakitis et al., 2015; Suda & Miltenberger, 1993). The factors that contribute to these variable outcomes have not been thoroughly evaluated in research. It seems likely that several variables might explain discrepant results, such as the clarity and completeness of self-monitoring checklists, the effort involved in the job tasks, the effort involved in self-monitoring, history of training and feedback for both job tasks and the self-monitoring procedure, the presence of competing job tasks, and additional reinforcement contingencies that might influence both target behaviors and competing behaviors.

It should be noted that research has *not shown* that that performance will maintain over lengthy periods of time with *only* self-monitoring, and it is unlikely that this outcome will be established in future research. The available research suggests that supervisor feedback and reinforcement contingencies are needed to maintain performance over time. Further, it is unethical and unprofessional to eliminate supervisor feedback altogether. Thus, self-monitoring can be viewed as a supplementary intervention that increases the overall quality and quantity of supervision by empowering the staff members to take an active role in evaluating their own performance.

Recommendations for Practice

Self-monitoring has the potential to increase the efficiency of performance management and improve staff performance, if used wisely and in combination with other organizational behavior management procedures. While more research is needed to better understand the conditions under which self-monitoring is an effective tool for performance management in human services organizations, it is nevertheless possible to generate some recommendations for practice. We suggest that the following steps are likely to be important in most situations:

1. Supervisors should ensure that the staff members have been trained to proficiency on the target job tasks prior to implementing ongoing self-monitoring. If self-monitoring is used as part of training, the training should also include other components (e.g., behavioral skills training).
2. Self-monitoring systems that are relatively effortless and do not significantly increase response requirements are more likely to be used with fidelity. It is generally wise to avoid measurement systems that interrupt the natural flow of behavior and get in the way of staff performing their tasks (Critchfield, 1999). To that end, supervisors might consider using permanent product measurement when possible, or have staff score data after they have completed the tasks.
3. Supervisors should train staff members to use self-monitoring checklists and deliver initial feedback on accuracy until the staff members demonstrate proficiency with scoring their own behavior.
4. When possible, supervisors should implement systems that include cues that set the occasion for tasks, such as checklists that detail the relevant components of the job tasks (Dunlap & Dunlap, 1989).
5. To increase the likelihood of treatment integrity, supervisors should consider implementing self-monitoring along with a dense schedule of supervisor feedback initially. When staff members demonstrate proficiency both with the job task and self-monitoring, feedback schedule can be thinned to sustainable levels.
6. After the staff members have been trained to accuracy, supervisors should primarily evaluate treatment integrity and productivity with periodic checks for accuracy of self-monitoring. If job performance fails to maintain at acceptable levels, it might be advisable to more thoroughly evaluate self-monitoring accuracy along with other relevant variables that might account for insufficient performance, such as reinforcement contingencies or competing tasks.
7. When implementing self-monitoring with staff, supervisors should also evaluate potential concomitant effects on the behavior of students, clients, residents, and other consumers. If self-monitoring improves treatment integrity, short and long-term improvements in client behavior should also be realized. If improvement does not occur, the treatment procedures themselves are likely ineffective. Continuing to spend time and effort to improve integrity of ineffective treatments is counterproductive.

8. Supervisors should incorporate technology to make tasks easier, such as digital devices that facilitate data collection. However, while these devices are convenient, they might not always set the occasion for behavior in the same way that posted checklists do, unless programmed to provide reminders (e.g., Petscher & Bailey, 2006).

9. It can be beneficial for staff members to observe video recordings and score their own treatment integrity (Belfiore et al., 2008; Kissel et al., 1983). However, supervisors would be wise to use this tactic sparingly, because it involves additional time and effort. Thus, it might be best used during initial training and to correct particularly glaring or challenging performance deficits.

10. Organizational leaders should consider implementing self-monitoring at all levels. Supervisors can monitor their own performance in creating and implementing performance management systems for the staff members they supervise.

11. Finally, we advise that supervisors continuously evaluate the social validity of the self-monitoring intervention, particularly its acceptability with the staff members themselves. When possible, it is beneficial to include staff members in decisions regarding the design and implementation of self-monitoring and other performance management systems.

Future Directions

The literature suggests that self-monitoring can be an effective performance management tool to improve treatment integrity and productivity of staff members in human service organizations. Nevertheless, its effects are not always consistent (e.g., Mouzakitis et al., 2015) and varying levels of supervisor feedback are sometimes needed to maintain criterion level performance achieved through self-monitoring (e.g., Suda & Miltenberger, 1993). Therefore, the field could benefit from further research on the effectiveness of self-monitoring, the conditions under which it is likely to be more or less effective, and the extent to which it can increase the efficiency of performance management in human service organizations.

Consecutive case series studies might help further evaluate the effectiveness of self-monitoring as a practical tool for performance management. A consecutive case series prevents publication bias by enrolling all eligible participants within a specific time period. Studies could focus on staff implementation of a specific set of common intervention procedures, notably preference assessments, discrete trial instruction, naturalistic teaching, prompting, and differential reinforcement. Each participant would be trained to proficiency in the target skill and those who did not maintain acceptable treatment integrity over a specific period of time would enter the self-monitoring phase. Supervisor feedback would be added if performance does not maintain at criterion levels. This kind of study would help establish the probability that self-monitoring alone can maintain high treatment integrity following initial staff training. Follow-up studies could then evaluate the optimal schedule of self-monitoring.

Research on the extent to which self-monitoring can improve the efficiency of performance management over periodic supervisor feedback would also be useful for directors of human service organizations. Group studies with random assignment might be necessary to answer that question. After comparing feedback with and without self-monitoring across groups, researchers could evaluate the extent to which supervisor feedback can be faded in the self-monitoring group while maintaining acceptable levels of treatment integrity.

Further research on additional components of self-monitoring (e.g., those included in the broader concept of *self-management*) would also be beneficial. For example, the importance of setting specific goals, self-evaluation of progress towards these goals through graphing own performance, and self-delivered reinforcement might improve the effectiveness of self-monitoring (e.g., Suda & Miltenberger, 1993). It is also possible that self-monitoring might be more effective if preceded by a period of frequent performance feedback (Mouzakitis et al., 2015). Researchers could also explore the effects of self-monitoring competing behaviors that interfere with treatment integrity and productivity (e.g., checking phone, engaging in off-task discussions with colleagues).

Finally, it would be beneficial to explore whether the effectiveness of self-monitoring is dependent on the variables responsible for performance deficits, that is, the functional properties of performance problems (Gravina et al., 2018). For example, it is possible that self-monitoring is more likely to be effective when the performance issues are due to insufficient or unclear antecedent conditions, but less likely to be effective when they are due to insufficient or maladaptive reinforcement contingencies.

Despite the questions that remain unanswered, the available research has shown that self-monitoring can be an effective component of performance management in human services organizations. Program directors can follow the path carved by researchers, but in doing so, should take care to evaluate effects on both staff and client behavior, as well as the social acceptability of the procedures.

References

Ackerman, A. M., & Shapiro, E. S. (1984). Self-monitoring and work productivity with mentally retarded adults. *Journal of Applied Behavior Analysis, 17,* 403–407. doi:10.1901/jaba.1984.17-403

Behavior Analyst Certification Board. (2019). *US employment demand for behavior analysts: 2010–2018*. Littleton, CO: Author.

Behavior Analyst Certification Board (2019). *US employment demand for behavior analysts: 2010–2017*. Littleton, CO: Author. https://www.bacb.com/wp-content/upl oads/2020/05/US-Employment-Demand-for-Behavior-Analysts_2019.pdf

Belfiore, P. J., Fritts, K. M., & Herman. B. C. (2008). The role of procedural integrity using self-monitoring to enhance discrete trial instruction (DTI). *Focus on Autism and Other Developmental Disabilities, 23*, 95–102. doi:10.1177/1088357607311445

Burg, M. M., Reid, D. H., & Lattimore, J. (1979). Use of a self-recording and supervision program to change institutional staff behavior. *Journal of Applied Behavior Analysis, 12*, 363–375. doi:10.1901/jaba.1979.12-363

Burgio, L. D., Engel, B. T., Hawkins, A., McCormick, K., & Scheve, A. (1990). A staff management system for maintaining improvements in continence with elderly nursing home residents. *Journal of Applied Behavior Analysis, 23*, 111–118. doi:10.1901/jaba.1990.23-111

Clayton, M. C. (2006). Self-management contingencies. *European Journal of Behavior Analysis, 7*, 143–145. doi:10.1080/15021149.2006.11434268

Codding, R. S., Feinburg, A. B., Dunn, E. K., & Pace, G. M. (2005). Effects of immediate performance feedback on implementation of behavior support plans. *Journal of Applied Behavior Analysis, 38*, 205–219. doi:10.1901/jaba.2005.98-04

Cooper, J. O., Heron, T. E., & Heward, W. L. (2020). *Applied behavior analysis* (3rd edition). Hoboken, NJ: Pearson.

Critchfield, T. S. (1999). An unexpected effect of recording frequency in reactive self-monitoring. *Journal of Applied Behavior Analysis, 32*, 389–391. doi:10.1901/jaba.1999.32-38

Deochand, N., & Fuqua, R. W. (2016). BACB certification trends: State of the States (1999 to 2014). *Behavior Analysis in Practice, 9*, 243–252. doi:10.1007/s40617-016-0118-z

Dunlap, L. K., & Dunlap, G. (1989). A self-monitoring package for teaching subtraction with regrouping to students with learning disabilities. *Journal of Applied Behavior Analysis, 22*, 309–314. doi:10.1901/jaba.1989.22-309

Fryling, M. J., Wallace, M. D., & Yassine, J. N. (2012). Impact of treatment integrity on intervention effectiveness. *Journal of Applied Behavior Analysis, 45*, 449–453. doi:10.1901/jaba.2012.45-449

Gravina, N., Villacorta, J., Albert, K., Clark, R., Curry, S., & Wilder. D. (2018). A literature review of organizational behavior management interventions in human service settings from 1990 to 2016. *Journal of Organizational Behavior Management, 38*, 191–224. doi:10.1080/01608061.2018.1454872

Harris, K. R. (1986). Self-monitoring of attentional behavior versus self-monitoring of productivity: Effects on on-task behavior and academic response rate among learning disabled children. *Journal of Applied Behavior Analysis, 19,* 417–423. doi:10.1901/jaba.1986.19-417

Hartmann, D. P. (1984). Assessment strategies. In D. H. Barlow & M. Hersen (Eds.), *Single-case experimental designs, strategies for studying behavior change* (pp. 107–139). Boston: Allyn & Bacon

Kazemi, E., Shapiro, M., & Kavner, A. (2015). Predictors of intention to turnover in behavior technicians working with individuals with autism spectrum disorder. *Research in Autism Spectrum Disorders, 17,* 106–115. doi:10.1016/j.rasd.2015.06.012

Kissel, R. C., Whitman, T. L., & Reid, D. H. (1983). An institutional staff training and self-management program for developing multiple self-care skills in severely/profoundly retarded individuals. *Journal of Applied Behavior Analysis, 16,* 395–415. doi: jaba.1983.16-395

Kogan, M. D., Vladutiu, C. J., Schieve, L. A., Ghandour, R. M., Blumberg, S. J., Zablotsky, B., Perrin, J. M., Shattuck, P., Kuhlthau, K. A., Harwood, R. L., & Lu, M. C. (2018). The prevalence of parent-reported autism spectrum disorder among US children. *Pediatrics, 142*(6), e20174161. doi:10.1542/peds.2017-4161

Korotitsch, W. J., & Nelson-Gray, R. O. (1999). An overview of self-monitoring research in assessment and treatment. *Psychological Assessment, 11,* 415–425. doi:10.1037/1040- 3590.11.4.415

LeBlanc, L. A., & Luiselli, J. K. (2016). Refining supervisory practices in the field of behavior analysis: Introduction to the special section on supervision. *Behavior Analysis in Practice, 9,* 271–273. doi:10.1007/s40617-016-0156-6

Maag, J. W., Reid, R., & DiGangi, S. A. (1993). Differential effects of self-monitoring attention, accuracy, and productivity. *Journal of Applied Behavior Analysis, 26,* 329–344. doi: jaba.1993.26-329

Mouzakitis, A., Codding, R. S., & Tryon, G. (2015). The effects of self-monitoring and performance feedback on the treatment integrity of behavior intervention plan implementation and generalization. *Journal of Positive Behavior Interventions, 17,* 223–234. doi:10.1177/1098300715573629

Nelson, R. O. (1977). Methodological issues in assessment via self-monitoring. In J. D. Cone & R. P. Hawkins (Eds.), *Behavioral assessment: New directions in clinical psychology* (pp 217–240). New York: Brunner/Mazel.

Pelletier, K., McNamara, B., Braga-Kenyon, P., & Ahearn, W. H. (2010). Effect of video self-monitoring on procedural integrity. *Behavioral Interventions, 25,* 261–274. doi: 10.1002/bin.316

Petscher, E. S., & Bailey, J. S. (2006). Effects of training, prompting, and self-monitoring on staff behavior in a classroom for students with disabilities. *Journal of Applied Behavior Analysis, 39,* 215–226. doi:10.1901/jaba.2006.02-05

Pipkin, C. S. P., Vollmer, T. R., & Sloman, K. N. (2010). Effects of treatment integrity failures during differential reinforcement of alternative behavior: A translational model. *Journal of Applied Behavior Analysis, 43,* 47–70. Doi:10.1901/jaba.2010.43-47

Plavnick, J. B., Ferreri, S. J., & Maupin, A. N. (2010). The effects of self-monitoring on the procedural integrity of a behavioral intervention for young children with developmental disabilities. *Journal of Applied Behavior Analysis, 43,* 315–320. doi:10.1901/jaba.2010.43-315

Quilitch, H. R. (1975). A comparison of three staff-management procedures. *Journal of Applied Behavior Analysis, 8,* 59–66. doi:10.1901/jaba.1975.8-59

Richman, G. S., Riordan, M. R., Reiss, M. L., Pyles, D. A. M., & Bailey, J. S. (1988). The effects of self-monitoring and supervisor feedback on staff performance in a residential setting. *Journal of Applied Behavior Analysis, 21,* 401–409. doi:10.1901/jaba.1988.21-401

Sarokoff, R. A., & Sturmey, P. (2004). The effects of behavioral skills training on staff implementation of discrete-trial teaching. *Journal of Applied Behavior Analysis, 37,* 535–538. doi:10.1901/jaba.2004.37-535

Shapiro, M., & Kazemi, E. (2017). A review of training strategies to teach individuals implementation of behavioral interventions. *Journal of Organizational Behavior Management, 37,* 32–62. doi:10.1080/01608061.2016.1267066

Simonsen, B., MacSuga, A., Fallon, L. M., & Sugai, G. (2013). The effects of self-monitoring on teachers' use of specific praise. *Journal of Positive Behavior Interventions, 15,* 5–15. doi:10.1177/1098300712440453

Skinner, B. F. (1953). *Science and human behavior.* New York: Free Press.

Stephenson, K. M., & Hanley, G. P. (2010). Preschoolers' compliance with simple instructions: A descriptive and experimental evaluation. *Journal of Applied Behavior Analysis, 43,* 229–247. https://doi.org/10.1901/jaba.2010.43-229

Sturmey, P. (2008). Best practice methods in staff training. In J. K. Luiselli, D. C. Russo, W. P. Christian, & S. M. Wilczynski (Eds.), *Effective practices for children with autism* (pp. 159–178). New York: Oxford University Press.

Suda, K. T., & Miltenberger, R. G. (1993). Evaluation of staff management strategies to increase positive interactions in a vocational setting. *Behavioral Interventions, 8,* 69–88. doi:10.1002/bin.2360080202

Tiger, J. H., Fisher, W. W., & Bouxsein, K. J. (2009). Therapist and self-monitored DRO contingencies as a treatment for the self-injurious skin picking of a young man with Asperger syndrome. *Journal of Applied Behavior Analysis, 42,* 315–319. doi:10.1901/jaba.2009.42-315

Winett, R. A., Neale, M. S., & Grier, H. C. (1979). Effects of self-monitoring and feedback on residential electricity consumption. *Journal of Applied Behavior Analysis, 12,* 173–184. doi:10.1901/jaba.1979.12-173

8
Supervision and Mentoring

Amber L. Valentino

A supervisor can assume various roles and responsibilities depending on the context in which the position is placed. For example, a labor supervisor may oversee the direct manual labor of a crew of helpers to ensure safe practices and manage a project to a timeline. A clinical psychology supervisor may be responsible for developing the supervisee's competence, ensuring the protection of clients, and directly teaching new skills to prepare the supervisee for independent practice. Within the field of behavior analysis, a supervisor can also assume different roles and responsibilities depending on the context. These roles can range from serving as a fieldwork supervisor for an aspiring BCBA™ (thus taking responsibility for the individual's competency across a variety of skills) to serving as a workplace supervisor, providing performance feedback and oversight of a certified individual. Regardless of the specific role of the supervisor, there is a consensus in the field of behavior analysis that effective supervision is critical to ensuring high-quality services, to the professional development of the supervisor and supervisee, and to the continuing development of our profession (Sellers et al., 2016b).

In this chapter, I review and synthesize pertinent research literature and the implications for mentoring and supervision in applied behavior analysis within human services organizations (HSOs) and other settings caring for persons with intellectual and developmental disabilities. I also cover recommended practices with guidelines for supervising and mentoring individuals toward competent performance of on-the-job responsibilities. Finally, I discuss the current state of literature and offer ideas for future research in the area of supervision and mentoring.

Review of Literature and Synthesis of Research Findings

Other disciplines have a long history in the literature of proposing supervision models and frameworks (e.g., Counseling: Chang, 2012; Special Education:

Holley, 2005; Martial and Family Therapy: Morgan & Sprenkle, 2007), in much the same way behavior analysts have begun to do in the past several years. Though we can draw upon this literature to build a behavior analytic knowledge base on supervision, specific behavior analytic research and conceptualization of the supervisor role using a behavior analytic framework is necessary. In the behavior analytic literature, there is a vast body of work that focuses on training and performance management (e.g., Parsons et al., 2012; Parsons et al., 1996; Reid & Green, 1990; Reid et al., 2003, 2005; Schepis & Reid, 1994). Typically, the focus of this literature has involved the use of behavioral skills training (BST), which is a training procedure that involves active trainee participation. BST has proven effective for teaching individuals a variety of new skills (e.g., Fleming et al., 1996). The BST model involves training to a criterion level, and monitoring performance to ensure maintenance and generalization of acquired skills over time.

Supervision encompasses effective training procedures but also refers to a broader set of activities focused on professional development, oversight of work, and thoughtful mentoring (LeBlanc & Luiselli, 2016). While historically behavior analysts may have viewed supervision as a requirement, checking boxes, and the simple event of a meeting, the meaning of supervision and its purpose has evolved and become more sophisticated within the past five to six years. Several events aided in this evolvement and sophistication while also contributing to a surge of ABA-specific supervision research. First, in 2012 the Behavior Analyst Certification Board (BACB®; BACB, 2012) began requiring completion of eight hours of curriculum-based training focused on supervisory skills. Additionally, the BACB now requires continuing education units focused on supervision. Finally, in 2016, the journal *Behavior Analysis in Practice* (BAP) released a special section on supervision practices. Although a few articles had been published on the topic before this date, the BAP special section introduced some seminal supervision articles. After that special section, the number of articles published on the topic of supervision increased, compared to the publication trends prior to BAP's special section. Figure 8.1 shows the frequency of publications from 2016 to September of 2019. The literature from 2016 and beyond conceptualizes supervision as encompassing many activities and as a very supportive practice in our field. The overall focus of the literature has been that of questioning and answering—that is, how do we truly teach, train, and establish the next generation of behavior analysts? The focus of this literature has also been on supervisors taking responsibility for the supervisor–supervisee relationship, and for the actions of the supervisee, while shaping complete behavior analytic repertoires fully, even when the demands to do so as quickly as possible are high (Pilgrim, 2018).

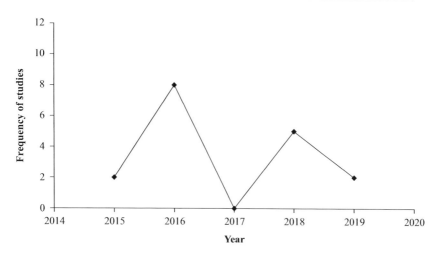

FIGURE 8.1 This graph depicts the number of articles focused on supervision in the ABA literature, beginning in 2015 and ending in September of 2019. A large increase can be seen in the year 2016, likely due to the introduction of a special section devoted to supervision practices in the journal *Behavior Analysis in Practice* (BAP).

The literature can be divided into the categories of (a) conceptualization of the supervisor role, (b) structural and logistical guidelines, (c) survey research, and (d) expansion and growth, explained and reviewed below.

Conceptualization of the Supervisor Role

Several authors have focused on more clearly defining the role of an ABA supervisor. Often, these authors' work focuses on expanding the definition of a supervisor, specifically when a supervisee is seeking to become a BCBA and the supervisor is providing formal fieldwork supervision (e.g., Sellers et al., 2016b). However, some authors have focused on other types of supervisory relationships, such as the one between student and professor (e.g., Barnes-Holmes, 2018).

Along with more clearly defining the role, recommendations for how to approach and structure supervision until recently had never been established. Sellers et al. (2016c) published recommendations that included five practices for supervision with detailed strategies and resources for structuring the experience. The rationale for this article was that although ABA has a rich literature base on teaching BCBAs using BST, as of the date of that paper, there had been no literature to guide supervisory practices. These five recommendations included (1) establish an effective supervisor–supervisee relationship, (2) establish a structured approach with specific content and competencies, (3) evaluate the effects of your supervision, (4) incorporate ethics and professional development into supervision, and (5) continue the professional relationship post certification. In this article, a large focus was placed on the supervisor taking responsibility for the relationship and ensuring the supervisee obtains the skills needed for independent practice. This article was a call to supervisors to embrace their role, and for many, to conceptualize it differently than they had before. These authors cautioned that their work was following the trend for publication of various practice guidelines in the field, but the recommendations had not yet been empirically validated. Nonetheless, this article can serve as a roadmap for supervisors to develop effective systems and relationships.

Recommendations for how to structure and approach supervision are new, and even when followed, supervisors may encounter obstacles. Sellers et al. (2016a) wrote another arrticle geared towards guiding the supervisor to identify and address barriers to successful supervision. This identification could have to do with issues related to a damaged supervisory relationship and/or persistent interpersonal and professional skills of the supervisee. This article extends the research on conceptualization of the role, in that it puts the supervisor in the position of detective: ensuring awareness and continuous reflection on how their own behavior influences supervision. Barnes-Holmes (2018) extends upon this theme of one's history influencing the supervisory relationship and discusses how this relationship (specifically between a student and professor) evolves over time. Uniquely, Barnes-Holmes conceptualizes the relationship as changing over time as the supervisor's reputation in the field grows. Simultaneously, the students' perception of the supervisor changes. These events, among others, can change the supervision dynamic. Barnes-Holmes goes on to describe that the supervisory relationship is so powerful that it can provide a sense of meaning and purpose in the supervisor's working life.

It is important to connect the role of the supervisor closely to our profession's ethics code. Some authors have provided a stronger foundation for supervisors to fully conceptualize the weight of their role as not only taking responsibility to further develop the field, but also to adhere to our field's ethical standards and commitments. Sellers et al. (2016a) discuss rationales and consequences relative to supervision issues and provides directions for professional development in each of seven identified supervisory areas within the ethics code. This article is useful for the supervisor wishing to understand the nuances in the ethics code related to supervision and to critically analyze their own repertoire while enhancing it. The authors offer powerful insight into the effects of supervisor behavior on individual supervisees as well as the field, stating, as individuals move into the role of providing supervision to others, it is likely that they will engage in the behavior modeled for them by past supervisors. In this way, an endless cycle of either ethical and productive behavior or unethical and inappropriate or harmful behavior may be created.

(p. 299)

The article serves as a resource to ensure the behavior modeled is ethical and the supervisor sees their role as prompting ethical and productive behavior. Turner et al. (2016) presented a practice model and considerations for supervising applied behavior analytic trainees. This model demonstrated consistency with BACB training curriculum outline and professional and ethical compliance code for behavior analysts, with a specific focus on bidirectional feedback and collaboration between supervisor and supervisee. Garza et al. (2018) published a model like Turner et al.'s (2016) that involved tips for establishing a good relationship, conducting supervisee skills assessments, goal setting, and training. These articles provide a foundation for supervisors viewing the supervision model as a vehicle for collaboration and ethical oversight.

Structural and Logistical Guidelines

Several authors have offered suggestions and models for how to structure the supervisory experience. Some of this work has focused on specific types of supervision such as group formats (Valentino et al., 2016), whereas other work has zoomed in on how to manage a specific supervision component such as electronic records (Cavaleri et al., 2015). Together, these articles present specific steps and tasks a supervisor can complete to manage the logistics of many components of building an effective supervisory experience for supervisees and themselves.

Notably, different types of supervision are both allowable by governing bodies and deemed beneficial. Valentino et al. (2016) highlight that group supervision provides unique opportunities to establish critical professional repertoires. While it is possible to conceptualize the role of the group leader as simply engaging in the same activities performed during individual supervision but with more listeners, this conclusion is not ideal. Valentino et al. provide critical supervision characteristics and ways to optimize group learning experience. Examples of these unique characteristics and benefits include peer feedback, observational learning, and development of empathy. The authors provide several suggestions on group structure that can maximize these benefits, such as creating a schedule and incorporating public speaking opportunities.

It is also critical to evaluate the specific variables that make supervision most effective. For example, Dixon et al. (2016) examined the relationship between mastery of learning objectives and credentials, supervision hours, years of experience, and caseload. They found that a simple increase in the number of supervision hours does not increase the number of mastered learning objectives. However, the BCBA credentials and the number of years of supervisor experience impact client outcomes. This study demonstrates that having the BCBA credential is powerful and can impact how clients respond to supervision. Thus, the investment in high-quality supervision of BCBAs is clearly worth the effort. Additionally, given the impact of years of experience, Dixon et al. (2016) encouraged the more experienced members of the field to mentor and share knowledge with less experienced BCBAs.

Supervision is provided in many HSOs as well as for-profit companies and, thus, models that fit within the organizations' framework are important to explore. Hartley et al. (2016) share the structural setup for an apprenticeship supervision model that has been successful in their organization. The authors acknowledge the constraints of a for-profit agency while supporting the mission of growing the next generation of behavior analysts. This apprenticeship model allows BCBAs to supervise future BCBAs by mentoring, educating, and training in a format that is mutually beneficial. Hartley and colleagues emphasize the original mission of the BCBA that each interaction a certificant has with others is an opportunity for behavior analysts to positively impact and support the field of behavior analysis. The structural guidelines offered in this article could be replicated by similar size agencies to help them overcome some of the difficulties associated with providing supervision while investing in high-quality supervision. A common experience in university programs, for example, is to establish a practicum training experience. Along a similar theme to Hartley et al.'s (2016) recommendations, Dubuque and Dubuque (2018) provide guidelines and recommendations for establishing a type of university-based practical training system using community-based sites. They offer practical suggestions to organize the practicum within a higher education training program. Dillon et al. (2008) offer a supervisory system focused on helping supervisees accomplish long-range projects, specifically master theses. Their model includes elements such as written task specifications, weekly subgoals and deadlines, regular monitoring and feedback, and added incentives. Finally, Mason et al. (2013) recommend that school districts in rural settings focus on training teachers and parents to be BCBAs to address the shortage in these geographic locations. In summary, these models provide a helpful framework for individuals in different settings to support the supervisory experience.

Organization of specific activities associated with the supervision experience is also important to consider. Cavalari et al. (2015) discuss ethical and practical challenges on records creation, storage, access, transfer, and disposal as well as recommendations such as identifying people to be responsible, specify guidelines, and set security standards. The authors also provide a helpful checklist for conducting periodic needs assessment and for ongoing compliance monitoring. This article is particularly relevant for supervisors to ensure adherence to our ethical code of conduct, which requires documentation of professional work and research (code 2.11, BACB.com) and the maintenance of records and data (code 2.12, BACB.com). Finally, Shuler and Carroll (2018) provide data that support a model wherein supervisors provide performance feedback using video modeling with voiceover instructions. This procedure was quite effective in that all supervisors mastered feedback skills and the intervention has the potential to be less time-consuming than packaged interventions. As aforementioned, training is a critical part of supervision and this article extends the literature on behavioral skills training (BST) applied specifically to critical supervisee skills.

Survey Research

Given the novelty of the supervision research, gathering data via survey is a useful way to identify global issues, questions, and areas for future research. In illustration, DiGennaro & Henley (2015) conducted a survey that inquired about different types of staff and supervisory training procedures in applied settings. The survey found that only a small percentage of respondents indicated they received any pre-service supervisory training before working independently, but 75% indicated they were responsible for supervising staff. DiGennaro & Henley (2015) concluded that employers are not consistently adopting best practice pre-service or in-service training guidelines. Based on these findings, the authors offer several suggestions for enhancing training for supervisors in the workplace, such as video-based BST, peer training, adoption of a supervisory training curriculum, and assessment of employee preferences.

Sellers et al. (in press) conducted a survey to gather information about current practices and barriers. Respondents included 284 BCBAs who had provided supervision for an average of 5.68 years. They presented the top areas of success and top areas of need as identified by respondents. The top five areas of success included using a contract, evaluating supervisor capacity, setting clear expectations, employing a range of performance evaluation strategies, and incorporating ethics and literature. The top five areas for improvement included setting clear expectations for receiving feedback, conducting ongoing evaluation of the supervisory relationship, using competency-based evaluations and tracking outcomes, directly assessing and teaching professionalism skills, and obtaining feedback on supervisory practices. Finally, these authors identified common barriers which included limited time, cost-prohibitive materials, poor access to examples, unawareness of certain requirements, and insufficient knowledge about how to measure or teach new skills. This article can serve as a helpful tool for supervisors wishing to specifically guide efforts toward areas of need by following a "to do" list for supervisors to ensure they adopt best practice guidelines and overcome barriers related to effective supervision.

Expansion and Growth

One final category pertinent to synthesizing the literature is that of expansion and growth of supervision. To date, there has only been one article published that specifically draws back to the supervisory experience and falls into this category. This article is also a survey study but warrants its own category given the focus on establishing a new area of potential supervision growth. Conners et al. (2019) discuss diversity issues in graduate training and fieldwork to produce more culturally competent professionals. They attest that there are no standards for training of this kind and as such our field lacks cultural competence. The authors utilized a survey to examine perceptions about experiences with multiculturalism and diversity issues. Respondents included 575 BCBAs representing a variety of geographic locations. The results indicated respondents perceived their training, fieldwork and supervision to be lacking in the area of cultural competency. Conners et al. (2019) and Fong et al. (2016) suggest several approaches for developing cultural awareness skills of behavior analysts that could be incorporated into training and supervision programs.

Research Implications

There are several conclusions that can be drawn from the supervision research thus far. These research implications can serve as a call to the field to consider the factors involved in high-quality supervision, facilitate further discussion, promote professional development, and support further research on the topic.

Supervision is Intimately Connected to the Quality of Services Our Field Provides

The way in which supervision is experienced can influence the quality of services our field provides, and this is particularly evident for the supervisory experience that occurs prior to an individual becoming professionally certified. As a field, we should feel the gravity of the role of the supervisor and take direct responsibility for ensuring supervision is of the highest quality. Luckily, several authors have provided practice guidelines, structural models, and ethical considerations to make this responsibility easier. Although particularly relevant to budding BCBAs, this implication also holds true for supervisory relationships that exist post certification. Continuing to provide high-quality supervision and mentoring in the workplace and to others in the field is just as important as during the fieldwork experience. While much of the literature discusses the responsibility of the supervisor in ensuring high-quality supervision, the supervisee also has a responsibility to invest in the supervision experience and actively engage with the supervisor to get the most out of the relationship. When both the supervisor and supervisee actively engage and take responsibility, the quality of services provided naturally improves.

Supervision Encompasses a Variety of Areas of Focus

These areas of focus include effective training, professional development, ethical decision-making, oversight of work, and mentoring. The supervision experience should be considered one that is far-reaching—above and beyond simply meeting a necessary requirement. When each of these activities is developed and considered in the context of practice recommendations, the supervisor and supervisee are likely to benefit. As our field progresses and as the literature on supervision develops, so will the activities that supervision encompasses.

The Supervision Experience Must Be Structured

Supervisors and supervisees must have a roadmap. This roadmap can consist of competencies linked to the BACB checklist (Sellers et al., 2016a) to be completed over the course of fieldwork hours for individuals seeking supervision to become a BCBA or can consist of professional development opportunities for the already practicing certified professional. The roadmap can be tailored, and the field has started to provide models for supervisors to include this structure at the onset of supervision. In addition to an overall roadmap, detailed plans regarding training procedures (Shuler & Carroll, 2018), and ethical documentation management (Cavalari et al., 2015) are also necessary.

There are Many Opportunities for Growth and Expansion of ABA Supervision

The literature thus far has provided us with one large area for potential growth, namely diversity (Conners et al., 2019). These areas of expansion could be accomplished on an individual basis (e.g., a supervisor developing a diversity training plan for her group of supervisees) or could be accomplished by large professional groups or organizations (e.g., a state professional organization sponsoring diversity training focused on individuals in coursework). Other potential areas for expansion and growth include incorporation of training on public speaking (Friman, 2014), expansion of a mentorship model that would match experienced BCBA supervisors with new BCBA supervisors regardless of work location, further development of supervisory training (e.g., video-based training packages; DiGennaro Reed & Henley, 2015), and use of pyramidal training. There is also a need for a structured curriculum to be developed and freely available to aid supervisors in creation of roadmaps and to ensure consistency. More formal assessment of supervisory skills and performance is needed, and tools can be developed to aid in this assessment. These are just a few ideas of practical ways supervision can grow and develop.

The Relationship Between the Supervisor and Supervisee is Important

Multiple authors (e.g., Sellers et al., 2016b, Barnes-Holmes, 2018) have written about the connection between high-quality supervision and the supervisory relationship. There are very clear and concrete activities that a supervisor can engage in to establish a positive relationship, such as clarifying performance expectations and developing a contract. There are also ongoing interpersonal actions that are important such as smiling, greeting, meeting deadlines, and being professional. Supervisors may encounter personalities that do not match their supervision style, and, in these cases, it is important to detect this mismatch as early as possible. After detection, the supervisor must work to address the barriers or identify an alternative supervisor for the supervisee. Allowing a supervision relationship to continue despite conflicts and barriers is likely to manifest itself in conflict. This conflict may occur over logistical issues (e.g., number of hours, frequency of supervision) but can typically be drawn back to larger more systemic barriers that were not overcome in the relationship. Ongoing dialogue, openness to bidirectional feedback, and willingness to adapt are critical for establishing an effective relationship.

Supervisors Need More Resources

As of July 1, 2019, there were 34,471 BCBAs and 3,631 Board Certified Assistant Behavior Analysts (BCaBAs; Behavior Analyst Certification Board [BACB], bacb.com, retrieved July 1, 2019), with this number rising significantly at each quarterly exam cycle. This rapid growth means that the number of people in supervisory roles who are new to the field is also growing. While supervisors often report knowing the necessity of certain supervisory skills, they often face barriers to providing effective supervision (Sellers et al., in press). In almost every article in the supervision literature thus far, authors discuss the need to develop more resources, support, processes, systems, and structure to ensure excellent supervision). As we develop as a field and continue to focus on this newly defined supervisor role, establishing these resources will be imperative.

Practice Recommendations

Thus far, as a field, we have produced several practice guidelines for discrete components of supervision (e.g., identifying and correcting issues in the supervisory relationship, practices for supervising individuals in coursework). These efforts have contributed to progress in our conceptualization of supervisory practice. There is yet to be an overarching set of practice guidelines to support supervisors serving in a variety of roles, supervisory relationships and frameworks, and skill sets of differing supervisees. The term "supervise" can serve as a starting point for these overall practice guidelines. The recommendations are intentionally global and meant to capture the behaviors supervisors should attend to in order to successfully promote positive, objective, and modern supervision practices.

Practice 1: Structure Your Time

Entering supervision blindly and without a plan may place the supervisor at risk for several events. First, the relationship with the supervisee may quickly deteriorate, and the supervisee may not view the supervisor as competent to provide the instruction and support they need. Second, critical repertoires may be missed, and the supervisee could exit the supervisory relationship with missing skills that are critical for successful on-the-job performance. Thus, supervisors should structure the time with each supervisee and structure their own supervisory approach for all supervisees. This does not mean that the supervisor must carry the burden of developing materials for each supervision session. It does suggest, however, that the supervisor must create a structure for the supervisee to complete assignments, engage in various professional development activities, and respond to supervision so that the time spent is productive and leads to continued growth and development.

Practice 2: Understand Individual Differences

There will naturally be personality and interaction style differences among supervisees. Some personality characteristics may "match" the supervisor's style perfectly, whereas others may create tension and frustration. Cultural considerations are also imperative and communication problems can occur in cross-cultural supervisory relationships (Daniels et al., 1999). As a behavior analytic supervisor, it is important to understand these individual differences and to adapt one's supervision style to the learner. Just as we would for clients, supervisees also need learning and support plans that are matched to their learning style. It is important to address these differences directly and to develop a plan for matching styles to best support the supervision experience.

Practice 3: Plan Ahead

There are many opportunities for supervisees to grow and flourish. In order to take advantage of these opportunities, advance planning is necessary. Examples of these opportunities could be participation in a unique functional analysis for a client, attendance at a workshop on public speaking, or the opportunity to serve on a committee through one's local professional organization. Planning for these opportunities will allow the supervisee to take ample advantage of them. Additionally, these experiences will positively augment supervision that takes place more traditionally in an office setting (or via remote 1:1 meeting time). Finally, planning your own approach and resources is critical. For example, preparing to deliver performance feedback during supervision has been shown to maximize the benefits, increase response and receptiveness to feedback, and to create a supportive supervisory environment (Hulse & Robert, 2014).

Practice 4: Encourage Growth

It can be easy to fall into the trap of meeting weekly, checking boxes, and even engaging in off-topic conversation. The supervisor should actively work to create a culture of growth. This culture can be accomplished through direct performance feedback, immediate reinforcement of self-reflection, humility, initiative, and spontaneous volunteering by the supervisee to expand horizons, take on a new challenge, or engage in less familiar behavior. By continuously focusing on and encouraging growth throughout the supervisory relationship, behavior analysts can quickly create a culture where our field is continuously striving to improve. This will inevitably benefit our clients, ourselves, and future budding behavior analysts.

Practice 5: Reflect on Your Approach

A threat to providing high-quality supervision is becoming complacent with one's approach, such that over time no change or evolution occurs. It is imperative that supervisors reflect on their approach to supervision, refining it as needed based on the individual, changes in the field, changes in oneself, and the overall need to constantly improve. As supervision tools and resources develop, self-monitoring and management guides will be beneficial to aid in this self-reflection.

Practice 6: Value Your Supervisees

The opportunity to supervise and mentor someone is special. As supervisors, we can shape the way our field progresses by how and what we teach the next generation of behavior analysts. We should feel the gravity of this role and value the fact that the individual has chosen behavior analysis as their field of study. This is especially important given the influx of people becoming certified. We could easily lose sight of providing quality supervision in the face of these numbers, writing some people off as just not as competent as others. However, doing so would minimize the impact supervisors can have to ensure all our supervisees become excellent supervisors to their supervisees and provide the best services possible.

Practice 7: Identify Ways to Improve

After reflection, supervisors must identify areas for improvement. We need to continuously evolve our supervision approach. These improvements could span a variety of areas, such as changes in interaction style, updates to support materials, modifications to instructional approach, or changes to arrangement of group activities.

Practice 8: Support New Ideas

The ABA supervision literature is growing every day with ideas for how we can improve supervisory practices. Embracing these ideas will facilitate progression. Additionally, colleagues, peers, and supervisees may have new ideas regarding how to change supervision practice for the better. Supporting and embracing these ideas is important for the individual supervisor as well as for the field's overall focus on evolvement of supervision practices.

Practice 9: Explore Opportunities for Expansion

The literature on ABA supervision is still new and we are just beginning to identify areas for expansion and growth. Continuing to explore these areas, both as a field and at the individual level, will enable supervision practices to expand. As the number of behavior analysts grows, so will the populations with whom we work. Thus, identifying areas for expanding the supervisory relationship and types of support offered to supervisees will aid in supporting this growth. For example, supervision practices will need to change as behavior analysts enter new workforces (LeBlanc et al., 2012), consider special variables (e.g., medical issues) when treating different clinical presentations (Copeland & Buch, 2019), and collaborate with different and more varied funding sources.

Research Direction

There are some evident deficits in the supervision literature that are ripe for further study. First, we have not objectively defined nor task analyzed the concepts that have been proposed in the literature as best practice. Second, while there have been several recommendations for engaging in good supervisory practices, none of these recommendations have been experimentally evaluated to determine if they have an impact on the variables that would suggest high-quality supervision has been provided. There is a rigor and science to delivering supervision (LeBlanc & Luiselli, 2016), and future research should be conducted accordingly. We can conceptualize this gap in the literature as needed to establish and define both our dependent variables (i.e., what behaviors or outcomes do we wish to influence through supervision?) and our independent variables (i.e., what does high-quality vs. low-quality supervision look like?). Further, we can examine the factors that influence the quality of supervision, for example, with the use of certain training models and mentoring arrangements. Figure 8.2 shows a simple visual of the broad categories for future research and a possible progression of study for future researchers to follow. Below, I discuss more specific research categories and questions for the interested researcher.

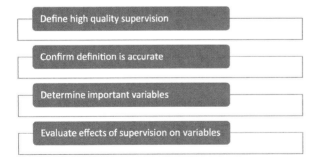

FIGURE 8.2   Broad areas of supervision research that need investigation. This visual provides a possible progression of research in the area of supervision and may help future researchers identify the general category within which their research falls.

Experimentally Evaluate Existing Recommendations

Several authors have offered practice recommendations that are based on experience, existing models in large organizations, and apparent face validity. For example, Valentino et al. (2016) provide several benefits of a group supervision model. Researchers could develop an assessment of professional behaviors and deliver it at the beginning and end of the group supervision experience to determine the effects of group supervision that adheres to these recommendations. As an example from the counseling literature, Agnew et al. (2000) evaluated the effects of a group supervision model on confidence and found that their peer group supervision model had a positive impact on counselors' confidence and professionalism.

There are several other models that could be validated (e.g., Hartley et al.'s 2016 apprenticeship model, Sellers et al.'s 2016 recommended practices). As well, several logistical and practical recommendations in the literature (e.g., Cavalari et al., 2015) to manage certain aspects of supervision would benefit from experimental evaluation. The researcher wishing to identify a gap in the literature could review the studies outlined in this chapter and identify a model that could be experimentally evaluated. To this end, the possibilities for research are nearly endless.

Define Supervisory Behavior and Identify Effective Training Methods

Supervisory behaviors are complex and involve constructs that the behavior analytic community has yet to define precisely. The first step in identifying effective training methods is to more clearly define those behaviors, which include interpersonal skills such as warmth, approachability, responsiveness, engagement, flexibility, reliability, and likeability. Additionally, supervisory behaviors involve problem-solving, interviewing, and ethical decision-making (Turner et al., 2016), all of which are imperfectly defined in the context of behavior analytic supervision. A great exercise for the aspiring supervision researcher would be to observe an optimal supervision session and list all the high-quality behaviors the supervisor demonstrates. Once these behaviors have been listed, they can be defined, and specific training methods can be developed and tested to address each behavior or groups of related behaviors.

Some literature in other disciplines can serve as a model for approaching this line of research. For example, Subramaniam et al. (2015) defined and evaluated different supervision styles (i.e., coaching, mentoring, and abusive supervision) on talent development of physicians. Their results were that coaching and mentoring styles had a positive impact on talent development whereas abusive styles had no impact. Additionally, Clark et al. (2008) evaluated the effects of a workshop on interactional skills of supervisors and found that interactional skills influence employee satisfaction and productivity and when trained appropriately can improve this repertoire. Behavior analysts have some work to do to define such constructs as "talent development" and to further define supervision styles, but these models from other disciplines will help expand the behavior analytic literature on supervision. Over time, training methods could be developed and evaluated for different types of supervision needed based on population, characteristics of the supervisee, and workplace. In the marriage and family therapy literature, Palmer-Olsen et al. (2011) evaluated a systematic model to train therapists to effectively deliver emotionally focused therapy (EFT), which is a specific type of therapy that focuses on the complexities inherent in couples' emotional interactions. An area for future research in behavior analysis may be to develop a model for effective supervision and corresponding training methods for training parents with children who engage in severe problem behavior.

Develop Assessment Tools

Once these definitions are developed, assessment tools are needed to evaluate those behaviors. Future researchers could develop an objective scoring tool that involves observation of the supervisor across several of these variables and computes a score to identify the quality of the supervision. This tool would need to be validated in some way, likely involving observation of different types of supervision to determine the spectrum of quality that exists across supervisors on these variables. Once this spectrum is established, researchers could make recommendations for scoring that would be grounded in this variety, thereby establishing objective supervision standards. Objective scoring criteria and self-monitoring could provide excellent models for assessing efficacy of supervisory behavior. LeBlanc and Luiselli (2016) recommend a functional behavior assessment (FBA) of supervision practices that includes rating scales, behavior checklists, and direct observation to promote isolation of procedures that are associated with great performance, procedural fidelity, and social validity. Researchers could use the Performance Diagnostic Checklist-Human Services (PDC-HS; Carr et al., 2018) creatively and apply to different aspects of supervision.

Establish Supervision Outcomes

There is a need to operationally define the competency of supervisees to determine whether and how supervision impacts supervisees' competency, outcomes (e.g., client progress and client satisfaction), BCBA exam pass rate (Turner et al., 2016), and learning objectives achieved (LeBlanc & Luiselli, 2016). Specific case factors may need to be taken into consideration and different models of supervision provided based on that variability in case presentation (e.g., symptom severity, skill level, age).

Develop New Models and Frameworks

Though the work that has been done to establish models is meritorious, there is still a clear need to establish additional models and frameworks for how we conduct supervision and specifically focus on areas of growth and expansion. For example, a framework for cultural competency, training standards for multiculturalism, and diversity issues are needed (Conners et al., 2019). The interested researcher could assess gaps in existing supervisees and develop ideas for new frameworks to address those gaps. Examples might include models for teaching "soft skills," engaging in empathetic care, public speaking, appropriately delivering feedback, time and stress management, or interdisciplinary collaboration (Brodhead, 2015). Taking the models that exist in the literature today and expanding them to these areas of need would provide the field with new practice recommendations while setting the stage for further experimental evaluation of these new models.

Establish Maintenance and Generalization Teaching Procedures

Although we are in the beginning stages of development of supervision best practices, our field would benefit long-term from establishing teaching procedures that promote maintenance and generalization of skills once they have been established. This effort will be particularly important as behavior analysts merge into new practice areas, as supervision skills will need to maintain and stretch to address new populations and new workplaces. Once high-quality supervision has been defined, assessed, and taught per the lines of suggested research above, the interested researcher could evaluate the utility of an assessment to determine whether skills have maintained and generalized and, if they have not, develop a set of teaching procedures to promote these two important variables.

Appendix A provides 30 research questions and ideas in each of the aforementioned categories that future researchers could ask to further the literature base on ABA supervision.

Conclusion

The field of behavior analysis has experienced a shift in the way we conceptualize and engage in supervisory practices. This shift has been positive and directed the field away from solely meeting requirements to a broader approach of mentoring, professional development, and support. In the past five years, a surge in behavior analytic literature on the topic of supervision has provided the field with practice models, guidelines, and more structure for various components of the supervisory process. Key features of effective supervision include (a) incorporation of a wide variety of areas of focus, (b) a structured experience, (c) focus on the supervisory relationship, (d) reflection, and (e) revision of supervisory practice and support of growth both at the individual level and for the field as a whole. As a result of our existing literature, we now have several very clear directions for practice and ideas about future research and resources. This chapter provides a starting point for readers wishing to more fully understand the ABA supervision literature, implement recommended practices, and develop a supervision research agenda within HSOs and other practice settings. Following these best practices and continuing to support the growth on this topic will enable behavior analysts to provide high-quality services to consumers and uphold high standards for budding behavior analysts in the field.

Appendix A Ideas and Questions for Supervision Research

Experimentally Evaluate Existing Recommendations

1. Do the recommendations for digital communication and records suggested by Cavalari et al. (2015) result in better compliance? Do they allow for better analysis for clinical and research decision-making? Does the "assessment and ongoing compliance monitoring checklist" proposed by these authors result in better compliance, more understanding, and/or less risk?
2. Do the considerations and recommendations provided by Dubuque and Dubuque (2018) impact the quality of practical training systems? Do they result in better adherence to BACB guidelines?
3. Does Hartley et al.'s (2016) apprenticeship model have good social validity? Does it help organizations overcome barriers associated with supervision provision?
4. Does Shuler and Carroll's (2018) training model for providing supervision result in maintenance of feedback skills over time?
5. Experimental evaluation of Sellers et al. (2016b) recommended practices— are these recommendations best practices compared to other practices?

6. Can the recommendations provided by Sellers et al. (2016b) be used to improve the supervisory relationship? Can an assessment tool be created to objectively detect these barriers? Once a tool is created, can interventions based on this article be put in place to match the intervention to the barrier identified?

7. Experimental evaluation of Turner et al. (2016) approach. Does the monitoring form provided in this article result in accurate identification of supervisory competence?

8. Does the group supervision model presented by Valentino et al. (2016) result in higher competence on the part of supervisees? Conduct an assessment of skills at the beginning of the group experience and then at the end to determine effects of group supervision using this model.

9. Is the model for supervision of accomplishing long-range projects proposed by Dillon et al. (2008) effective with other types of projects that employees might face on the job (e.g., writing skill acquisition programs for various types of clients, managing authorization reports and deadlines, etc.)?

Define Supervisory Behavior and Identify Effective Training Methods

10. Objectively define positive and negative supervisory behaviors and test to see if the definitions match supervision styles.

11. Objectively define negative supervisory behaviors and test to see if the definitions match supervision styles.

12. More clearly define different supervision styles and the behaviors associated with each.

13. Create supervision tools to match the supervisor's style with the best supervision technique.

14. Establish and evaluate training procedures to teach various supervisory behaviors (e.g., smiling, rapport development, trustworthiness, etc.)

Develop Assessment Tools

15. Develop and evaluate an objective assessment tool to assess supervision quality.

16. Develop and evaluate a functional behavior assessment of supervision practices.

17. Develop and evaluate an assessment tool to identify barriers in supervision delivery.

Establish Supervision Outcomes

18. Define the variables that supervision should impact.
19. Assess whether and how various supervision models impact those identified variables.
20. Define variables for different settings, populations, and case presentations and evaluate the effects of different types of supervision on them.

Develop New Models and Frameworks

21. Develop and test a framework for cultural competency.
22. Develop and evaluate training standards for teaching multiculturalism and diversity.
23. Develop a tool to assess skill deficits in existing supervisees and develop a framework based on those skill deficits.
24. Develop a model for teaching soft skills.
25. Create a framework for teaching time and stress management.
26. Establish recommended practices for interdisciplinary collaboration.
27. Establish guidelines for teaching (and improving) public speaking skills.

Establish Maintenance and Generalization Teaching Procedures

28. Create and evaluate the efficacy of a tool to assess maintenance of supervisory skills.
29. Create and evaluate the efficacy of a tool to assess generalization of skills.
30. Establish recommended guidelines for maintaining supervision skills once established.
31. Establish recommended guidelines for generalization of supervision skills once established to novel populations, places of employment, and with different types of supervisees.

References

Agnew, T., Vaught, C., Getz, H., & Fortune, J. (2000). Peer group clinical supervision program fosters confidence and professionalism. *Professional School Counseling, 4*, 6–12.

Barnes-Holmes, D. (2018). A commentary on the student-supervisor relationship: A shared journey of discovery. *Behavior Analysis in Practice, 11* (2), 174–176. doi: 10.1007/s40617-018-0227-y

Behavior Analyst Certification Board (2012). *Supervisor training curriculum outline.* Littleton: Behavior Analyst Certification Board.

Brodhead, M. (2015). Maintaining professional relationships in an interdisciplinary setting: Strategies for navigating nonbehavioral treatment recommendations for individuals with autism. *Behavior Analysis in Practice, 8,* 70–78. doi: 10.1007/s40617-015-0042-7.

Carr, J.E., Wilder, D.A., Majdalalny, L., & Mathisen, D. (2018). An assessment-based solution to a human-service employee performance problem. *Behavior Analysis in Practice, 11,* 129–138. doi: 10.1007/s40617-018-0243-y.

Cavalari, R.N.S., Gillis, J.M., Kruser, N., & Romanczyk, R.G. (2015). Digital communication and records in service provision and supervision: Regulation and practice. *Behavior Analysis in Practice, 8* (2), 176–189. doi: 10.1007/s40617-014-0030-3

Chang, J. (2012). A contextual-functional meta-framework for counselling supervision. *International Journal for the Advancement of Counselling, 2,* 71–87. doi:10.1007/s10447-012-9168-2.

Clark, H.B., Wood, R., Kuehnel, T., Flanagan, S., Mosk, M., & Northrup, J.T. (2008). Preliminary validation and training of supervisory interactional skills. *Journal of Organizational Behavior Management, 7,* 95–116. doi: 10.1300/J075v07n01 07.

Conners, B., Johnson, A., Duarte, J., Murriky, R., & Marks, K. (2019). Future directions of training and fieldwork in diversity issues in applied behavior analysis. *Behavior Analysis in Practice, 12,* 767–776. doi: 10.1007/s40617-019-00349-2.

Copeland, L., & Buch, G. (2019). Addressing medical issues in behavior analytic treatment. *Behavior Analysis in Practice, 13,* 240–246. doi:10.1007/s40617-019-00342-9.

Daniels, J., D'Andrea, M., & Kim, B.S. (1999). Assessing the barriers and changes of cross-cultural supervision: A case study. *Counselor Education and Supervision, 38,* 191–204. doi: 10.1002/j.1556-6978.1999.tb00570.x.

DiGennero, F.D., & Henley, A.J. (2015). A Survey of Staff Training and Performance Management Practices: The Good, the Bad, and the Ugly. *Behavior Analysis in Practice, 8,* 16–26. doi: 10.1007/s40617-015-0044-5

Dillon, M.J., Kent, H.M., & Malott, R.M. (2008). A supervisory system for accomplishing long-range projects: An application to master's thesis research. *Journal of Organizational Behavior Management, 2,* 213–227. doi: 10,1300/J075v02n03 07.

Dixon, D.R., Linstead, E., Granpeesheh, D., Novack, M.N., French, R., Stevens, E. Stevens, L., & Powell, A. (2016). An evaluation of the impact of supervision intensity, supervisor qualifications, and caseload on outcomes in the treatment of autism spectrum disorder. *Behavior Analysis in Practice*, 9 (4), 339–348. doi: 10.1007/s40617-016-0132-1.

Dubuque, E.M., & Dubuque, M.L. (2018). Guidelines for the establishment of a university-based practical training system. *Behavior Analysis in Practice*, 11 (1), 51–61. doi: 10.1007/s40617-016-0154-8.

Fleming, R.K., Oliver, J.R., & Bolton, D.M. (1996). Training supervisors to train staff: A case study in a human service organization. *Journal or Organizational Behavior Management*, 16, 3–25.

Fong, E.H., Catagnus, R.M., Brodhead, M., Quigley, S., & Field, S. (2016). Developing the cultural awareness skills of behavior analysts. *Behavior Analysis in Practice*, 9, 84–94. doi: 10.1007/s40617-016-0111-6.

Friman, P.C. (2014). Behavior analysts to the front! A 15-step tutorial on public speaking. *Behavior Analyst*, 37, 109–118.

Garza, K.L., McGee, H.M., Schenk, Y.A., & Wiskirchen,R.R. (2018). Some tools for carrying out a proposed process for supervising experience hours for aspiring board certified behavior analysts. *Behavior Analysis in Practice*, 11 (1), 62–70. doi: 10.1007/s40617-017-0186-8

Hartley, B.K., Courtney, W.T., Rosswurm, M., & LaMarca, V.L. (2016). The apprentice: An Innovative approach to meet the behavior analyst certification board's supervision standards. *Behavior Analysis in Practice*, 9 (4), 329–338. doi: 10.1007/s40617-016-0136-x

Holley, W. (2005). Supervision: Using the evidence to support our practice. *Kairaranga*, 6, 41–48.

Hulse, D., & Robert, T. (2014). Preplanning for feedback in clinical supervision: Enhancing readiness for feedback exchange. *Journal for Counselor Preparation and Supervision*, 6 (2), 2–17 doi: 10.7729/62.1091

LeBlanc, L.A., & Luiselli, J.K. (2016). Refining supervisory practices in the field of behavior analysis: Introduction to the special section on supervision. *Behavior Analysis in Practice*, 9 (4), 271–273. doi: 10.1007/s40617-016-0156-6

LeBlanc, L.A., Heinicke, M.R., & Baker, J.C. (2012). Expanding the consumer base for behavior-analytic services: Meeting the needs in the 21st century. *Behavior Analysis in Practice* (5), 4–14.

Mason, L.L., Perales, J., & Gallegos, Er. (2013). Community-based development of rural behavior analysts. *Rural Special Education Quarterly*, 32, 20–23.

Morgan, M.M., & Sprenkle, D.H. (2007). Toward a common-factors approach to supervision. *Journal of Marital and Family Therapy*, 33, 1–17.

Palmer-Olsen, P., Gold, L.L., & Woolley, S.R. (2011). Supervising emotionally focused therapists: A systematic research-based model. *Journal of Marital and Family Therapy, 37*, 411–426.

Parsons, M.B., Reid, D.H., & Green, C.W. (1996). Training basic teaching skills to community and institutional support staff for people with severe disabilities: A one-day program. *Research in Developmental Disabilities, 17*, 467–485.

Parsons, M.B., Rollyson, J.H., Iverson, J., & Reid, D.H. (2012). Evidence-based staff training: A guide for practitioners. *Behavior Analysis in Practice, 5* (2), 2–11.

Pilgrim, C. (2018). Some thoughts on shaping future behavior analysts: A call to stay true to our roots. *Behavior Analysis in Practice, 11*, 204–205. doi: 10.1007/s40617-018-0233-0

Reid, D.H., & Green, C.W. (1990). Staff training. In J.L. Matson (Ed.), *Handbook of behavior modification with the mentally retarded* (2nd ed.) (pp. 71–90). New York: Plenum Press.

Reid, D.H., Parsons, M.B., Lattimore, L.P., Towery, D.L., & Reade, K.K. (2005). Improving staff performance through clinician application of outcome management. *Research in Developmental Disabilities, 26*, 101–116.

Reid, D.H., Rotholz, D.A., Parsons, M.B., Morris, L., Braswell, B.A., Green, C.W., & Schell, R.M. (2003). Training human service supervisors in aspects of PBS: Evaluation of a statewide, performance-based program. *Journal of Positive Behavior Interventions, 5*, 35–46.

Schepis, M.M., & Reid, D.H. (1994). Training direct service staff in congregate settings to interact with people with severe disabilities: A quick, effective and acceptable program. *Behavioral Interventions, 9*, 13–26.

Sellers, T.P., Alai-Rosales, S., & MacDonald, R.P. (2016a). Taking full responsibility: The ethics of supervision in behavior analytic practice. *Behavior Analysis in Practice, 9*, 299–308. doi:10.1007/s40617-016-0144-x

Sellers, T.P., LeBlanc, L.A., & Valentino, A.L. (2016b). Recommendations for detecting and addressing barriers to successful supervision. *Behavior Analysis in Practice, 9* (4), 309–319. doi: 10.1007/s40617-016-0142-z

Sellers, T.P., Valentino, A.L., & LeBlanc, L.A. (2016c). Recommended practices for individual supervision of aspiring behavior analysts. *Behavior Analysis in Practice, 9* (4), 274–286. doi: 10.1007/s40617-016-0110-7.

Sellers, T.P, Valentino, A.L., Landon, T., & Aielo, S. (2019). Board certified behavior analysts' supervisory practices: Survey results and recommendations. *Behavior Analysis in Practice, 12*, 536–546. doi: doi.org/10.1007/s40617-019-00367-0

Shuler, N., & Carroll, R.A., (2018). Training supervisors to provide performance feedback using video modeling with voiceover instructions. *Behavior Analysis in Practice*, 12, 576–591. doi: 10.1007/s40617-018-00314-5

Subramaniam, A., Silong, A.D., & Ismail, I.A. (2015). Effects of coaching supervision, mentoring supervision, and abusive supervision on talent development among trainee doctors in public hospitals: Moderating role of clinical learning environment. *Medical Education*, 15, 129–137. doi: 10.1186/s12909-015-0407-1.

Turner, L.B., Fischer, A.J., & Luiselli, J.K. (2016). Towards a competency-based, ethical and socially valid approach to the supervision of applied behavior analytic trainees. *Behavior Analysis in Practice*, 9 (4), 287–298. doi: 10.1007/s40617-016-0121-4

Valentino, A.L., LeBlanc, L.A., & Sellers, T.P. (2016). The benefits of group supervision and a recommended structure for implementation. *Behavior Analysis in Practice*, 9 (4), 320–328. doi: 10.1007/s40617-016-0138-8

PART IV
Systems Interventions

9
Employee-Focused Incentive-Based Programs

Amy J. Henley

Incentives are putative consequences delivered to an employee contingent on the occurrence of a desired behavior or reaching a performance criterion (e.g., training modules completed, percent procedural integrity).[1] The myriad conditions under which the contingent delivery of incentives has been successfully applied is a notable advantage of this behavior change tactic. Incentives have been effectively used to improve employee performance in laboratory (e.g., Oah & Dickinson, 1992) and applied settings (e.g., Luiselli et al., 2009), when delivered alone (e.g., Lee & Oah, 2015) or in combination with other employee behavior change procedures (e.g., Goomas & Ludwig, 2007), with lottery or probabilistic arrangements (e.g., Cook & Dixon, 2006), when delivered contingent on individual employee behavior (e.g., Bucklin et al., 2004) or the collective behavior of a group of employees (e.g., Honeywell et al., 1997), and with varied behaviors in diverse industries.

Incentives may also lead to reliable increases in net organizational profits. For example, George and Hopkins (1989) compared the effects of hourly pay to performance-contingent pay with restaurant servers. When participants earned 7% of gross sales based on performance, individual income was 20%–30% higher, restaurant sales increased 18%–36%, and labor costs were unchanged. Thus, adopting an incentive system may have financial benefits for employees and organizations despite requiring the expenditure of time and money to implement the system. Performance and economic gains achieved under an incentive system have also proved durable when the system is maintained long-term. Wagner et al. (1988) found substantial long-term increases in productivity and decreases in labor costs over a nine-and-a-half-year period using a group incentive system with unionized ironworkers who previously received hourly pay. The reliable, lasting, and robust findings based on multiple measures of employee and organizational performance have resulted in sustained interest in incentives as an attractive and viable employee behavior change procedure in the experimental literature.

Incentives are the second most common *consequent* intervention to change employee behavior (see Chapter 7 for a discussion of antecedent and consequent interventions), appearing in a quarter of empirical research articles published in the *Journal of Organizational Behavior Management* between 1998 and 2009 (VanStelle et al., 2012). Despite the prevalence in the literature, incentives appear less common in applied settings providing behavior analytic services to individuals with intellectual and developmental disabilities (hereafter referred to as human service organizations; HSOs). DiGennaro Reed and Henley (2015) evaluated the frequency with which HSOs provide training and performance management practices to employees. Although 27% of respondents indicated that their employer provides incentives in *some* capacity, a mere 8% receive incentives delivered *contingent* on performance more than twice per year. These findings suggest that of the small percentage of HSOs that offer incentives, few provide them in a way that is consistent with the principles of effective reinforcement.

The paucity of incentive use in HSOs is concerning because performance issues that occur when employees are well-trained and capable of correct responding are reported at a much higher rate than issues that could be resolved with additional training or practice (VanStelle et al., 2012). In the absence of effective contingencies to support desired employee behavior in the post-training work environment, even high-quality empirically supported staff training is insufficient to maintain desired performance over time (Lerman et al., 2015). Degradations in performance warrant particular attention because compromises in the integrity with which employees implement teaching and treatment protocols negatively affect consumer outcomes (Fryling et al., 2012). Unfortunately, the prevailing natural contingencies in many HSOs are not sufficient to evoke and maintain desired behavior and, in some cases, may favor undesirable employee behavior.

For example, following consumer behavior guidelines or implementing teaching procedures produces immediate, probable, aversive consequences, including increased time and effort. Such procedures also place demands on consumers and increase the likelihood that the individual will engage in challenging behavior, further compounding these undesirable consequences. On the other hand, deviating from behavior guidelines to reduce the time or effort required for correct implementation, or engaging in behavior that delays completion of teaching procedures, results in immediate, probable, positive consequences (e.g., social interaction). The numerous available response alternatives that are unrelated to an employees' job responsibilities may unfortunately provide higher rates of reinforcement. In the absence of supervisory oversight, the former scenario is unlikely to lead to punitive consequences (e.g., reprimand) and the latter rarely results in positive consequences such as praise. Sadly, consumer progress is unlikely to maintain correct implementation. Improvements in consumer skills or functioning, and the improved conditions that such gains may occasion (e.g., lower rates of challenging behavior), are considerably delayed and probabilistic. Under these conditions, employees will maximize reinforcement by allocating more responding to the less effortful option that provides more immediate, positive, and probable consequences. It is, therefore, necessary to supplement the inadequate natural contingencies operating in the post-training work environment with additional programmed consequences that effectively compete with concurrently available reinforcers. The practices most frequently used to accomplish these aims are largely unsuccessful, however.

Compensation, in the form of hourly or salary wages, is the primary means by which organizations hope to motivate employees. Often referred to as pay for time (Wine, 2018), these arrangements undermine established guidelines for effective reinforcement because pay is only loosely tied to performance. Such loose contingencies place a greater emphasis on attendance than measurable output and are more likely to generate behavior patterns in which employees engage in only that which is minimally necessary to avoid termination. As a result, organizations often attempt to supplement typical compensation arrangements with other employee motivation programs. Among the most common are annual bonuses and salary increases or employee recognition programs. Although these strategies are easy to implement, they are not often successful because they also violate much of the critical components for effective reinforcement. For example, among the many reasons that employee of the month programs have been criticized is that the behavior of a single employee contacts reinforcement while commendable performance of many others goes unreinforced (Johnson & Dickinson, 2010). Other programs provide reinforcement at great delays (e.g., annual bonus) or delivered noncontingently (e.g., Employee Appreciation Day).

The limited efficacy of pay for time arrangements and traditional motivational programs underscores the need for procedures that are grounded in the principles of behavior analysis and aligned with research on reinforcement. The addition of incentives creates a direct link between measurable performance outcomes and reinforcement that is tenuous in the above approaches. This contingency is necessary for the reinforcement associated with work behavior to compete with the many sources of reinforcement for nonwork behavior and generate high levels of desirable performance. In contrast, however, incentive systems do not have the advantage of simplicity in design and implementation. They may take many forms and selection of these parameters is challenging. What follows is a discussion of several thematic research lines comparing variations in incentive system implementation.

Review of Pertinent Research

Quality

Reinforcement-based interventions are more effective when higher quality reinforcers (i.e., more preferred) are made contingent on behavior relative to when
lower-quality consequences are used (Neef et al., 1992). Thus, it is imperative
to carefully select the items for use in an incentive system. Incentives may have
a monetary value (i.e., monetary incentives) and include money and gift cards/
certificates. Nonmonetary incentives may include myriad tangible or intangible
consequences such as time off from work (Austin et al., 1996), food (Kortick &
O'Brien, 1996), social celebrations (Hagge et al., 2017), and numerous others. An
advantage of monetary incentives is that they are likely to function as generalized
conditioned reinforcers—making their efficacy relatively independent of fluctuating motivating operations. Using incentives that are not dependent on particular
motivative conditions is beneficial when employees have frequent opportunities
to earn the incentive and satiation is a concern, when it is difficult or impossible
to assess preference, or when developing a system to change the behavior of many
employees with varied individual preferences. The efficacy of monetary incentives, then, is largely dependent on the monetary amount (i.e., magnitude) or the
range of items for which a gift card may be exchanged (Holt et al., 2016). Despite
the noted advantages, long-term use of monetary incentives may not be economi-
cally feasible unless performance improvements offset the costs. This limitation is
relevant to HSOs in which financial resources are often limited and few employee
responsibilities directly translate to increased profits.

Nonmonetary incentives are a flexible means to mediate the cost associated
with monetary incentives. The countless nonmonetary options make it possible
to identify desirable low-cost items such as access to a preferred parking spot
and telecommuting options. There is also some promising evidence to suggest
that employees may prefer nonmonetary items over money (Wine et al., 2013).
Unfortunately, the innumerable possible options can make it challenging for
supervisors to accurately select preferred nonmonetary incentives for employees,
a supposition supported by recent empirical work (Wilder et al., 2011; Wilder
et al., 2007). Individual preferences may also change rapidly and it is unlikely
supervisors will be able to identify the conditions that lead to preference shifts
and accurately select new items (Wine et al., 2012). The inadequacy of manager
selection underscores the need for the use of preference assessments. A detailed
account of these methodologies can be found in Chapter Three of this text and
thus will not be considered here.

In general, though, comparisons of employee preference assessment methods
have reported higher accuracy (i.e., consistently classified reinforcing stimuli as
high-preferred) when participants reported preference in terms of the *amount of*

work they would be willing to complete for each item relative to when they are asked to report *preference* for the items without consideration for the response requirement (Wilder et al., 2006; Wine et al., 2014). Although tenuous, this interpretation aligns with numerous evaluations of reinforcer and preference assessments with nonemployee populations. These studies have consistently observed shifts in preference with increases in the response requirement (e.g., DeLeon et al., 1997). Methods in which reinforcers are identified at low work requirements or without consideration of the requirement are not representative of conditions employees will experience. Incentives identified using such methods may not be effective in practice or may be less effective than other available alternatives. Taken together, research on reinforcer selection suggests that organizations would be well served to solicit information regarding preference from employees at regular intervals using formal assessments that incorporate the work requirement rather than rely on supervisor selection.

Reinforcement Schedules

A series of laboratory and applied studies from the 1970s and 1980s compared hourly pay to fixed and variable ratio reinforcement schedules on work behavior to identify the most efficacious incentive schedule. Several thorough reviews have detailed, critiqued, and synthesized this research (Bucklin & Dickinson, 2001; Dickinson & Poling, 1996; Hantula, 2001). By all accounts, the authors agree; the results are idiosyncratic and preclude any firm conclusions about the effects of ratio schedules on employee behavior. Despite this ambiguity, one clear finding emerged, namely that performance was consistently better when participants earned incentives when compared to hourly pay. If supported by future research, these findings could have positive implications from a practical standpoint.

Many restrictions in organizations, such as payroll processing, constrain when and how often incentives can be delivered. It may be easier for organizations to adopt incentive systems if specific schedule arrangements are not necessary to be effective. Flexibility in scheduling would allow organizations to integrate an incentive system within existing organizational processes with minimal disruptions. However, similar practical restrictions may also make it difficult to deliver earned incentives immediately, introducing a delay that may be problematic.

Delay

Extensive empirical evidence has shown systematic decreases in reinforcer efficacy as the delay between the behavior and reinforcer delivery increases (Lattal,

2010). An understanding of how delayed reinforcement affects work behavior is a needed area of inquiry because it is not always logistically feasible to deliver incentives immediately or at short delays. Notwithstanding a few recent exceptions, evaluations of this important parameter with incentives are virtually nonexistent.

In the second of a three-study analog experiment, Wine et al. (2019) examined the effects of monetary incentives delivered at six progressively increasing delays from 1 to 32 days among participants completing analog tasks. Responding was generally comparable with no consistent differences among the delays tested. This finding stands in contrast to decades of research with human and nonhuman animals. A possible explanation for these incongruent results is that the effects of delay may interact with the response requirement, similar to that of reinforcer quality previously discussed. That is, responding may be less sensitive to delay when the response requirement is low, leading to undifferentiated responding. Increases in the schedule may reveal differences in the efficacy of identical reinforcers delivered at varying delays (Roane et al., 2001). Promising research integrating behavioral economic concepts and quantitative models to understand employee behavior provides a potential method to evaluate this possibility.

Sub-disciplines within behavior analysis are increasingly integrating behavioral economics to understand and improve upon existing application technologies with much success (Hursh et al., 2013). A principle advantage of adopting a behavioral economic approach is the precise quantification of the efficacy of qualitatively different reinforcers across a wide range of response requirements using demand curve analyses. Demand analyses applied to the organization may help identify the extent to which employees will work to obtain a given incentive (providing valuable information about preference), as well as the requirement at which employees will complete the maximum amount of work to access that incentive. This application of demand would help inform durable resource-efficient incentive arrangements capable of maintaining high levels of responding.

In one of the first experiments to apply demand curve analyses to employee behavior, Henley et al. (2016a) assessed the effects of delay of monetary reinforcement using an adapted self-report procedure commonly used in behavioral economics (Reed et al., 2015). Undergraduate participants completed two surveys that differed only in the delay to payment. Consistent with previous research on delayed reinforcement, peak reported work output was 45% higher when compensation was delayed by one hour as compared to four weeks. This difference was not present at the lowest work requirements but emerged and became more pronounced as the requirement increased. These findings suggest reinforcer efficacy was equivalent when accessing it required relatively little effort, but the delayed reinforcer was less effective at maintaining responding when the work requirement increased. This outcome lends some initial credibility to the possibility that previous research, in which responding was insensitive to manipulations of reinforcer dimensions, may have used low-effort tasks (e.g., check processing, filing) or work requirements that were not sufficiently difficult to generate observable differences. The external validity of these findings is limited, however, because participants were not employees and did not experience the study outcomes and should be interpreted with caution. These data nonetheless highlight the potential benefits from adopting an economic perspective for employee incentive systems and the need to evaluate the interactive effects of different incentive dimensions and contingency arrangements.

Magnitude

Responding and reinforcer efficacy can also be modulated by manipulating the magnitude of reinforcement (Catania, 1963). The reinforcer magnitude necessary to evoke behavior change is important to organizations because it must be financially feasible to implement a system involving reinforcers that cost money, directly or indirectly (e.g., personnel time). Identifying the lowest magnitude reinforcer that can effectively maintain behavior may be especially important for HSOs where finances are often limited. There are numerous published reports in which relatively small incentives were effective in applied settings (Bucklin & Dickinson, 2001) but comparisons of incentive magnitude are sorely lacking.

In one of the only studies to date, Henley and colleagues used a similar behavioral economic framework (described above) to compare the effects of two incentive magnitudes using an experiential procedure with workers recruited from Amazon Mechanical Turk (www.mTurk.com; Henley et al., 2016b). Workers completed a computerized task in exchange for a monetary incentive across a progressively increasing response requirement. The results were generally consistent with what one might expect from the basic research on magnitude. Participants in the higher magnitude group completed slightly more work than that observed in the smaller magnitude. An interesting finding was that participants who received the smaller magnitude incentive completed more work per penny earned. Put another way, increases in responding were not proportional to increases in incentive magnitude. Therefore, the lower magnitude condition resulted in a more efficient use of financial resources from a cost-benefit perspective.

Although relatively few in number, some studies have indirectly evaluated incentive magnitude using variable piece-rate pay systems (Oah & Dickinson,

1992; Smoot & Duncan, 1997). Unlike traditional arrangements in which the incentive magnitude remains constant—referred to as a linear arrangement—the magnitude per-piece increases or decreases with consecutive opportunities in accelerating and decelerating schedules, respectively. The findings were mixed within and between studies and will require more research to understand the relation between performance and changing per-piece arrangements. The inconsistent results notwithstanding, participants from Oah and Dickinson (1992) earned more money in the accelerating arrangement despite comparable performance among groups, which may limit the financial viability of an accelerating system.

Researchers wishing to extend this line of work may benefit from consulting the contingency management literature concerned with programmed incentives to treat substance abuse. Magnitude has emerged as one of the most powerful variables for treatment efficacy and may be worthy of further consideration for employee incentive systems. Moreover, ascending schedules, which are similar to the accelerating schedules, are one of the most commonly used and frequently effective arrangements (Dallery et al., 2015). Ascending schedules can also include a reset contingency in which the incentive amount returns to the initial low value when an individual fails to meet the reinforcement criteria. Adding a reset contingency to an accelerating pay plan may be one way to mediate costs.

Lotteries

Probabilistic or lottery-based schedules of reinforcement are another variation that appears to be used with regularity in applied settings (e.g., Luiselli et al., 2009). There are many ways to arrange a lottery system, such as the number of entries allowed per employee, that appear to be effective regardless of the particular variation used (e.g., Cook & Dixon, 2006; Miller et al., 2014). Lottery-based incentives involve a contingency in which, upon meeting the performance criteria, employees have the opportunity to earn an incentive but its delivery is not guaranteed. A major advantage of lotteries is the potential to reduce costs because organizations only need to pay out incentives to one or a few employees as opposed to every employee that meets the requirement. This feature makes it possible to use incentives that are more highly preferred, of higher magnitude, or available more frequently without increasing costs. Although lottery systems seem to be working well, several features would benefit from empirical justification. For example, the value of the probability is a central feature in every lottery system, and yet, little is known about the probability that is necessary to evoke and maintain desired behavior.

Several recent analog studies have conducted parametric evaluations of incentive probability ranging from 75% to as little as 3% (Gravina et al., 2005; Wine et al., 2017). Across studies, the 3% probability evaluated by Wine and colleagues (2017) was the only condition in which participants failed to consistently meet the response requirement. The authors tentatively suggested that percentages as low as 6% (the lowest effective probability examined) may be sufficient to maintain responding. In a 2019 study, however, Wine et al. imposed a 32-day delay to incentive receipt and found that a 10% probability was not effective but responding was unaffected by this delay when the incentive was guaranteed (i.e., 100%). This was one of the first studies to demonstrate the interactive effects of reinforcer dimensions on incentive efficacy with employees. Based on these data, probability may be a less influential determinant of behavior at short delays but exert more control over responding at greater delays. It is conceivable that the common practice of combining lottery earnings with a biweekly paycheck could introduce a delay that renders previously effective probabilities ineffective. Future research should explore this possibility.

Percentage of Pay

Several studies have examined the effects of varying percentages of incentive pay by constraining total compensation and manipulating the proportion of pay available through incentives relative to base pay (i.e., guaranteed wages; see Bucklin & Dickinson, 2001, for a review). Incentive pay ranges between 0% (i.e., no incentives) and 100% (i.e., piece-rate pay only) with higher percentages constituting a higher proportion of pay dependent on measurable performance. In an applied case study by LaMere et al. (1996), performance of truck drivers improved and maintained over a three-year period when participants earned between 3% and 9% of their pay in incentives. These findings provide evidence of the long-term efficacy of small percentages of incentive pay.

Evaluations of the percentage of incentive pay consistently demonstrated higher performance when participants earned incentives relative to base pay. However, Oah and Lee (2011) provide the only evaluation of the percentage of incentive pay in which performance varied across percentages. Oah and Lee's study is noteworthy because the authors made several modifications to the experimental arrangement that increased the ecological validity relative to previous laboratory-based incentive research. For example, Oah and Lee recruited individuals with a three-year history of socializing with one another to jointly participate and increased the number and length of sessions to better approximate a typical work schedule (30 sessions each lasting 6 hours conducted 5 days a week). They found consistently higher productivity and duration of time spent working when participants earned 100% of their pay from incentives compared to conditions in which participants earned 10% and 0% of their pay from incentives. Although more research is needed, these initial findings suggest that higher percentages of incentive pay may result in higher levels of performance. Additionally, the findings suggest researchers can modify laboratory settings to better approximate the workplace.

Feedback

A final line of investigation involves the effect of incentives when combined with performance feedback (i.e., information about performance). Several early reports found that performance increases obtained with feedback can be further enhanced when incentives are added (e.g., Dierks & McNally, 1987; Gaetani et al., 1985). Gaetani et al. found that performance of two auto mechanics increased nearly 100% following the introduction of feedback. When feedback was combined with incentives, performance increased another 50%, totaling an average increase of 192% over baseline. Such impressive gains demonstrate the potent influence of incentives when added to a feedback intervention. Without an evaluation of incentives in isolation, the question remained as to whether feedback augments the effectiveness of an existing incentive contingency. A laboratory study by Bucklin et al. (2004) found superior performance when individuals earned incentives relative to hourly pay. In addition, they found that feedback enhanced the effects of incentives for nearly all participants.

Data from Johnson et al. (2008) reveal at least one potential limitation on the efficacy of feedback and incentives delivered together, however. The authors failed to observe meaningfully higher performance when feedback was combined with either incentive or hourly pay, despite considerable evidence that feedback improves performance. They attributed this discrepant finding to the type of feedback provided; participants received objective information about the number of tasks completed. Objective feedback may not be effective in the absence of or may be less effective relative to evaluative statements about performance (e.g., praise). It is possible that features of the incentive and feedback interventions may interact and influence efficacy in currently unpredictable ways. Because feedback is a vital part of the workplace, it is likely that feedback contingencies will be in place in most settings where incentive systems are implemented. Additional studies examining the effects of feedback and incentive variations when combined would be a valuable contribution to the literature. What can be ascertained from the limited research is that performance is generally better, and unlikely to be worse, when feedback and incentives are combined. Nonetheless, it is premature to make conclusions about the specific relation between these interventions.

Synthesis of Research Findings and Implications

The focus of this chapter has been to review what is known about employee incentive systems with an emphasis on comparisons within implementation variations. The research covered thus far demonstrates how much remains to be learned about the conditions under which incentives are maximally effective. There are numerous examples of conflicting results within and across experiments. In other cases, responding was undifferentiated or was inconsistent with predictions derived from well-established behavioral processes. Despite these idiosyncrasies, there are several areas of general agreement across thematic research lines.

The most consistent finding is that individuals perform better when they earn incentives than when they receive hourly pay. This effect was observed in nearly every experiment containing comparisons between incentives and hourly pay. Decades of research also provides compelling evidence that incentives yield impressive performance improvements with all sorts of settings, target behaviors, incentive types, contingency arrangements, and populations (Jenkins et al., 1998). Thus, incentive arrangements may take many forms and still be effective. This finding is promising because it suggests that it is likely possible to identify an arrangement that fits within existing organizational processes or modify a system to find the most feasible and efficacious arrangement. Several studies described previously, however, raise the possibility that variations in the particular arrangement may differentially influence performance, but these variations appear to exert comparatively less influence on responding than the contingency. Therefore, the most critical determinant of the efficacy of an incentive system is the contingency between performance and pay. Demonstrations of the long-term efficacy of incentives are another commonality across research areas. These studies suggest that incentive arrangements can effectively maintain desired performance as long as the system remains in place and is implemented as intended.

The above points suggest at least several features that are necessary for the effective application of incentives in practice. First, to ensure there exists a contingency between performance and pay, it is necessary to carefully select and clearly define the behavior for which incentives will be made contingent. This contingency also requires systems for monitoring the behavior to ensure that incentives are delivered accurately and consistently. Third, it is necessary to be strategic in system design by (a) carefully considering organizational resources and incorporating strategies to promote maintenance and (b) ensuring organizational processes and available resources support continued correct implementation. Although some applied implications have already been discussed, in the next section I offer some practical recommendations for the implementation of incentive systems in the light of these conclusions.

Practice Recommendations

The first step in the development of an incentive system is to select a target behavior. Although the specific behavior will vary based on the context, some general guidelines exist. The first guideline is to select behavior that is under the employees' control (Komaki & Minnich, 2008). Uncontrollable variables unrelated to the employee's performance may unduly influence the measure and produce inaccurate performance estimates. Again, the contingency between behavior and reinforcement is of critical importance. Outside factors that employees cannot fully control weaken that relation, compromise reinforcer efficacy, and could potentially lead to an increase in conditioned emotional responding (e.g., frustration, complaining). Evaluating employee performance by measuring consumer outcomes is one example of a common performance measure in HSOs that may violate this suggestion. It is imperative to track consumer outcomes to detect a worsening or lull in progress that could be related to employee performance issues (e.g., low treatment integrity). Nonetheless, many factors outside of the employees' control can influence consumer progress (e.g., medication changes) and it is not recommended as the sole measure upon which incentive delivery be made contingent.

Next, it is important to complete a systems check to assess whether a change in the target behavior, as a result of the change in reinforcement contingencies, may have unintended negative effects on other job responsibilities or organizational processes (Bailey & Austin, 2001). A systems check requires one to consider how employee responsibilities and organizational processes are related and if they may be adversely affected by a change in the target behavior. In an incentive system designed to increase the number of teaching trials, for example, it is possible for an employee to allocate a disproportionate amount of time to the target task at the expense of developing leisure skills or creating opportunities for incidental teaching. It may be useful to set an upper and lower limit on the reinforcement criteria such that exceeding a certain value no longer results in more reinforcement. Selecting multiple targets to support a more equal distribution of critical responsibilities is another method to avoid undesirable response allocation.

A number of factors should be considered when selecting multiple target responses. First, incorporating a behavior that has monetary benefits for the organization could offset the costs of the program and result in a more sustainable intervention. For example, targeting safety skills may lead to fewer injuries and save on workers' compensation payments. Interventions aimed at reducing absenteeism have also been shown to reduce costs (e.g., Luiselli et al., 2009). Incorporating measures that can be tracked automatically or via permanent product (e.g., meeting attendance) may help reduce the effort involved in tracking multiple performance measures and allow time to track other important employee behavior that require direct observation. Regardless of the effort required to track such behaviors, I strongly encourage the inclusion of measures such as program implementation that are linked to positive outcomes for consumers. It may also be beneficial to select behaviors that span the diverse repertoires required of behavior analysts. Targeting effective communication and problem-solving skills or ethical repertoires, for example, may facilitate the professional development of employees and have positive benefits to the organization. Last, limiting the number of performance measures to fewer than seven is recommended to moderate the resources required to implement the system and increase the likelihood of continued implementation over time.

Developing a system for measuring and monitoring employee performance is the next step in the process. An effective system must be standardized and based on clearly defined objective measures. Measurement should occur on a regular basis as more frequent measurement and feedback is generally associated with greater gains in employee performance. Frequent measurement makes it possible to ensure employees are contacting reinforcement and to quickly detect areas of concern. Supervisors can evaluate the function of the performance problem and provide support to employees that are not consistently meeting expectations before the issue becomes pervasive or leads to more serious consequences. One barrier to frequent measurement is the time and resources involved in tracking performance. To increase the likelihood that a measurement system will be used consistently and reliably, it must be constructed in a way that maximizes sustainability and minimizes the complexity of the system and the effort required to implement it. For example, incorporating automatic color coding based on performance level into the tracking mechanism or data display can help supervisors identify any employee exceeding or failing to meet expectations at a glance. Although creating features such as this may require additional resources up-front, the cumulative savings in time or effort make these undertakings a worthwhile investment. Transparency is also a key factor. It is critical to communicate with employees what behaviors are being measured, how they are defined, how observations will be conducted, and the consequences for surpassing or failing to meet expectations. Once the basic procedures are developed, it is important to arrange a system of delivery and accountability for accurate and consistent implementation of behavior measurement, incentive delivery, and monitoring over time.

Following the identification of a valid and reliable measurement system, the next step is to select items that will be delivered contingent on behavior. Supervisors may not accurately identify preferred items and it is crucial to involve employees in this process either informally through collaborative discussions (Daniels & Bailey, 2014) or through the use of formal preference assessments. An array of items to populate the assessment is needed prior to its use, which can be generated by supervisors or by soliciting ideas from employees. Reassessing preferences frequently to account for shifts in preference is important but may be time-consuming to complete and employees may become frustrated with the process. One solution is to use an array of items from which employees may select their preferred incentive upon meeting the performance criteria that can be updated on a less frequent basis.

At this point, specific parameters of the incentive program will need to be chosen. The challenge is to select values that effectively change and maintain employee behavior and offer maximal cost-efficiency. For example, supervisors must select an appropriate incentive amount for use in a system. Erring on the side of providing *larger* incentives may not be financially sustainable and lead to the discontinuation of an effective program before obtaining the desired behavior change. Incentives that are *too small* may not be sufficient to motivate employees to change their behavior and may result in the expenditure of valuable resources on an ineffective system. Supervisors must also select the work requirement, frequency of delivery, delay to delivery, as well as make decisions about many other variables. Decisions such as these can be detrimental if made arbitrarily.

Unfortunately, the limited evaluations of reinforcer dimensions and arrangements as well as the individual requirements of each setting make it impossible to recommend any exact values. Generally speaking, the basic literature on reinforcer dimensions suggests efficacy is greatest with the use of high versus low magnitude items, immediate versus delayed delivery, high versus low preferred items, and more relative to less frequent delivery. Satiation may be a concern if each of the aforementioned parameters is maximized. To narrow the possible values, I suggest beginning the selection process by first considering what is logistically feasible in terms of monetary and staffing resources needed to carry out the system long-term. It may then be helpful to "field-test" the system prior to its introduction. Field-testing involves hypothetically implementing a contingency arrangement for a period of time and make any final adjustments (Cooper et al., 2020). This practice uses current performance levels to make *a priori* determinations including the likelihood that behavior will contact reinforcement, and whether the number of reinforcer deliveries is realistic for the organization or may lead to satiation. The specific parameters selected for an incentive program will ultimately need to be modified iteratively until the optimal values are identified. Ideally, adjustments will be data-based, although practical exigencies may arise that necessitate changes as well.

One strategy to promote acceptability and continued implementation of an incentive system is to seek employee participation during development. This practice is thought to be associated with the effectiveness of a system as well as employee satisfaction and acceptability with the arrangement (Bucklin & Dickinson, 2001). For example, it is possible to encounter resistance to the use of lotteries because of the similarities with gambling (e.g., Yukl & Latham, 1975). Soliciting employee input during development may help avoid potential resistance and promote creative modifications to address any concerns. To extend the previous example, in lieu of complete lottery system, a raffle ticket for a higher magnitude item may be included among an array of smaller magnitude incentives from which employees may choose. This approach would capitalize on the potential benefits for individuals who are motivated by the lottery without imposing undesirable conditions on others. Employee perceptions of a given system may change after experiencing the contingencies and soliciting input during development is not sufficient. I strongly suggest recruiting ongoing feedback from employees whose behavior is targeted by the program as well as those individuals charged with implementation. This information should then be used to revise the procedures to promote acceptability and further system efficacy.

As a point of caution, incentives are not an appropriate intervention under all conditions and may not be effective for all performance problems. It is improbable that incentives will be effective when deficient performance is the result of insufficient knowledge or skills necessary to complete the target behavior or if the work setting precludes accurate performance (e.g., broken equipment), for example. Evidence to this effect is demonstrated in a unique study by Roscoe et al. (2006) that compared acquisition of a task using either contingent money based on implementation accuracy, absent descriptive information about performance, or feedback about correct and incorrect performance for each step of the task. Feedback produced clear and immediate improvements with all participants mastering the task. In contrast, performance was unchanged when contingent money was introduced, unless participants had already received feedback. These results are not intended to advocate for the use of one intervention over another. Incentives and feedback are commonly provided simultaneously, a strategy that I encourage to best support employees working in HSOs. The failure of incentives to evoke criterion performance in the absence of behavior-specific information is meant to underscore the need to consider the function of deficient employee performance prior to planning treatment (Austin, 2000). Incentives are best suited for situations in which employees have already acquired the skill, but the prevailing workplace contingencies are insufficient to support maintenance and improvement of trained skills over time.

Research Directions

As noted previously, individual incentive plans are implemented with relative paucity in HSOs, which contrasts sharply with their frequent use in large for-profit organizations. The financial resources available to larger corporations to fund an incentive plan and hire experts to develop and oversee implementation may be one factor contributing to the disparity in adoption rates. The many variations discussed to this point make designing and implementing incentive systems somewhat challenging, requiring considerable expertise to skillfully construct. Even though many individuals working in HSOs have experience creating reinforcement programs for consumers, many struggle to translate the basic principles and adapt intervention procedures for use with employees. Complicating this challenge further, it is difficult to draw clear conclusions from the extant literature comparing incentive variations that would be needed to guide the design of an empirically supported incentive system. This literature covers a modest portion of possible variations and the findings are often conflicting. Addressing these barriers calls for more comparison studies to facilitate the identification of the most robust arrangements, thereby requiring fewer resources to help lower program costs and hopefully increase the adoption potential of incentive systems in HSOs. A few possibilities for future research that may accomplish such aims are listed below.

A lack of simulation fidelity is a frequent supposition for the failure to observe differentiated responding among incentive conditions in studies comparing the various contingency arrangements. Many of the contingencies for engaging in on- and off-task behavior, motivating operations, and competing response alternatives present in the workplace are often lacking from laboratory-based studies despite researchers' best efforts. To illustrate, Matthews and Dickinson (2000) did not observe performance differences among percentages of incentive pay using a single 70-minute session. Oah and Lee (2011) observed differentiated responding when they evaluated the same percentages across 30 six-hour sessions. Experimental preparations with lower ecological validity may not be sufficiently sensitive to detect differences that would otherwise be apparent in naturalistic settings with extended exposure to the contingencies. Therefore, more advanced laboratory arrangements that better simulate the complex and competing contingencies with attractive alternatives that are present in real work settings may be a necessary requisite for the evaluation of more nuanced comparisons.

A potentially fruitful line of research comprises a greater understanding of the relative efficacy of reinforcer dimensions and how parametric manipulations of their values differentially influence performance. If successful, this line of inquiry could reveal some of the critical variables that compete most effectively with concurrent sources of reinforcement in the workplace. Such critical variables could then be leveraged when developing an incentive system to maximize the effectiveness of the intervention while minimizing the required resources. Further, the findings of Wine et al.'s (2019) evaluation of incentive probability and delay mirrors other research findings of the interactive effects of two or more dimensions on responding. The ways in which combinations of reinforcer dimensions interact and influence behavior in the workplace are largely unknown and could yield useful information for application.

The substantial literature on the effects of transitions among schedules of varying reinforcer density (e.g., rich to lean) suggest an avenue for novel research poised to yield interesting findings with potential applied utility. For an incentive program to remain effective over time will almost surely require some modification. It may be necessary, for example, to decrease the schedule of delivery or incentive magnitude to ensure maintenance under economic constraints. Changes in parameters within an existing incentive system may influence behavior in unknown and possibly detrimental ways. Rich-to-lean transitions, in particular, are associated with pausing and problem behavior (Jessel and Hanley, 2016; Williams et al., 2011); to my knowledge, this research has not been sufficiently extended to employee behavior. Given the wealth of literature demonstrating the effect of transitions with myriad populations and settings, it seems plausible that similar disruptions in behavior may occur when parameters are adjusted or possibly when transitioning between incentivized and non-incentivized work tasks. It remains difficult to predict how changes in parameters may influence employee behavior at the current time. Research extending basic and applied work on transitions to employees would be a valuable contribution to both literatures.

As previously mentioned, lottery-based incentive arrangements are a possible cost-saving strategy with demonstrated efficacy. In addition to parametric comparisons of probability, several aspects of lottery systems would benefit from empirical evaluation. For example, when used in naturalistic settings, employees may be unaware of the likelihood of winning a drawing once entered. The probability may also vary depending on the number of employees who meet the entry criteria. Evaluations of known versus unknown probabilities as well as variable probabilities would be interesting areas for future research. The potential for employees to experience early or prolonged periods without winning is a potential drawback of lottery systems. Employees must receive the reinforcer at least sometimes to be effective. Performance may deteriorate below criterion levels if an employee does not earn an incentive shortly following program inception. It is also possible that early contact with reinforcement may be sufficient to sustain responding during longer periods without reinforcement. Thus, efficacy may be influenced by the sequence in which employees contact reinforcement in a lottery system.

Organizational researchers may also wish to evaluate the use of incentives embedded within a token economy (for a discussion of token economies, see Hackenberg, 2018). The use of a token economy with an array of backup reinforcers would functionally eliminate the need to habitually assess preference once the system is in place. The use of an array of reinforcers (Slowiak, 2014) and token arrangements (Vergason & Gravina, 2019) have been effective with employees. There are a multitude of ways in which a token economy may be configured. The systematic evaluation of varied token arrangements in work contexts is underexplored.

A fifth area for future research that could make substantive contributions to HSOs surrounds the identification and development of methods to assess employee burnout and satisfaction as well as variables contributing to turnover. Turnover is a pervasive problem affecting HSOs with detrimental consequences such as disruptions in services, compromised treatment integrity, and potentially crippling financial ramifications for an organization. In a recent survey among behavior analytic service providers, approximately half reported being unsatisfied with their current work conditions and nearly two-thirds were experiencing moderate to high levels of burnout (Plantiveau et al., 2018). Supervisor behavior and the supports provided to employees, including ongoing training and frequent feedback and praise, are related to improved satisfaction and retention (Kazemi et al., 2015; Plantiveau et al., 2018). It stands to reason that the contingent delivery of incentives may have similar positive effects. Behavior analysts currently have limited methods for evaluating these important constructs and their relation to incentives remains to be explored.

Although not a thematic line of research per se, the cost-effectiveness of differing incentive arrangements is a critical measure of the social validity of a system. The financial feasibility ultimately dictates program adoption and continuation. Cost-benefit analyses provide organizational leaders with an efficient means to assess the economic viability of an intervention. Despite numerous calls urging the use of such analyses (e.g., Andrasik, 1979; Poling et al., 1993), between 10% and 18% of studies include cost-benefit analyses (VanStelle et al., 2012; Wells et al., 2013). Cost-benefit analyses of incentive systems may identify more resource-sensitive arrangements and hold researchers accountable for developing interventions in a cost-sensitive manner.

Note

1 Although I have used the term *incentive* here, I do not intend to suggest that incentives are functionally different than reinforcers. Organizational behavior management (OBM) researchers and practitioners often work with stakeholders who are not familiar with behavior analysis and may find the less technical *incentive* more acceptable compared to *reinforcer* (Becirevic, Critchfield, & Reed, 2016). Moreover, because OBM interventions often seek to change the behavior of many employees, the items selected for use in an incentive system may not function as reinforcers for all employees. These factors may have led to the more frequent adoption of *incentive* in OBM, which I have retained to remain consistent with the broader OBM literature.

References

Andrasik, F. (1979). Organizational behavior modification in business settings: A methodological and content review. *Journal of Organizational Behavior Management*, *2*(2), 85–102.

Austin, J. (2000). Performance analysis and performance diagnostics. In W. Fisher, C. Piazza, & H. Roane (Eds.), *Handbook of applied behavior analysis* (pp. 321–349). Reno, NV: Context Press.

Austin, J., Kessler, M. L., Riccobono, J. E., & Bailey, J. S. (1996). Using feedback and reinforcement to improve the performance and safety of a roofing crew. *Journal of Organizational Behavior Management*, *16*, 49–75. doi: 10.1300/J075v16n02_04.

Bailey, J. S., & Austin, J. (2001). Deconstructing the performance management process. In J. Austin & J. E. Carr (Eds.), *Handbook of applied behavior analysis* (pp. 67–86). Oakland, CA: Context Press.

Becirevic, A., Critchfield, T. S., & Reed, D. D (2016). On the social acceptability of behavior-analytic terms: Crowdsourced comparisons of lay and technical language. *Behavior Analyst*, *39*, 305–317. doi: 10.1007/s40614-016-0067-4.

Bucklin, B. R., & Dickinson, A. M. (2001). Individual monetary incentives. *Journal of Organizational Behavior Management*, *21*(3), 45–137. doi: 10.1300/J075v21n03_03.

Bucklin, B. R., McGee, H. M., & Dickinson, A. M. (2004). The effects of individual monetary incentives with and without feedback. *Journal of Organizational Behavior Management*, *23*(2–3), 65–94. doi: 10.1300/J075v23n02_05.

Catania, A. C. (1963). Concurrent performances: A baseline for the study of reinforcement magnitude. *Journal of the Experimental Analysis of Behavior*, *6*, 299–300.

Cook, T., & Dixon, M. R. (2006). Performance feedback and probabilistic bonus contingencies among employees in a human service organization. *Journal of Organizational Behavior Management, 25*, 45–63. doi: 10.1300/J075v25n03_04.

Cooper, J. O., Heron, T. E., & Heward, W. L. (2020). *Applied behavior analysis* (3rd ed.). Upper Hoboken, NJ: Pearson Education.

Dallery, J., Defulio, A., & Meredith, S. E. (2015). Contingency management to promote drug abstinence. In H. Roane, J. Ringdahl, & T. Falcomata (Eds.), *Clinical and organizational applications of applied behavior analysis* (pp. 395–424). London, UK: Elsevier. doi: 10.1016/B978-0-12-420249-8.00016-2.

Daniels, A. C., & Bailey, J. S. (2014). *Performance management: Changing behavior that drives organizational performance* (5th ed.). Atlanta, GA: Performance Management Publications.

DeLeon, I. G., Iwata, B. A., Goh, H. L., & Worsdell, A. S. (1997). Emergence of reinforcer preference as a function of schedule requirements and similarity. *Journal of Applied Behavior Analysis, 30*(3), 439–449. doi: 10.1901/jaba.1997.30-439.

Dickinson, A. M., & Poling, A. D. (1996). Schedules of monetary reinforcement in organizational behavior management: Latham and Huber (1992) revisited. *Journal of Organizational Behavior Management, 16*, 17–91. doi: 10.1300/J075v16n01_05.

Dierks, W., & McNally, K. (1987, March). Incentives you can bank on. *Personnel Administrator, 32*, 61–65.

DiGennaro Reed, F. D., & Henley, A. J. (2015). A survey of staff training and performance management practices: The good, the bad, and the ugly. *Behavior Analysis in Practice, 8*, 16–26. doi: 10.1007/s40617-015-0044-5

Fryling, M. J., Wallace, M. D., & Yassine, J. N. (2012). Impact of treatment integrity on intervention effectiveness. *Journal of Applied Behavior Analysis, 45*, 449–453. doi: 10.1901/jaba.2012.45-449.

Gaetani, J. J., Hoxeng, D. D., & Austin, J. T. (1985). Engineering compensation systems: Effects of commissioned versus wage payment. *Journal of Organizational Behavior Management, 7*, 51–63.

George, J. T., & Hopkins, B. L. (1989). Multiple effects of performance-contingent pay for waitpersons. *Journal of Applied Behavior Analysis, 22*, 131–141.

Goomas, D. T., & Ludwig, T. D. (2007). Enhancing incentive programs with proximal goals and immediate feedback. *Journal of Organizational Behavior Management, 27*, 33–68. doi: 10.1300/J075v27n01_02

Gravina, N., Wilder, D. A., White, H., & Fabian, T. (2005). The effects of raffle odds on signing in at a treatment center for adults with mental illness. *Journal of Organizational Behavior Management, 24*, 31–42. doi:10.1300/J075v24n04_02

Hackenberg, T. D. (2018). Token reinforcement: Translational research and application. *Journal of Applied Behavior Analysis, 51*, 393–435. doi: 10.1002/jaba.439

Hagge, M., McGee, H., Matthews, G., & Aberle, S. (2017). Behavior-based safety in a coal mine: The relationship between observations, participation, and injuries over a 14-year period. *Journal of Organizational Behavior Management, 37,* 107–118. doi: 10.1080/01608061.2016.1236058

Hantula, D. A. (2001). Schedules of reinforcement in organizational performance, 1971–1994: Application, analysis and synthesis. In C. M. Johnson, W. K. Redmon, & T. C. Mawhinney (Eds.), *Handbook of organizational performance: Behavior analysis and management* (pp. 139–166). New York: Haworth Press.

Henley, A. J., DiGennaro Reed, F. D., Kaplan, B. A., & Reed, D. D. (2016a). Quantifying efficacy of workplace reinforcers: An application of behavioral economic demand to evaluate hypothetical work performance. *Translational Issues in Psychological Science, 2,* 174–183. doi: 10.1037/tps0000068

Henley, A. J., DiGennaro Reed, F. D., Reed, D. D., & Kaplan, B. A. (2016b). A crowdsourced nickel-and-dime approach to Analog OBM research: A behavioral economic framework for understanding workforce attrition. *Journal of the Experimental Analysis of Behavior. 106,* 134–144. doi: 10.1002/jeab.220

Holt, D. D., Glodowski, K., Smitts-Seeman, R. R., & Tiry, A. M. (2016). The domain effect in delay discounting: The roles of fungibility and perishability. *Behavioural Processes, 131,* 47–52. doi: 10.1016/j.beproc.2016.08.006

Honeywell, J. A., Dickinson, A. M., & Poling, A. (1997). Individual performance as a function of individual and group pay contingencies. *Psychological Record, 47,* 261–274.

Hursh, S. R., Madden, G. J., Spiga, R., DeLeon, I. G., & Francisco, M. T. (2013). The translational utility of behavioral economics: Experimental analysis of consumption and choice. In G. Madden, W. Dube, T. Hackenberg, G. Hanley, & K. Lattal (Eds). *APA handbook of behavior analysis, Vol. 2: Translating principles into practice* (pp. 191–224). Washington, DC: American Psychological Association.

Jenkins, G. D., Gupta, N., Mitra, A., & Shaw, J. D. (1998). Are financial incentives related to performance? A meta-analytic review of empirical research. *Journal of Applied Psychology, 83,* 777–787.

Jessel, J., & Hanley, G. P. (2016). A translational evaluation of transitions. *Journal of Applied Behavior Analysis, 49,* 359–376. doi: 10.1002/jaba.283.

Johnson, D. A., & Dickinson, A. M. (2010). Employee-of-the-month programs: Do they really work? *Journal of Organizational Behavior Management, 30,* 308–324. doi:10.1080/01608061.2010.520144.

Johnson, D. A., Dickinson, A. M., & Huitema, B. E. (2008). The effects of objective feedback on performance when individuals receive fixed and individual incentive pay. *Performance Improvement Quarterly, 20,* 53–74.

Kazemi, E., Shapiro, M., & Kavner, A. (2015). Predictors of intention to turnover in behavior technicians working with individuals with autism spectrum disorder. *Research in Autism Spectrum Disorders, 17,* 106–115.

Komaki, J. C., & Minnich, M. R. (2008). In C. M. Johnson, W. K. Redmon, & T. C. Mawhinney (Eds.), *Handbook of organizational performance: Behavior analysis and management* (pp. 51–80). Binghamton, NY: Haworth Press.

Kortick, S. A., & O'Brien, R. M. (1996). The world series of quality control: A case study in the package delivery industry. *Journal of Organizational Behavior Management, 16,* 77–93. doi: 10.1300/J075v16n02_05.

LaMere, J. M., Dickinson, A. M., Henry, M., Henry, G., & Poling, A. (1996). Effects of multicomponent monetary incentive program on the performance of truck drivers. *Behavior Modification, 4,* 385–405.

Lattal, K. A. (2010). Delayed reinforcement of operant behavior. *Journal of the Experimental Analysis of Behavior, 93,* 129–139.

Lee, J., & Oah. S. (2015). A comparison of the effects of incentive and penalty procedures on work performance: A simulation. *Journal of Organizational Behavior Management, 35,* 336–345. doi: 10.1080/01608061.2015.1093056.

Lerman, D. C., LeBlanc, L. A., & Valentino, A. L. (2015). Evidence-based application of staff and caregiver training procedures. In H. Roane, J. Ringdahl, & T. Falcomata (Eds.), *Clinical and Organizational Applications of Applied Behavior Analysis* (pp. 321–351). doi: 10.1016/B978-0-12-420249-8.00014-9

Luiselli, J. K., DiGennaro Reed, F. D., Christian, W. P., Markowski, A., Rue, H. C., St. Amand, C., & Ryan, C. J. (2009). Effects of an informational brochure, lottery-based financial incentive, and public posting on absenteeism of direct-care human services employees. *Behavior Modification, 33,* 175–181. doi: 10.1177/0145445508320624.

Matthews, G. A., & Dickinson, A. M. (2000). Effects of alternative activities on productivity under different percentages of incentive pay. *Journal of Organizational Behavior Management, 20,* 3–27. doi:10.1300/J075v20n01_02.

Miller, M. V., Carlson, J., & Sigurdsson, S. O. (2014). Improving treatment integrity in a human service setting using lottery-based incentives. *Journal of Organizational Behavior Management, 34*(1), 29–38. doi: 10.1080/01608061.2013.873381

Neef, N. A., Mace, F. C., Shea, M. C., & Shade, D. (1992). Effects of reinforcer rate and reinforcer quality on time allocation: Extensions of matching theory to educational settings. *Journal of Applied Behavior Analysis, 25,* 691–699.

Oah, S., & Dickinson, A. M. (1992). A comparison of the effects of a linear and an exponential performance pay function on work productivity. *Journal of Organizational Behavior Management, 12,* 85–123. doi: 10.1300/J075v12n01_05

Oah, S., & Lee, J. H. (2011). Effects of hourly, low-incentive, and high-incentive pay on simulated work productivity: Initial findings with a new laboratory method. *Journal of Organizational Behavior Management, 31*(1), 21–42. doi: 10.1080/01608061.2011.541820

Plantiveau, C., Douvani, K., & Virues-Ortega, J. (2018). High levels of burnout among early-career board-certified behavior analysts with low collegial support in the work environment. *European Journal of Behavior Analysis, 19*, 195–207.

Poling, A., Smith, J., & Braatz, D. (1993). Data sets in organizational behavior management: Do we measure enough? *Journal of Organizational Behavior Management, 14*(1), 99–116

Reed, D. D., Kaplan, B. A., & Becirevic, A. (2015). Basic research on the behavioral economics of reinforcer value. In F. D. DiGennaro Reed & D. D. Reed (Eds.), *Autism Service Delivery: Bridging the Gap Between Science and Practice* (pp. 279–306). New York: Springer.

Roane, H. S., Lerman, D. C., & Vorndran, C. M. (2001). Assessing reinforcers under progressive schedule requirements. *Journal of Applied Behavior Analysis, 18*, 249–255. doi: 10.1901/jaba.2001.34-145.

Roscoe, E. M., Fisher, W. W., Glover, A. C., & Volkert, V. M. (2006). Evaluating the relative effects of feedback and contingent money for staff training of stimulus preference assessments. *Journal of Applied Behavior Analysis, 39*, 63–77. doi: 10.1901/jaba.2006.7-05.

Slowiak, J. M. (2014). "How may I help you?" Improving telephone customer service in a medical clinic setting. *Journal of Organizational Behavior Management, 34*, 39–51. doi: 10.1080/01608061.2013.873382.

Smoot, D. A., & Duncan, P. K. (1997). The search for the optimum individual monetary incentive pay system: A comparison of the effects of flay pay and linear and non-linear incentive pay systems on worker productivity. *Journal of Organizational Behavior Management, 14*(2), 5–75.

VanStelle, S. E., Vicars, S. M., Harr, V., Miguel, C. F., Koerber, J. L., Kazbour, R., & Austin, J. (2012). The publication history of *Journal of Organizational Behavior Management*: An objective review and analysis: 1998–2009. *Journal of Organizational Behavior Management, 32*(2), 93–123. doi: 10.1080/01608061.2012.675864.

Vergason, C. M., & Gravina, N. E. (2019). Using a guest- and confederate-delivered token economy to increase employee-guest interactions at a zoo. *Journal of Applied Behavior Analysis, 53*, 422–430. doi: 10.1002/jaba.599.

Wagner, J. A., Rubin, P. A., & Callahan, T. J. (1988). Incentive payment and nonmanagerial productivity: An interrupted time series analysis of magnitude and trend. *Organizational Behavior and Human Decision Processes, 42*, 47–74.

Wells, J., Reimer, D., & Houmanfar, R. (2013). Money and the Journal of Organizational Behavior Management interventions: A review. *Journal of Organizational Behavior Management, 33*, 276–289.

Wilder, D. A., Harris, C., Casella, S., Wine, B., & Postma, N. (2011). Further evaluation of the accuracy of managerial prediction of employee preference. *Journal of Organizational Behavior Management, 31*, 130–139. doi: 10.1080/01608061.2011.569202.

Wilder, D. A., Rost, K., & McMahon, M. (2007). The accuracy of managerial prediction of employee preference: A brief report. *Journal of Organizational Behavior Management, 27*, 1–14. doi: 10.1300/J075v27n02_01.

Wilder, D. A., Therrien, K., & Wine, B. (2006). A comparison between survey and verbal choice methods of identifying potential reinforcers among employees. *Journal of Organizational Behavior Management, 25*(4), 1–14.

Williams, D. C., Saunders, K. J., & Perone, M. (2011). Extended pausing by humans on multiple fixed-ratio schedules with varied reinforcer magnitude and response requirements. *Journal of the Experimental Analysis of Behavior, 95*, 203–220. doi: 10.1901/jeab.2011.95-203.

Wine, B. (2018). Incentive-based performance improvement. In J. Luiselli (Eds), *Applied behavior analysis: Advanced guidebook* (pp. 117–134). doi: 10.1016/ B978-0-12-811122-2.00007-3.

Wine, B., Chen, T., & Brewer, A. (2019). An examination of reward probability and delivery delays on employee performance. *Journal of Organizational Behavior Management, 39*, 179–193. doi: 10.1080/01608061.2019.1666776.

Wine, B., Edgerton, L., Inzana, E., & Newcomb, E. T. (2017). Further effects of lottery odds on responding. *Journal of Organizational Behavior Management, 37*, 75–82. doi:10.1080/ 01608061.2016.1267064.

Wine, B., Gilroy, S., & Hantula, D. A. (2012). Temporal (in)stability of employee preference for rewards. *Journal of Organizational Behavior Management, 32*, 58–64. doi: 10.1080/01608061.2012.646854.

Wine, B., Gugliemella, C., & Axelrod, S. (2013). An examination of generalized-conditioned reinforcers in stimulus preference assessments. *Journal of Organizational Behavior Management, 33*(4), 244–251.

Wine, B., Reis, M., & Hantula, D. A. (2014). An evaluation of stimulus preference assessment methodology in organizational behavior management. *Journal of Organizational Behavior Management, 34*, 7–15. doi: 10.1080/01608061.2013.873379.

Yukl, G. A., & Latham, G. P. (1975). Consequences of reinforcement schedules and incentive magnitudes for employee performance: Problems encountered in an industrial setting. *Journal of Applied Psychology, 60*, 294–298. doi: 10.1037/h0076755.

10
Safety and Injury Prevention

Nicole Gravina and Nicholas Matey

In 2018, the Bureau of Labor Statistics reported an average injury rate of 3.1 for every 100 full-time workers across all industries. In healthcare and social assistance organizations, the injury rate reported was 3.9 for every 100 full-time workers (BLS.gov, 2019). These data suggest workers in healthcare and social assistance organizations are 1.26 times as likely to be injured compared to workers across all industries. The healthcare and social assistance injury rate is higher than many other historically risky industries, including coal mining (3.3), construction (3.0), and manufacturing (3.4), and above the average across all industries. These data indicate that injury rates are high in healthcare and social assistance organizations, such as those that serve individuals with intellectual and developmental disabilities (IDD). Therefore, these organizations should design and employ strategies to support and improve employee safety.

Although the prevalence of injuries specific to organizations that provide behavior analytic services (hereto referred to as human service organizations or HSOs) is not known, the most common types of injuries in these healthcare settings are assaults from patients, overexertion, strains from lifting, and falls (BLS.gov, 2010). At least some of these injury types are relevant to organizations that provide services to individuals with IDD. Behavior therapists could sustain an injury while lifting an individual during therapy, or could incur an injury while using a restraint procedure during problem behavior (Luiselli, 2011). Assaults from clients during problem behavior can include biting, hitting, and being struck by objects thrown by the client, possibly requiring employees to wear different types of protective equipment (Lin et al., 2012; Urban et al., 2011). Some individuals with IDD have treatment plans designed to explicitly address aggressive behaviors, meaning that both the employee and the client may be vulnerable to injury during therapy, especially if the program is not implemented correctly. Moreover, behavior therapists work with clients in multiple settings, including outpatient clinics, schools, residential facilities, hospitals, homes, and out in the community, and each of these settings presents different potential safety hazards. Thus, behavior therapists and their clients are at risk for a variety of injuries, depending on the context for services and behaviors being addressed.

Workplace injuries negatively affect the individual who sustained the injury and the organization in numerous ways, and both incur costs following an injury. The organization may pay for medical expenses, workers' compensation, legal services, damaged equipment, training, increased insurance premiums, and they may earn less revenue due to reduced productivity. The National Safety Council (2019) estimates that an organization pays an average of $39,000 for each injury requiring medical consultation. Additionally, injuries can also cost the injured employee money, including reduced wages for days off, loss of job or demotion, medical costs, decreased ability to work, and payment for assistance with home activities (e.g., hiring lawn-mowing services or paying for grocery delivery).

Furthermore, there are several other documented adverse outcomes of injuries. Employees who have been injured are more likely to experience depression, anxiety, persistent pain, headaches, and other adverse physical and psychological effects (e.g., Kim, 2013). Injuries may affect an employee's basic ability to function, and they may require modified work assignments and assistance with tasks outside of work like carrying groceries and caring for children. Injuries also lead to distrust by all employees, not just the injured person, and affect the overall culture of the workplace, including worker satisfaction and attitudes (e.g., Barling et al., 2003). These outcomes could prove even more costly for organizations.

In healthcare settings, employee injuries are also associated with adverse outcomes for patients and clients. Provider fatigue, injury, and stress appear to be associated with a higher risk of errors in medication delivery and higher rates of infection transmission (Rogers et al., 2004). For behavior therapists, injuries and associated stress and fatigue could reduce the quality of program implementation. Employees who experience injuries may be more reluctant to provide certain types of treatments or work with specific clients in the future, which could affect care. In some cases, the risks and hazards that caregivers face are in relation to the patient or client or in the same work area. For example, a employees who suffers a back injury while lifting a client may also drop the client, resulting in an injury for the client as well. Injuries are harmful not only for the injured but also for the organization and the clients they serve.

Because the safety of employees in human service settings is so intertwined with client safety and care, organizational systems aimed at improving employee safety should be extended to include the client (Weatherly, 2019). Some interventions could address the immediate physical environment where individuals with IDD are served. For example, an intervention aimed at keeping the floor free of debris could improve safety for both employees and clients by reducing trip hazards. Other interventions focused on direct care staff will indirectly impact the client. For example, programs that improve safety can lead to a reduction in employee turnover (Knoblauch & Bethel, 2010), which could result in a more experienced workforce and cost savings (Celona et al., 2010), benefitting both the client and the organization.

The weight of the data strongly suggests that HSOs, including those serving individuals with IDD, should invest in safety systems aimed at preventing and reducing workplace injuries (Luiselli, 2013; Sanders, 2009). Injuries can occur during myriad work tasks and, therefore, interventions for improving safety must be comprehensive. Behavioral safety offers tools for improving workplace safety in concert with more traditional safety approaches. The remainder of this chapter will review the current literature on behavioral safety, offer considerations for best practices specific to HSOs that serve individuals with IDD, and point to needs in future research.

Safety Research

Behavioral safety is a package intervention, based on principles of behavior analysis, designed to promote safe practices while working and prevent injuries (McSween, 2003). Behavioral safety is implemented as a part of an organization's comprehensive safety program, along with other safety programs such as specialized training in restraint techniques and procedures in place to meet safety regulations and laws (e.g., fire escape route plan, building inspections). At a high level, organizations using behavioral safety programs identify behaviors and conditions necessary to work safely, create a checklist to observe those behaviors and conditions, and provide feedback and praise based on the observations to individuals and the group. If employees engage in more safe practices and keep conditions around them safe (e.g., no trip hazards in the walkway), the likelihood of injuries is reduced. Reviews of behavioral safety studies have demonstrated that variations of this approach can improve safe practices and reduce injuries (Krause et al., 1999; Sulzer-Azaroff & Austin, 2000; Tuncel et al., 2006).

Selecting Safety Targets

In behavioral safety, researchers and practitioners use a variety of assessment tools to identify behaviors to target and select interventions. The goal is to identify *leading measures*, meaning measures that occur before incidents that can help prevent them. For example, using good posture while lifting a client may reduce the likelihood of a back injury, or keeping the floor clear of debris may reduce the likelihood of a fall resulting in an injury. Identifying leading measures allows leaders to manage these indicators to prevent injuries, rather than only managing performance after the injury occurs (a *lagging* measure).

There are several ways to identify leading measures in organizations. A review of assessment approaches found that 90% of behavioral safety applied research studies used a historical assessment to help identify intervention targets (Wilder et al., 2017). A historical assessment involves examining the past two to five years of injury and first aid data to identify common trends in injuries. For example, injury and first aid data may reveal that back and shoulder injuries while lifting clients are the most commonly occurring type of injury. These data indicate that lifting may need to be one of the behaviors targeted by the behavioral safety program. A historical assessment can be complemented by examining reports of common procedural missteps, interviewing employees to identify the riskiest aspects of a job, examining hazards and other safety reports, and gathering any additional information that could help determine appropriate safety performance targets.

Observation Checklist

In most behavioral safety programs, the safety assessment is used to develop an observation checklist for observing safety behaviors and providing feedback (McSween, 2003). An observation checklist should be intuitive and easy to complete. If the response requirement for recording at-risk behaviors is substantially higher than the response effort for recording safe behaviors, less at-risk behaviors may get reported (Hinz et al., 2014). Behaviors and conditions that are certain to be 100% safe need not be included on the checklist. Sometimes organizations will rotate checklist items off if there appears to be no performance issue. The length of checklists varies from short to comprehensive. A scan of safety checklists available online revealed an average checklist length of approximately 20 items, with some as brief as five items and some as long as 30 items. Longer checklists will require more extensive observation periods but may provide more information.

HSOs often collect data on other activities like progress during treatment and treatment integrity. It may be efficient for these organizations to add safety items to existing data collection procedures. Conversely, safety behaviors and conditions may garner more attention when they are on a standalone checklist. Checklists for HSOs might include items related to safe lifting and positioning, responses during problem behavior, safe hygiene practices, wearing appropriate attire, and keeping work areas free of trip hazards and other dangerous items such as choking hazards and items that can cause harm during problem behavior. Figure 10.1 is an example of a standalone checklist that may be appropriate for an HSO serving individuals with IDD.

Sometimes, separate observation checklists or other measurement tools are developed for leaders. For example, Cooper (2006) created a checklist for leaders that measured visible ongoing support (VOS) on a construction site. Items on the checklist asked questions about whether the leader accompanied an employee on an observation that week, if feedback on safety performance was delivered during the weekly meeting, and whether hazards identified were remediated. Observer workgroups filled out the VOS checklist each week and provided feedback to the leaders. Results showed a statistically significant correlation between VOS scores and safety performance, indicating that leader involvement in the safety process is beneficial. Another study conducted by Zohar and Luria (2003) found that employee at-risk behaviors in a manufacturing setting decreased when supervisors spent more time talking with their direct

Name: / Date: / Time:	**Instructions:** For each component you observe, place a checkmark in the column for "safe", "at-risk", or "N/A." If further explanation is needed, please use "barriers" section. Following the observation, providing feedback to the observed can help reinforce safe behavior and derease hazards. Turn in completed cards to dropbox at front desk.					
With Client				**Sanitation**		
	Safe	At-risk	N/A		Safe	At-risk	N/A
1. Lift Posture				1. Hand Sanitation			
2. Body Position/Sitting Posture				2. Toys/Stimuli			
				Barriers to Safe Behavior		
3. Use of Restraint				Barriers are things that may prevent safe behavior or influence at-risk behavior. If you notice anything making it difficult for the performer to work safely, please comment above.		
4. Call for assist				**Behavior/Condition**	**Explanation**	
5. Safe Distance						
Conditions						
	Safe	At-risk	N/A			
1. Housekeeping						
2. Chemicals out of reach						
3. Clutter						
4. Tripping Hazards						
6. Hair/Jewelery						
7. Footwear						
8. Attire						
Other Comments						

FIGURE 10.1 A potential safety checklist for human service settings

reports. These results suggest that a separate checklist for leaders of HSOs may include items that indicate support of the measurement process, feedback delivery, and talking with employees about safe practices. Including leader behaviors on a checklist demonstrates to employees that everyone is responsible for creating a safe work environment and that leaders care about safety. And, researchers have demonstrated that engaging leaders in improving safety can reduce injuries (Gravina et al., 2019).

In addition to identifying behaviors and conditions that can be observed daily, leaders should also identify unexpected events like fires, tornadoes, earthquakes, and active shooter situations that may occur in their organization. State safety regulations may require that procedures be in place for these events. Unexpected events do not need daily management; however, appropriate responses in those situations should be identified through a task analysis, which can be used to develop secondary observation checklists for written procedures and practice drill designed to prepare employees for unexpected events.

Measurement System

Once checklists have been created, they can then be used to establish the measurement and feedback system. Typically, observations are conducted by peers and/or supervisors (McSween, 2003). When employees work alone, they may score their own behavior (Hickman & Geller, 2003). Observation scorecards usually do not include the name of the person observed in order to create anonymity, avoid aversive consequences for the observed, and encourage accurate observations. The observation scorecards typically include the name of the person *conducting* the observation so that observers can be recognized for their effort. The anonymous data are then aggregated and examined for trends by work area, behavior, and time of day. The data can be used to select more targeted interventions when there appear to be large performance issues for a specific behavior or condition. The aggregated data can also be used to provide group feedback and recognize achievements.

The measurement system in behavioral safety can be implemented in many ways. For example, observations can be conducted by front-line employees only (e.g., Cooper et al., 1994), supervisors only (e.g., Chhokar & Wallin, 1984), both front-line employees and supervisors (e.g., Cooper, 2006), or everyone in the organization. Observations can occur in real-time, or observers can score videos. Conducting observations can be voluntary or mandatory. Preliminary data do not suggest that mandatory observations are superior as previously believed. Rather, mandatory observations may lead to an increase in "pencil whipping" or giving more positive ratings (DePasquale & Geller, 1999). To ensure quality observations, organizational leaders should train observers to competency in using the checklist and providing feedback, deliver feedback on quality in addition to or instead of quantity of observations, and make the value of the data collected visible to the workforce. Furthermore, including employees in the development of the measurement system may increase buy-in (Geller, 2002).

Research suggests that one advantage of employees conducting peer observations is a phenomenon known as the "observer effect" (Alvero & Austin, 2004). The observer effect occurs when the observer improves his or her own behavior after observing a peer. Alvero et al. (2008) conducted a study aimed at identifying the potential underlying mechanism of the observer effect. They used a talk-aloud protocol to capture participants' verbal behavior while they worked and saw an increase in rule statements related to safety when participants began the peer observation intervention. Then, a distraction task was introduced to disrupt rule statements, and safety performance declined. When the distraction task was removed, rule statements increased, and so did safety performance. These results suggest that peer observations may increase rule-statements that observers make to themselves about safety, and this may improve their safety performance. More recent research found that the observer effect only occurred when participants knew they were being observed (King et al., 2018). Regardless, preliminary evidence suggests that having employees conduct observations may produce benefits beyond capturing safety performance data (Sasson & Austin, 2008).

In addition to an observation system, organizations should create a system to collect information from employees about hazards, equipment, and other working conditions that may impede working safely. This information can be gathered as part of the observation process, but organizations may get more input by designating a second method for collecting the data. Some ideas include having a dropbox where input can be submitted on paper, asking for input during weekly meetings, and creating an online system for input. More ideas will be shared if employees can submit suggestions anonymously and if leaders make it clear that they are reading employee responses and acting on the suggestions.

Safety Training

After important safety behaviors and conditions are identified, it is vital to communicate the expectations to employees and ensure they are adequately trained on performing the required skills. Most organizations communicate policies through a manual and didactic training. While having an easily accessible manual is considered best practice, research suggests that information and didactic training alone is insufficient to create high levels of safety performance

(Alvero & Austin, 2004; Sasson & Austin, 2008). To create and maintain high levels of performance, behavior analysis offers effective tools for training new skills, including discrimination training, video modeling, and behavioral skills training (BST).

Discrimination Training

Discrimination training for safety is designed to help participants accurately identify safe and at-risk behavior. Taylor and Alvero (2012) taught participants to discriminate between safe and at-risk postures and evaluated whether the training improved the participants' own safety performance. The computer-based discrimination training began with a review of the definitions of safe behaviors and was followed by scoring videos of safe and at-risk behavior with feedback on accuracy. Following discrimination training, peer observations were added. Discrimination training alone improved the participant's safety performance by 21%, and engaging in observations of others further increased their own safety performance by 15%. Thus, it may be essential to ensure employees can discriminate between safe and at-risk performance, particularly for behaviors like posture or lifting, which may be difficult to discern without practice.

Video Modeling and Scoring

Video modeling and scoring can also be an effective strategy for training safety performance. Nielson et al. (2009) used information, video scoring, and feedback to train nursing assistants on safe lifting practices. The researchers found that performance improved following the information phase and further improved during video scoring. The participants exposed to feedback improved their performance the most. The advantage of video modeling and scoring is that it can be used outside of the clinical environment to train staff, and once videos are created, it is an efficient training tool. Also, videos can be used to train difficult or infrequently used skills in a safe environment.

Behavioral Skills Training (BST)

BST is another option for training employees on important safety behaviors. BST includes four components: instruction, modeling, rehearsal, and feedback (Miltenberger, 2015). Skills can be practiced in situations that simulate real events, making this a useful tool for training for unexpected or rare events.

Researchers have used BST to prepare children and staff to follow procedures for fire drills (Garcia et al., 2016) and active shooter situations (Noto et al., in review). However, BST can be time-consuming and, therefore, organizational leaders should reserve this training procedure for the most critical and riskiest skills and skills that employees don't know how to perform, not skills that they can already perform well, given the right conditions.

Antecedent Interventions

Along with training, other antecedent interventions such as prompts, goals, and environmental manipulations can be useful for improving safety practices. For example, posted signs alert employees to hazards and prompt them about rules while they are in the environment relevant to the rule. In HSOs, signs can instruct employees to store cleaning supplies safely, wash hands, and keep the therapy area clean. Checklists or photos indicating desired behaviors and conditions may be posted. Although signs and posted checklists can serve as helpful prompts, they may be insufficient for sustaining long-term behavior change. Preliminary research suggests that dynamic and humorous signs may be more effective than static signs (Warman et al., 2019). In most cases, coupling a sign with other interventions will produce the best results.

Goal Setting

Goal setting is another antecedent intervention commonly used in behavioral safety, including manufacturing (Reber & Wallin, 1984), construction (Cooper et al., 1994), and healthcare (Stephens & Ludwig, 2008). Goals serve as discriminative stimuli, indicating when performance will be reinforced. Cunningham and Austin (2007) used goal setting along with feedback to increase the use of a hands-free technique by hospital operating staff in inpatient and outpatient surgery units. The package intervention improved performance markedly and it maintained at a five-month follow-up.

Goal setting may be more effective when employees are included in the process. Preliminary research on participative versus assigned goals indicates that participative goals may lead to improvements in the performance of safety behaviors beyond those targeted by the goal. For example, Ludwig and Geller (1997) compared participative and assigned goals for pizza delivery drivers. Participants were divided into an assigned goals group and a participative goals group, and three safety behaviors were observed, namely complete stopping, turn signal use, and seatbelt use. Both groups improved their performance on the targeted behavior (complete stopping), but the participative goals group also improved their performance of the non-targeted behaviors (turn signal use and seatbelt use). Research also suggests that individuals who participate in goal setting may be more productive than those in assigned goals or "do your best" groups (Latham & Yukl, 1975). These results suggest that engaging employees in goal setting related to safety participation and performance may be a useful intervention strategy.

Technology-Based Prompts

More recently, researchers have used technology-based prompts such as scrolling signs, texts, and emails to encourage safe performance. For example, Cruz and colleagues (2019) conducted a study to evaluate and refine the Performance Diagnostic Checklist-Safety (PDC-Safety; Martinez-Onstott et al., 2016) in an HSO that served children diagnosed with autism spectrum disorder (ASD). Researchers sought to increase the use of hand sanitizer by behavior technicians to reduce the spread of illness among clients and staff. The PDC-Safety assessment found that an antecedent intervention (email prompts) was likely to improve handwashing while another intervention to increase availability of hand sanitizer was not indicated. Researchers first implemented the non-indicated intervention and did not observe improvement in performance across three participants. The indicated intervention improved performance but one participant required additional feedback to improve and maintain performance. Thus, low-effort technology-based solutions can be included in safety programs to encourage safe practices.

Environmental Manipulations

Environmental manipulations are another type of antecedent intervention used to encourage safety, often by reducing the response effort to perform critical behaviors. For example, Casella et al. (2013) evaluated the impact of response effort on frequency of glove use, hand sanitation, and electrical outlet precautions by child therapists under low-, medium-, and high-effort conditions. Results showed that safe behavior occurred more often in the low-effort condition compared to the medium- and high-effort conditions. Another study found that providing ergonomically correct equipment increased the safety performance of office employees (Gravina et al., 2007). Although antecedent interventions, such as environmental manipulations, are a valuable component of behavioral safety programs, they are usually combined with feedback and other consequences.

Consequence Interventions

Feedback and Recognition

Feedback is a crucial intervention component in most behavioral safety programs. The feedback provided is based on peer observations and is usually delivered both immediately after the observation to the individual and in an aggregated format to the group (McSween, 2003). Alavosius and Sulzer-Azaroff (1986) evaluated continuous, intermittent, and no-feedback conditions on three healthcare routines (feeding, positioning, and transferring) for direct care workers who worked with individuals with physical disabilities. Results indicated that feedback was superior to no feedback, and continuous feedback resulted in faster acquisition of the skills, while both types of feedback promoted maintenance. Another study by Lee et al. (2014) found that both global and specific safety scores improved safety performance, but global feedback also improved untargeted safety behaviors. These results suggest that feedback should be frequent, and providing both specific feedback for target behaviors and a global feedback score may be useful.

In best practice, the observer and the observed employee have a two-way conversation about the checklist following an observation. For example, an observer might tell their peer that they performed tasks safely, except for wearing hearing protection in an area where it is required. The observed employee may respond, indicating that the earplug bin is empty, and the observer can record that information so that the bin can be filled. In other words, the observer provides feedback to the observed employee but ideally also gathers input on how to create a safer work environment. The input provided for improving the work environment is a critical dimension of the feedback process, and some organizations track the number of suggestions and the percentage addressed. The aggregated data from all observations conducted in a month are usually graphed and displayed in a common area like a break room and/or reviewed at meetings.

Incentives

Incentives may also be a useful tool for improving workplace safety, when used with caution. McSween (2003) suggests offering a menu of awards and incentives for participating in activities aimed at improving safety in the workplace, such as completing safety training, conducting peer observations, and participating in safety meetings. Hickman and Geller (2005) provided a small incentive (i.e., $1 per self-observation form) to short-haul truck drivers for completing self-observations before or after each shift. Participation in the pre-behavior group was 42%, and participation in the post-behavior group was 75%; both groups demonstrated an improvement in overspeed and extreme braking. Incentives can be useful for encouraging engagement with the process when participation is low.

In the past, researchers have provided incentives based on safety performance. Fox et al. (1987) employed a token economy that awarded tokens to employees for behaving safely *and* avoiding injuries at two open-pit mines. The tokens (stamps) were exchangeable for purchase products and services in the community. The intervention reduced injuries at both locations, and the reduction was sustained for several years. Furthermore, although the token economy cost between $9,000 and $22,000 per year per site, the return on investment was favorable, ranging from 13:1 to 28:1 across years. While these results are positive, basing incentives on safety performance rather than participating in the process could result in underreporting of safety incidents. Underreporting means that the organization obtains less information about the causes of safety issues and has less opportunity to remedy those issues before a more serious event occurs. Therefore, incentives should be based on *behaviors* and *conditions* that may lead to reduced incidents, not reduced incidents.

When an Injury Occurs

Safety professionals consider it best practice to document injuries and first aid cases and spend time discovering variables that may have contributed to the occurrence of the event. If organizations are large enough, they may be required to do this by law (OSHA, 2017). Typical documentation lists information about the injury itself, events leading up to the injury, possible causes, and recommendations for future actions. Common incident investigation recommendations include retraining, discipline, and environmental changes. However, understanding variables that led to the injury from a behavioral perspective may provide better insight and more precise solutions for preventing similar injuries in the future. Therefore behavior analysts should include lists of antecedents and consequences for both the event that led to the injury and behaviors that may have led to a different outcome in their incident analysis. Then a focused intervention can be implemented based on the results.

Practice Recommendations

Research offers several practical recommendations for HSOs. First, organizations must ensure that they are compliant with any state or federal regulations and laws. Requirements for safety vary by state and the size of the organization (smaller organizations are often subject to less regulation). Fines for noncompliance can be steep, and organizations may be prevented from practicing if violations are ongoing or egregious. Laws and regulations may change from year to year and, therefore, it is advised to update plans accordingly. Consult with local authorities to confirm compliance with these requirements.

The behavioral safety literature points to several practical recommendations beyond safety regulations and laws for HSOs. First, safety is the responsibility of everyone in the organization and it is beneficial to engage the entire workforce in safety program development and implementation. Research suggests that improvements may be amplified if employees are more engaged in data collection, intervention development, and intervention implementation (Sigurdsson & Austin, 2006). Employees may identify safety issues that leaders did not consider, and they may adapt the intervention to fit their work area and tasks better.

Organizational leaders and employees should identify tasks that put employees at risk for injury. Ideally, the risks identified would be eliminated. For example, the risk of chemical burns from cleaning products can be eliminated by switching to cleaning products that are equally effective but pose no risk. If the risk cannot be eliminated, leaders can establish best practice procedures for safe task completion and provide training that includes rehearsal and feedback as well as prompts in the environment. Protective equipment can be employed to block or reduce exposure as well. Next, leaders can establish a data collection system to sample safety performance and provide feedback to individuals and the team. Furthermore, it is important to create opportunities for people to bring up safety concerns in meetings or through an anonymous online system. Track these safety concerns and whether they have been addressed. Other observation tools like workplace, hazard, and home inspections can be added to the program. If participation in the process or bringing up safety concerns is infrequent, incentives can be used to increase engagement. Participation can also be promoted by leaders and supervisors regularly discussing safety with their employees and actively engaging in improving it.

Future Research

While several evidence-based strategies exist for improving workplace safety, questions remain. To start, although numerous studies have examined behavioral safety interventions in manufacturing and construction settings, very few studies have used human service settings, and none of those studies evaluated a comprehensive safety intervention that addressed a range of safety behaviors. Conducting research on programs aimed at improving several aspects of safety in HSOs will uncover issues and intervention strategies that are unique to these environments (Luiselli, 2013; Sanders, 2009).

Relatedly, there are several unanswered questions about the best way to implement various components of behavioral safety. For example, research could illuminate the ideal length of a safety checklist, frequency of observations, and whether safety observations should be conducted separately from other data collection occurring at the site. HSOs may afford less opportunity for individuals to conduct peer observations, and thus, different strategies like self-observation and manager observation should be investigated in these environments. Some industrial organizations report that as safety performance improves, business outcomes also improve (Acetate Fibers Division, Eastman, 2015). In healthcare and HSOs, the relationship between safety and service delivery could be evaluated, and strategies to promote both, simultaneously, could be developed.

Another area ripe for further exploration is the role of technology in improving workplace safety. Technology can provide real-time prompts, data collection, and feedback, helping guide workers to make safe decisions. For example, researchers could use wearable technology with clients to predict the occurrence of problem behavior, allowing the direct care technician more time to respond safely and appropriately. Wearable technology could also provide instant feedback on positioning during lifting and physically transporting clients. Light and noise signals could prompt technicians to sanitize their hands as they walk past hand sanitizer dispensers. And, photo technology could take pictures of the work environment periodically so that observers could collect momentary time sampling data on room conditions, evaluating whether they are free of trip hazards and other dangerous conditions (Schmidt et al., 2013).

Finally, more research is needed to examine the ways leaders contribute to safety performance in the workplace. Limited studies have suggested that leaders demonstrating support of the safety process and talking about safety performance can improve workplace safety. Research has also demonstrated that teaching leaders to use behavior analysis to conduct projects aimed at improving safety may reduce injuries (Gravina et al., 2019). However, this research was conducted in manufacturing and construction settings and may not be directly transferrable to settings that serve individuals diagnosed with IDD. Settings that serve individuals diagnosed with IDD do not usually employ full-time safety professionals to train and guide leaders and staff. When staff work with clients in their homes, supervisors may not be there to observe safety performance daily or even weekly. Also, staff who visit multiple home settings may face different safety challenges in each home. Thus, strategies to help leaders support staff in these unique conditions need to be identified.

Conclusion

Work performed in HSOs can put employees and clients at risk for injury. Therefore these organizations need systems in place to help employees learn safe practices and use them consistently. Behavioral safety offers a variety of tools that can be employed to support safe practices. These can be combined with other safety programs (e.g., restraint training programs) to create safer work environments for staff and clients. Because limited research has examined strategies for improving safety performance in HSOs, it is time for behavior analysis and OBM professionals to turn their attention to these settings so that tools can be refined and customized to the unique challenges faced by practitioners, service recipients, and organizational leaders.

References

Acetate Fibers Division, Eastman Chemical (2015). CCBS accreditation application. Retrieved from: https://behavior.org/wp-content/uploads/2017/06/896.pdf.

Alavosius, M. P., & Sulzer-Azaroff, B. (1986). The effects of performance feedback on the safety of client lifting and transfer. *Journal of Applied Behavior Analysis, 19,* 261–267.

Alvero, A. M., & Austin, J. (2004). The effects of observing on the behavior of the observer. *Journal of Applied Behavior Analysis, 37,* 457–468.

Alvero, A. M., Rost, K., & Austin, J. (2008). The safety observer effect: The effects of conducting safety observations. *Journal of Safety Research, 39*(4), 365–373.

Barling, J., Kelloway, E. K., & Iverson, R. D. (2003). Accidental outcomes: Attitudinal consequences of workplace injuries. *Journal of Occupational Health Psychology, 8*(1), 74–85.

Bureau of Labor Statistics (2010). Workplace safety and health in the health care and social assistance industry, 2003–07. Retrieved from: https://www.bls.gov/opub/mlr/cwc/workplace-safety-and-health-in-the-health-care-and-social-assistance-industry-2003-07.pdf.

Bureau of Labor Statistics (2019). Injuries, illnesses, and fatalities. Retrieved from: https://www.bls.gov/iif/oshsum.htm#17Summary_News_Release.

Casella, S. E., Wilder, D. A., Neidart, P., Rey, C., Compton, M., & Chong, I. (2013). The effects of response effort on safe performance by therapists at an autism treatment facility. *Journal of Applied Behavior Analysis, 43,* 729–734.

Celona, J., Hall, E., & Forte, J. (2010). Making a business case for safe handling. Presented at the 2010 West Coast Safe Patient Handling and Movement Conference. September 2010; San Diego, CA.

Chhokar, J. S., & Wallin, J. A. (1984). Improving safety through applied behavior analysis. *Journal of Safety Research, 15,* 141–151.

Cooper, D. M. (2006). Exploratory analyses of the effects of managerial support and feedback consequences on behavioral safety maintenance. *Journal of Organizational Behavior Management, 26,* 1–41.

Cooper, M. D., Phillips, R. A., Sutherland, V. J., & Makin, P. J., (1994). Reducing accidents using goal setting and feedback: A field study. *Journal of Occupational and Organizational Psychology, 67,* 219–240.

Cruz, N. J., Wilder, D. A, Phillabaum, C., Thomas, R., Cusick, M., & Gravina, N., (2019). Further evaluation of the performance diagnostic checklist-safety (PDC-Safety). *Journal of Organizational Behavior Management, 39,* 266–279.

Cunningham, T. R., & Austin, J., (2007). Using goal setting, task clarification, and feedback to increase the use of the hands-free technique by hospital operating room staff. *Journal of Applied Behavior Analysis, 40,* 673–677.

DePasquale, J. P., & Geller, E. S., (1999). Critical success factors for behavior-based safety: A study of twenty industry-wide applications. *Journal of Safety Research, 30*(4), 237–249.

Fox, D. K., Hopkins, B. L., & Anger, W. K., (1987). The long-term effects of a token economy on safety performance in open-pit mining. *Journal of Applied Behavior Analysis, 20,* 215–224.

Garcia, D., Dukes, C., Brady, M. P., Scott, J., & Wilson, C., (2016). Using modeling and rehearsal to teach fire safety to children with autism: Teaching fire safety. *Journal of Applied Behavior Analysis, 49,* 699–704.

Geller, E. S. (2002). *The participation factor: How to increase involvement in occupational safety.* Chicago, IL: ASSE.

Gravina, N., King, A., & Austin, J. (2019). Coaching leaders to use behavioral science to improve safety. *Safety Science, 112,* 66–70.

Gravina, N., Lindstrom-Hazel, D., & Austin, J., (2007). The effects of workstation changes and behavioral interventions on safe typing postures in an office. *Journal of Prevention, Assessment and Rehabilitation, 29,* 245–253.

Hickman, J. S., & Geller, E. S., (2003). A safety self-management intervention for mining operations. *Journal of Safety Research, 34*(3), 299–308.

Hickman, J. S., & Geller, E. S., (2005). Self-management to increase safe driving among short-haul truck drivers. *Journal of Organizational Behavior Management, 23,* 1–20.

Hinz, K., McGee, H., Huitema, B., Dickinson, A., & Van Enk, R. (2014). Observer accuracy and behavior analysis: Data collection procedures on hand hygiene compliance in a neurovascular unit. *American Journal of Infection Control, 42,* 1067–1073.

Kim, J. (2013). Depression as a psychosocial consequence of occupational injury in the US working population: Findings from the medical expenditure panel survey. *BMC Public Health, 13,* 303.

King, A., Gravina, N., & Sleiman, A. (2018). Observing the observer. *Journal of Organizational Behavior Management, 4,* 306–323.

Knoblauch, M. D., & Bethel, S. A. (2010). Safe patient-handling program "UPLIFTS" nurse retention. *Nursing, 40*(2), 67–68.

Krause, T. R., Seymour, K. J., & Sloat, K. C. M. (1999). Long-term evaluation of a behavior-based method for improving safety performance: A meta-analysis of 73 interrupted time-series replications. *Safety Science, 32,* 1–18. https://doi.org/10.1 016/S0925-7535(99)00007-7.

Latham, G. P., & Yukl, G. A., (1975). Assigned versus participative goal setting with educated and uneducated woods workers. *Journal of Applied Psychology, 60,* 299–302.

Lee, K., Shon, D., & Oah, D. (2014). The relative effects of global and specific feedback on safety behaviors. *Journal of Organizational Behavior Management, 34,* 16–28.

Lin, T., Luiselli, J. K., Gilligan, K., & Dacosta, S. (2012). Preventing injury from child aggression: Single-case evaluation of staff-worn protective equipment. *Developmental Neurorehabilitation, 15,* 298–303.

Ludwig, T. D., & Geller, E. S., (1997). Assigned versus participative goal setting and response generalization: Managing injury control among professional pizza deliverers. *Journal of Applied Psychology, 82,* 253–261.

Luiselli, J. K. (2011). Therapeutic implementation of physical restraint. In J. K. Luiselli (Ed.), *The handbook of high-risk challenging behaviors in intellectual and developmental disabilities* (pp. 243–256). Baltimore, MD: Paul H. Brookes.

Luiselli, J. K. (2013). Descriptive analysis of a staff injury reduction intervention in a human services setting for children and youth with intellectual and developmental disabilities. *Behavior Modification, 37,* 665–679.

Martinez-Onstott, B., Wilder, D. A., & Sigurdsson, S. (2016). Identifying the variables contributing to at-risk performance: Initial evaluation of the Performance Diagnostic Checklist-Safety (PDC-Safety). *Journal of Organizational Behavior Management, 36,* 80–93.

McSween, T. (2003). *The value-based safety process: Improving your safety culture with a behavioral approach.* New York: Wiley.

Miltenberger, R. G. (2015). *Behavior modification: Principles and procedures* (6th ed). San Francisco, CA: Cengage Learning.

National Safety Council (2019). Work injury costs. Retrieved from: https://injuryfacts. nsc.org/work/costs/work-injury-costs/.

Nielsen, D., Sigurdsson, S. O., & Austin, J. (2009). Preventing back injuries in hospital settings: The effects of video modeling on safe patient lifting by nurses. *Journal of Applied Behavior Analysis, 42*, 551–561.

Noto, J., Nicholson, K., Rajagopal, S., Riswick-Estelle, J., & Weatherly, N. (unpublished) (n.d.). Behavioral skills training for active shooter scenarios among human service staff. Submitted to *Journal of Applied Behavior Analysis*.

Occupational Safety and Health Administration (2017). Workers' rights. Retrieved from: https://www.osha.gov/Publications/osha3021.pdf.

Reber, R. A., & Wallin, J. A. (1984). The effects of training, goal-setting, and knowledge of results on safe behavior: A component analysis. *Academy of Management Journal, 27*(3), 544–560.

Rogers, A. E., Hwang, W. T., & Scott, L. D. (2004). The effects of work breaks on staff nurse performance. *Journal of Nursing Administration, 34*(11), 512–519.

Sanders, K. (2009). The effects of an action plan, staff training, management support, and monitoring on restraint use and costs of work-related injuries. *Journal of Applied Research in Intellectual Disabilities, 22*, 216–230.

Sasson, J. R., & Austin, J. (2008). The effects of training, feedback, and participant involvement in behavioral safety observations on office ergonomic behavior. *Journal of Organizational Behavior Management, 24*, 1–30.

Schmidt, J. S., Urban, K. D., Luiselli, J. K., White, C., & Harrington, C. (2013). Improving appearance, organization, and safety of special education classrooms: Effects of staff training in a human services setting. *Education and Treatment of Children, 36*, 1–13.

Sigurdsson, S. O., & Austin, J. (2006). Institutionalization and response maintenance in organizational behavior management. *Journal of Organizational Behavior Management, 26*, 41–77.

Stephens, S. D., & Ludwig, T. D. (2008). Improving anesthesia nurse compliance with universal precautions using group goals and public feedback. *Journal of Organizational Behavior Management, 25*, 37–71

Sulzer-Azaroff, B., & Austin, J. (2000). Does BBS work? Behavior-based safety & injury reduction: A survey of the evidence. *Professional Safety, 45*(7), 19–24.

Taylor, M. A., & Alvero, A. M. (2012). The effects of safety discrimination training and frequent safety observations on safety-related behavior. *Journal of Organizational Behavior Management, 32*, 169–193. http://dx.doi.org/10.1080/01608061.2012.698115

Tuncel, S., Lotlikar, H., Salem, S., & Daraiseh, N. (2006). Effectiveness of behaviour based safety interventions to reduce accidents and injuries in workplaces: Critical appraisal and meta-analysis. *Theoretical Issues in Ergonomics Science, 7*(3), 191–209. http://dx.doi.org.portal.lib.fit.edu/10.1080/14639220500090273

Urban, K. D., Luiselli, J. K., Child, S. N., & Parenteau, R. (2011). Effects of protective equipment on frequency and intensity of aggression-provoked staff injury. *Journal of Developmental and Physical Disabilities, 23,* 555–562.

Warman, A. S., Wine, B, Newcomb, E. T., Chen, T., & Morgan, C. A. (2019). An evaluation of static versus variable antecedents on employee performance. *Journal of Organizational Behavior Management,* 39, 257–265. DOI: 10.1080/01608061.2019.16666775.

Weatherly, N. L. (2019). A behavioral safety model for clinical settings: Coaching for Institutionalization. *Perspectives on Behavior Science, 42*(4), 973–985.

Wilder, D. A., Lipschultz, J. L., King, A., Driscoll, S. P., & Sigurdsson, S. (2017). An analysis of the commonality and type of preintervention assessment procedures in the Journal of Organizational Behavior Management (2000–2015). *Journal of Organizational Behavior Management 38,* 5–17.

Zohar, D., & Luria, G. (2003). The use of supervisory practices as leverage to improve safety behavior: A cross-level intervention model. *Journal of Safety Research, 34,* 567–577.

11

Employee Turnover and Workforce Stability

Michael C. Strouse and Florence D. DiGennaro Reed

As of 2013, there were about 1.3 million Direct Support Professionals (DSPs) serving approximately 1.8 million individuals with intellectual or developmental disabilities (I/DD) (President's Committee, 2017). The number of DSPs needed to deliver care in the coming years, however, will rise exponentially. Diament (2020) reports that about 473,000 people are on waiting lists for services nationally, while 871,420 persons with I/DD are residing with a family caregiver over 60 who soon will not be able to provide care (Braddock et al., 2017). Unfortunately, the DSP workforce has been one of the most unstable workforces nationally for over three decades (Braddock & Mitchell, 1992; Larson & Lakin, 1997; President's Committee, 2017). Annual DSP turnover rates now exceed 50% (National Core Indicators [NCI], 2019), while the turnover rate for all workforces averages about 3% (Bureau of Labor Statistics, 2020). These statistics predate the economic crisis and workforce instability caused by the COVID-19 pandemic, which we may discover has worsened the turnover rate.

Turnover data for DSPs, however, does not tell the full story of instability, because it does not capture the significant number of additional people involved in care caused by excessive reliance on part-time positions, chronic openings, call-offs, and vacation absences (Strouse et al., 2004, 2013). Nationally, the DSP workforce, for example, has 69% full-time employees with a 12% chronic vacancy rate, and 31% part-time employees with an 18% vacancy rate. Further, part-time employees have disproportionately high turnover (Braddock & Mitchell, 1992). To fill vacancies, community providers use staff pools and substitutes (7% of hours worked) or pay 10% overtime (President's Committee, 2017). The remaining vacant shifts either go uncovered or are worked by managers or supervisors. To compound this issue, 35% of the DSP workforce has been employed less than one year, while 35% of all those who do leave employment do so before working six months. Community service providers must recruit and train over 600,000 new people to employment each year just to tread water.

DSPs are often younger, female, culturally diverse (with English often as a second language), and the great majority are high school or GED graduates having little or no college experience (Engerman et al., 1997; Hewitt et al., 2008; Paraprofessional Healthcare Institute [PHI], 2011; President's Committee, 2017; Strouse et al., 2013). The majority of full-time DSPs work overtime or a second job to make ends meet (Braddock & Mitchell, 1992; President's Committee, 2017). About 75% of all agencies nationally *offer* health insurance to full-time employees (NCI, 2019). Studies, however, do not report the percentage of DSPs who actually participate in agency-provided health insurance. In a review of several agencies across the Midwest, we found only 10% to 20% of all DSPs enrolled in agency-provided healthcare—even when the agencies pay upwards of 80% or more of the monthly premium cost. This outcome matters because low participation increases the cost of health insurance by 15% to 25% (for those who do enroll). Also, the great majority of DSPs are young and typically qualify for the maximum subsidy and lowest rates for insurance on the Affordable Care Act (ACA) insurance exchange for themselves *and* their family. About 50% of DSPs receive publicly funded benefits (President's Committee, 2017) like food stamps, Medicaid, and housing subsidies. Finally, in our experience, many DSPs commute from less costly areas, live with family or roommates, often have unreliable transportation, and struggle to afford childcare.

Not surprisingly, DSPs want a good job where they can help people but also be supported and valued. They want a living wage (or as close to one as possible). They desire schedule flexibility for work/life balance so they can spend time with their families. In our experience, they want a good home in a safe neighborhood, a way to take better care of their children, reliable transportation, and the ability to work closer to home. Healthcare and retirement benefits are often not at the top of the need list if these resources are pitted against getting greater wages and because there is often access to less costly and subsidized insurance on the ACA exchange.

Influences on I/DD Workforce Instability

Several literature reviews have identified factors that are correlated with workforce instability. Braddock's State of the States in Developmental Disabilities series (e.g., Braddock et al., 2017) and a few pioneering national studies on staff stability (e.g., Braddock & Mitchell, 1992; Larson et al., 1998) remain among the best sources for gaining insight on the causes of workforce instability. More recent reviews and papers report many of the same factors that affect stability and/or improve the longevity of the I/DD workforce (e.g., Bogenshutz et al., 2014; Kazemi et al., 2015; President's Committee, 2017; Wine et al., 2020). In the following pages, we examine four of the most challenging barriers, namely (a) low pay; (b) poor work schedules; (c) ineffective hiring strategies; and (d) inadequate on-the-job training.

Low Pay Combined with an Increase of Better-Paid, More Attractive Employment Options

Not surprisingly, *low pay* is the most cited, consistent, and logical "cause" of job instability (Braddock & Mitchel, 1992; Engerman, et al., 1997; Strouse et al., 2013; President's Committee, 2017). Even though some people work in I/DD services for the love of the job, those who choose to work in this field still need a living wage. Nationally, wages range between $11 and $12 per hour (NCI, 2019). What makes pay more challenging, however, is the exponential increase of other better-paying jobs, because a reinforcer's true value is, of course, relative to what else is available (Jarmolowicz et al., 2016). There are simply too many alternatives that offer better pay, working conditions, schedules, and time off. The greatest competition is the growth of the senior care industry, fueled by over 10,000 baby boomers retiring each day, or once every eight seconds (Kohn & Taylor, 2010). Well-funded senior populations are creating many new service opportunities that offer caregivers a chance to make a meaningful difference, earn far better pay, and work more attractive schedules. Additionally, national movements for increasing minimum wages are in full swing with an eye on paying $15 per hour. Many regions have already either achieved this goal or have scheduled yearly increases for minimum wages. By the end of 2020, 20 states are poised to raise their minimum wage (De Lea, 2019). The unfortunate reality for I/DD service providers is that they must increase their wages beyond the minimum to recruit caring staff to work for them.

Unappealing and Problematic Work Schedules

Few factors create greater staffing instability than poorly designed work schedules (Engerman et al., 1997; Strouse et al., 2013). This issue is most problematic for residential services because they serve as staffing "backfill" for other I/DD services. For example, the most common "base" work schedule we see used in community programs is some version of a five-day workweek with eight-hour shifts (day, afternoon/evening, and overnight). Most agencies staff their traditional day services programs from about 8 AM to 4 PM, Monday through Friday. Because residential services operate seven days a week, they are left with afternoon, evening, and weekend shifts to fill—including a disproportionate number of part-time positions which have the highest turnover and vacancy rates

(Braddock & Mitchell, 1992; President's Committee, 2017). Five-day workweeks also have 104 days off a year (before any paid time-off days are earned); however, high vacancies and overtime in residential programs for agencies that use this approach often result in staff working double shifts (16 hours), six- or seven-day workweeks, or partial extra shifts (where two employees pick up part of an open shift), creating too many different people involved in care.

In this staffing approach, each time a preferred daytime schedule becomes available, DSPs working in less desired afternoon, evening, or weekend positions reliably migrate to more preferred schedules. This transition causes a cascading schedule migration that does not stop until the *least* desirable schedule is open (often two to three weeks *later*, after two or three employees move to better schedules in sequence). In the end, new DSPs are hired to fill the most undesirable full- or part-time schedules, often working in homes in the evening or weekends, without experienced direct support staff available to help them learn the skills they need to be successful. The resulting instability leads to excessive vacancies, causing overtime and use of substitutes and staff pools. Many shifts are only partly covered, or are covered by supervisors, causing even more DSP and management turnover (Braddock & Mitchell, 1992).

Ineffective Hiring Strategies

Hiring practices have a tremendous impact on workforce stability (Engerman et al., 1997; Strouse et al., 2013). Problems with the hiring process may be driven by regulations but many are self-inflicted. The overriding problem is the length of time it takes to hire, train, and place a person in a home or program. Our research (Engerman et al., 1997; Strouse et al., 2013) shows that the quality of the candidates *decreases* as the days to hire increase. The time from when a vacancy occurs in a home to when staff is replaced might be six to eight weeks or more. Sometimes it begins with delays in notifying HR of a potential vacancy. Other delays come from the previously described schedule migration, which can delay hiring by several weeks as people disruptively move to better schedules when openings occur. Once this sorts itself out, advertising/recruiting begins, the HR department reviews applicants, collects information, conducts the interview, schedules program/home visits, and makes a hiring decision, after which background checks and post-offer activities occur. Eventually, new staff training is held which is typically the first time an employee can earn a wage.

Bottlenecks and miscues can and do occur at each step. Human Resources (HR) departments often develop processes geared to making it efficient for them to collect and process applicants, rather than making it a better experience for the job candidate. We have seen DSP candidates make four or five trips to different locations spanning multiple weeks before they start earning a wage. Additionally, employees are often placed in a home or program by HR based upon the greatest need of the provider, instead of the one that might be the best match for the employee. To add to this, if turnover is a constant process (for us about 10 to 15 employees per month per region) long hiring practices simply become a hamster wheel where you never can "catch up" because an equal number of people will leave during this latency for hiring. This situation may explain why agency vacancy rates continue to hover between 12% to 18%.

Lack of Effective Training and On-the-Job Coaching for New Employees

There are many requirements that shape how pre-service and early training is provided for new employees, but there is also a lot of variability in how much (and how) training is provided. We reviewed multiple programs offering training that ranged from three days to two weeks, including one that provided 29 days of training. Some agencies offer a brief classroom orientation and then require the balance of training to be online, while other agencies offer more traditional didactic training workshops with none or only supplementary online modules. Most agencies create a new staff workshop that is a combination of required training, agency-specific training, and some type of in-home, person-centered, and program-specific shadow training by "experienced" staff or managers.

The consistent weakness across agency approaches is that limited skilled support is consistently available to help new staff *after training, during their first 60 to 90 days of employment.* Most new staff do not have the chance to receive effective on-the-job coaching, feedback, and encouragement to appropriately apply the skills that are taught during pre-service training in homes and programs as natural opportunities to use these skills present themselves. The best mentoring arguably would be offered by skilled supervisors and long-term DSPs. However, as previously described, the most experienced staff generally migrate across time to work weekdays in day services programs where they avoid evening and weekend work. As home sizes become smaller and services more individualized, new employees find themselves increasingly isolated without any other staff or supervisor present when they need it most.

Improving Workforce Stability

Our work at GoodLife Innovations is focused on creating better ways to help people live with greater independence, while also improving the lives of the

DSPs who must make our mission possible within the resources we have to spend. In the following pages, we present several strategies we use to improve workforce stability within the resources we have available to spend for labor.

Position, Schedule, Compensation, and Time Off Strategies

At GoodLife, we have created different types of positions, schedules, and compensation approaches for different purposes. We operate Kansas' largest "shared living" program (essentially a specialized foster care program designed for I/DD populations). We hire Professional Neighbors, Professional Families, and Professional Roommates (each described later in this chapter), and DSPs who work shifts. We use a combination of these positions, staffing approaches (i.e., schedules), and unique pay and benefits strategies that all work together to deliver quality services cost-effectively. The following is a brief discussion of these approaches, followed by illustrative case studies showing their impact on some important measures of stability.

GoodLife's "Front/Back" Staffing Model

While GoodLife uses a number of different shift schedules for hourly staff across its programs and services, about 60% of all shift schedules used are loosely based around DSPs working 12-hour shifts for three or four days a week (Figure 11.1). In this approach, there are two teams. One team works the "front half" of the week (Sunday, Monday, and Tuesday) and the other team works the "back half" of the week (Thursday, Friday, and Saturday). Staff from either team will typically "pick up" Wednesdays (the swing shift day) for extra work. Front half and back half teams either work daytime or nighttime shifts, creating four groups. With this staffing model, DSPs have three to four days off each week. Thus, each employee works one weekend day and two weekdays, for a total of 36 hours a week. If they pick up another day (e.g., Wednesdays) they might work 48–52 hours a week, but they still have three days off. Day DSPs begin between 7 AM to 9 AM and end their shift between 7 PM to 9 PM. Night employees, if needed, start in the evening (7 PM to 9 PM) and work overnight through the early morning (7 AM to 9 AM). There is sometimes an overlap of the night shift and day shift at a home for two hours each morning (each working 13 hours with the overlap in the day during the morning) to cover the extra care needed in the morning to prepare service recipients for their day (in the community or to attend day services programs).

GoodLife's front/back scheduling process was developed many years ago (Strouse et al., 2004), and has been refined across the past two decades and it has many

Position	Time	Mon	Tues	Wed	Thurs	Fri	Sat	Sun	Home Hours	DS Hours	Total Hours	Awake Total	Sleep Total
Day Front	In	7 AM	7 AM	7 AM				7 AM					
Half	Out	8 PM	8 PM	8 PM				8 PM	34	18	52	52	0
Day Back	In				7 AM	7 AM	7 AM						
Half	Out				8 PM	8 PM	8 PM		27	12	39	39	0
Night Back	In				8 PM	8 PM	8 PM						
Half	Out				9 AM	9 AM	9 AM		39	0	39	39	0
Night Front	In	8 PM	8 PM	8 PM				8 PM					
Half	Out	9 AM	9 AM	9 AM				9 AM	52	0	52	52	0

FIGURE 11.1 Front half/back half staffing model (with 2-hour overlap from 7–9 AM). *Note:* DS = day services

variations. This process serves as the base schedule approach for many of the homes and programs at GoodLife. It is not intended as a stand-alone staffing strategy, but rather as one strategy (our most frequent one) that is used in combination with other staffing strategies. This schedule is designed for programs like GoodLife that also offer day services. Thus, when the day staff on this schedule work during the weekdays, they begin their day at a home, then either provide individualized day services or travel to a GoodLife day services program to provide support for the same or a different caseload of persons, after which they return to the original home to complete their shift.

There are several additional strategies we combine with this staffing model. One significant feature we use with this specific schedule and most others at GoodLife is our "special day" pay strategy, which is a pay strategy allowed by 29 CFR §778.203 of the Department of Labor (DOL) and permitted by most states (DOL, n.d.). The details of this strategy are beyond our ability to fully describe in this chapter and require consultation with a labor expert of your state. It allows an employer to pay premium pay overtime for hours worked below 40 in a workweek for specific days (holidays, Saturdays and Sundays, the sixth or seventh days of the workweek, days of rest, and special days), and (under specific DOL guidelines) to use this overtime (OT) as a credit against regular OT worked in that same workweek by that same employee. Essentially, this special OT premium pay is paid electively by the employer for staff regardless of *whether they have worked over 40 hours or not*. GoodLife uses this special pay strategy for its 12-hour shifts that begin on Saturday or Sunday.

To illustrate, consider an example of an employee paid $10/hour working three 12-hour shifts in a workweek with one of these three days occurring on Sunday, which is a premium day. In this example, an employee is scheduled to regularly work 12 hours on Sunday (premium pay at time-and-a-half), Monday (straight-time pay), and Tuesday (straight-time pay) for a total of 36 hours in a workweek. Monday and Tuesday would be paid at $10/hour (or $120 per shift or $240 total). Sunday would be paid at $15 per hour (OT for 12 hours at $15 per hour or $180). As shown in Table 11.1, this work schedule calculates to be an average hourly rate of $11.67 (or $240 + $180 = $420/36 hours). Suppose the above employee picks up an *additional* 12-hour shift on Wednesday (the "swing day"). In this case, the employee would be paid straight time for hours worked on Wednesday (because the employer has a *credit* of 12 hours of OT for working Sunday). If this same employee picks up another shift on the weekend (e.g., picks up a Saturday) they would be paid OT (as a premium pay day), but not as an additional cost to the employer because Saturday was already budgeted to be OT. Two employees working the front and back half (both being paid $10/hour and $15/hour on the weekend) with one picking up Wednesday at $10/hour, would cost the

TABLE 11.1 Average wage calculation

Average Wage Calculation

Wages based on employee who works 24 hours during weekdays, and 12 hours on weekend

Base Hourly Rate	Weekday Hourly Rate	Weekend Hourly Rate	Average Hourly Rate	Average Hourly Cost Based on 7 Days of Coverage
$9.00	$9.00	$13.50	$10.50	$10.29
$9.50	$9.50	$14.25	$11.08	$10.86
$10.00	$10.00	$15.00	$11.67	$11.43
$10.50	$10.50	$15.75	$12.35	$12.00
$11.00	$11.00	$16.50	$12.83	$12.57
$11.50	$11.50	$17.25	$13.42	$13.14
$12.00	$12.00	$18.00	$14.00	$13.71

agency $11.43 per hour for all hours worked (i.e., $120 × 5 days, plus $180 × 2 days, divided by 84 hours). If the base pay was increased from $10 to $12/hour (and $18 for OT for special day pay), the average hourly rate is $14/hour for an employee working a 36-hour front or back half of the full-week schedule, yet the average hourly rate for two people working both the front/back schedule (with one person picking up the "Wednesday" shift) is $13.71.

The second feature of this scheduling approach is that GoodLife offers only a few vacation days per year but allows unlimited shift trades between the front/back team of employees to maximize flexibility. Employees working three-day work-weeks are scheduled to work about 12 days a month and are off work roughly 16 days each month. This arrangement results in 208 days off per year before accrued paid time off (PTO) days. In contrast, five-day workweek schedules organically permit employees to be off work only 104 days, and to compensate, agencies typically pay for 30 PTO days for employees working these schedules, a format that still only provides DSPs with 134 days off a year. In GoodLife's front/back schedule strategy, first-year employees are offered two paid days off, adding another few days off as tenure increases. One PTO day, however, allows them to take a weekend off and trade for other days. In the end, the front/back schedule approach provides about 60% more time off than their five-day-a-week colleagues who also are provided 30 days of paid leave that obligates an agency to arrange coverage.

From the provider's perspective, there are several benefits to the above front/back staffing model. This scheduling system is designed to produce fewer persons involved in care, fewer transitions across a day, and significantly fewer part-time weekend positions, all while offering greater capacity for a workforce to take time off or affordably work extra shifts. This approach reduces the number of staff to hire, schedule migration, training costs, employer-paid employee taxes, and the need for managers to work extra—especially on weekends. Unbudgeted OT using this approach is rare (typically less than 1.5%), and the payroll costs for services are less variable and more predictable. Fewer people involved in care generally means better services, more flexible and inclusive day schedules for persons served, and experienced persons (instead of part-time persons) working afternoons and weekends (when families visit or interact with staff the most).

From the DSP's perspective, this staffing model can provide $1.00 to $1.50 per hour better pay. Recently hired DSPs work alongside more experienced employees because there is less schedule migration. Employees working this schedule make 104 fewer trips to/from work and have 104 fewer days of childcare, reducing costs for these expenses and making it easier for employees with transportation challenges to get to and from work. More days off provides DSPs the ability to increase their income by picking up extra shifts while still having multiple days off each week. This scheduling strategy allows DSPs with trading to go to school, have more work flexibility, or spend more time with their families to recharge. While workdays are longer, there are natural downtimes in working longer schedules that are often not available for working shorter periods.

Professional Roommate Model

GoodLife's Professional Roommate (PR) model is a relatively new staffing approach. PRs work 24-hour shifts, living with and providing support for one to three roommates with I/DD who do not need frequent up-at-night support. PRs typically work three-day shifts and receive premium pay, as previously described, for working on a Saturday or Sunday. PRs have private sleeping quarters and are available if needs arise during the night.

Each PR is *paid* for 16 hours of work each day and sleeps on the premises overnight. Sleep time is *unpaid* unless the PR is called to work (a provider must comply with all DOL requirements for uncompensated sleep time). Across a three-day schedule, most PRs are paid for 32 hours of straight time for two 16-hour shifts during weekdays plus 16 hours of premium pay or OT for working on a Saturday or Sunday. Figure 11.2 provides a sample schedule for three PRs who support one home and provide inclusionary day services or work within a day services program during the week.

The average hourly cost for their three-day shift is about $14/hour, which includes regular and OT pay. If you add the housing cost to this hourly support cost, for example, $500 a month for use of one bedroom by the PR, the hourly

Position	Time	Mon	Tues	Wed	Thurs	Fri	Sat	Sun	Home Hours	DS Hours	Total Hours	Awake Total	Sleep Total
PR 1	In		3 PM	12 AM	12 AM	12 AM			36	12	64	40	24
	Out		11:59 PM	11:59 PM	11:59 PM	7 AM							
PR 2	In					7 AM	12 AM	12 AM	10	6	48	32	16
	Out					11:59 PM	11: 59 PM	7 AM					
PR 3	In	7 AM	7 AM					7 AM	36	12	56	40	16
	Out	11:59 PM	11:59 PM					11:59 PM					

FIGURE 11.2 Professional roommate (PR) staffing model. *Note:* DS = day services

"cost" increases about $1 (from $14 to $15). However, this strategy offers about 240 hours of very low-cost night "on-call" support each month.

GoodLife's PR approach can be an affordable solution to support people during waking hours and also provide occasional help at night. PRs typically earn about $1.50 per hour more than shift employees partly in consideration of not being compensated for uninterrupted sleep time. They also provide highly stable care that includes fewer people involved in care than traditional shift staffing. While PRs work long days (waking hours) there are longer periods of downtime, especially later in the evening. Additionally, PRs only make one trip a week to/from work which is a benefit for people who have transportation challenges and live long distances from work. Most PRs are recruited from GoodLife's front/back half "shift" workforce.

Professional Neighbors and Professional Families

Professional Families (PFs) and Professional Neighbors (PNs) are full-time paid employees and may be a single person or a couple. PFs live in homes that are attached or next to the home of the people they support, such as next-door homes, attached duplexes, or separate living quarters of the same home. PNs live in homes/apartments in proximity or in the same neighborhood to multiple homes of people they support. In both cases, these homes serve as the primary residences for PF/PNs and their families. The homes are provided and paid for by GoodLife and PF/PNs live there *as a requirement of work*, which means that housing can be a tax-free benefit if certain requirements are met. PFs and PNs work a variety of flexible schedules and provide support that ebbs and flows around need, as well as support occasional intermittent needs overnight (DOL WHD, 2016). For example, PF/PNs might work split shifts in the morning and then in the afternoon/evening weekdays to add support during high-need times in a home or across several nearby homes they support. They are paid an average starting wage of about $11 per hour at GoodLife, but they also receive housing and utilities as a tax-free benefit. As with PRs, the night support costs are very low, because you only pay PF/PNs for interrupted sleep time under requirements (DOL WHD, 2016). GoodLife uses its iLink Remote Support Technologies to virtually monitor all its homes (previously HomeLink Support Technologies; DiGennaro Reed & Reed, 2013). iCoaches monitor all homes at night and deploy sleeping staff (PFs, PNs, and PRs) to support nighttime care needs. The housing costs for a PF or PN are higher; however, the overall cost is affordable for people who need occasional up-at-night support. PRs and PNs are often recruited from shift staff positions at GoodLife, and turnover rates for PFs and PNs are about half the rate of traditional shift staff (Strouse et al., 2004).

Professional Extended Families

Professional Extended Families (EFs) provide shared living services which are essentially specialized adult (or child) foster care for one or two people with I/DD. GoodLife's EFs are families of all sizes, both with and without children. GoodLife supports about 114 persons in its EF model in 83 homes across 19 Kansas counties. In this approach, one or two persons with I/DD are placed in an EF home. The majority of EFs were previously PFs, PNs, DSPs, or even supervisors, managers, or clinicians at GoodLife. About 48 of all EFs were in one of these roles, and an additional 23 EFs had long relationships with the person they served before becoming an EF.

EF placements are made after considerable relationships are formed and must be approved by all stakeholders, including the person supported, guardian(s), the EFs, and GoodLife. Home studies are conducted to make sure the placement and EF families are compatible and the environment is appropriate. The expectation of each placement is that both the individual with I/DD and the EF's own family's needs are met (a win-win) and all lives are enriched.

Payment for EF services is a *difficulty of care payment* (Internal Revenue Service [IRS], 2014) that changes across levels of need for support but is a fairly constant fee month-to-month. Payments/compensation for EFs, under certain conditions, are tax-free. Some EFs provide full-day support and individualized 24/7 services (with respite support). Other EFs might provide only residential support. Some EFs may hold "outside" jobs during the day (while individuals with I/DD would attend a day services program at GoodLife or another day services provider).

As previously mentioned, GoodLife's EF services are the most stable of all its services, with turnover averaging less than 3% annually across the last few decades (1.2% in 2019). GoodLife has examples of EFs providing services for over 20 years; however, 18% of placements are greater than ten years, and over 50% of placements are greater than five years. Additionally, EF services have historically had the highest family satisfaction of all services (average rating of 3.8 on a 4-point scale, with 1 = Very Dissatisfied and 4 = Very Satisfied). The EF program is often a result of one to five years of relationship building. EFs are highly skilled and independent, and are considered the best example of an *advancement ladder* for DSPs at GoodLife (because advancement removes them from being a DSP).

Summary of Standard Schedules and Remnant Schedules

GoodLife offers a variety of standardized staffing models to include the above-described and other approaches. Collectively, all schedules are designed to

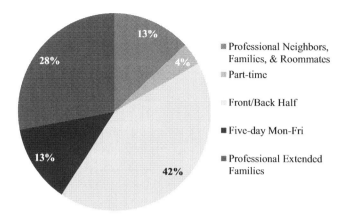

FIGURE 11.3 Percent distribution of schedules/positions for employees at GoodLife

efficiently meet the needs of persons served. Figure 11.3 shows the percent distribution of different types of schedules/positions for employees at GoodLife. The Monday to Friday schedules are designed to provide consistency across all five days of our "traditional" day services program and offer support for EFs who work or for natural families who send their son/daughter to typical day service programs. Note that the part-time positions are less than 4% compared to a national average of 31%.

GoodLife Workforce Management

GoodLife uses specialists called Workforce Managers (WMs) to manage, analyze, oversee, and fill shift vacancies; ensure schedules are implemented correctly; approve all shift trades and PTO usage; and approve any unbudgeted overtime request. The WM tracks and fills all open shifts (shift vacancies). This specialist also collects data on (a) vacancies due to position openings, (b) vacations or planned leave where at least one week notice was given, and (c) "call-offs" which are defined as openings where less than a week's notice is given. The WM records each type of vacancy and "reason" by manager, home/program, and shift type. Staff who want to trade shifts or work extra shifts put their preferences on an electronic scheduling board. Because of GoodLife's weekend premium pay, there is frequently a waiting list for working extra weekend shifts. The WM uses a vacancy management replacement staffing hierarchy to ensure replacement strategies are cost-effective for GoodLife, that no employee works excessively, and the fewest number of different people provide care. In effect, preferences are given to staff who regularly work in a home or program. Similarly, the WM must approve a program/home supervisor or manager to work any open direct support shifts to make sure there is not any other option available and collect data on the extent that this occurs.

The following three tables summarize vacancy data for one month for three differently staffed homes. Table 11.2 summarizes data for a "shift-staffed" group home serving six people with significant health and adaptive needs. Table 11.3 includes data for a home staffed by a Professional Family with additional shift staff. Table 11.4 shows vacancy data for a Neighborhood Network program that serves approximately 18 fairly independent people in an apartment program using a combination of Professional Neighbors and shift staffing. These tables differ on the numbers and types of vacancies that contribute to instability (too many people involved in care). These vacancy data shed more light on the kinds of issues that increase the number of different people involved in care. The group home has greater monthly vacancies compared to the home that uses a Professional Family or Professional Neighbors (41%, 13%, and 24%, respectively).

TABLE 11.2 Vacancy data for a "shift-staffed" group home serving six people

Group Home for Six People

	Vacation	Open Position	Call Off	Total	Shifts per Mo	% of Shift Vacant per Month
Sunday	0	3	1	4	15	27%
Monday	1	0	1	2	15	13%
Tuesday	0	3	2	5	15	33%
Wednesday	0	4	3	7	12	58%
Thursday	0	5	2	7	12	58%
Friday	0	5	2	7	12	58%
Saturday	0	5	1	6	12	50%
Total	1	25	12	38	93	41%

TABLE 11.3 Vacancy data for a professional family home

Professional Family Home for Three People

	Vacation	Open Position	Call Off	Total	Shifts per Month	% of Shift Vacant per Month
Sunday	0	4	0	4	10	40%
Monday	0	0	0	0	15	0%
Tuesday	0	1	0	1	15	7%
Wednesday	0	0	0	0	12	0%
Thursday	0	0	0	0	12	0%
Friday	0	2	0	2	12	17%
Saturday	0	4	0	4	8	50%
Total	0	11	0	11	84	13%

TABLE 11.4 Vacancy data for a Neighborhood Network Program

Neighborhood Network for 18 People

	Vacation	Open Position	Call Off	Total	Shifts per Month	% of Shift Vacant per Month
Sunday	0	3	0	3	15	20%
Monday	0	6	0	6	30	20%
Tuesday	0	7	0	7	30	23%
Wednesday	0	7	0	7	24	29%
Thursday	0	7	1	8	24	33%
Friday	0	4	0	4	24	17%
Saturday	0	3	0	3	12	25%
Total	0	37	1	38	159	24%

TABLE 11.5 Average replacement staff needed per day for a service region

Day	Frequency
Sunday	8
Monday	7.5
Tuesday	10.5
Wednesday	10.5
Thursday	10.5
Friday	10
Saturday	9
Total	9.29

Each cause of vacancy (open positions, call-offs, and vacation days) has different solutions.

Because GoodLife is a large community services provider, we can predict with reasonable accuracy the number of vacancies expected for each day of the week and by schedule type. For example, Table 11.5 shows a distribution of the number of additional staff that must be hired to work front/back half schedules each day based upon our vacancy data for a region of services. The vacancies are due to open positions, call-offs, and vacation days. The number of additional staff that we need to hire to work ranges between eight and ten per day. If we hired more than ten staff, the agency would assume extra cost because we would have more staff than needed to fill vacancies on certain days. With the information summarized in Table 11.5, HR can over-hire these front/back half positions and have trained full-time backup staff available to fill these openings before the opening even occurs. These superimposed DSPs in this example work front/back half schedules and their hours and shifts are guaranteed. In most cases, superimposed DSPs know their home assignment a week or more in advance to fill an open position or replace staff on a planned leave. When a call-off occurs with little notice, a superimposed DSP might be directed to a home by the WM via a text or phone call. If there is no superimposed staff available (all were used), the WM looks on the electronic job board and contacts a regular staff person who wants to work extra. There is little additional cost for hiring super-imposed positions because the number of superimposed positions roughly equals the number of predicted vacancies. From an accounting perspective, GoodLife assigns all superimposed employees to the "unassigned staff department." When the WM assigns a superimposed employee to fill an open shift, the hours are then reassigned to that home/program's department. The number of hours left at the end of the week in the "unassigned staff" department is reviewed and superimposed positions are adjusted so costs are low or zero.

Most new staff are hired to work superimposed DSP schedules as part of GoodLife's *Employee Choice Program*. New employees are supervised by the WM until they are permanently assigned a home so they can sample different home placements to find a great match. The Employee Choice Program is designed to help new employees have a say in where they work and find a place that best fits their preferences. For an Employee Choice DSP to become a permanent employee of a home, both the employee and the supervisor must agree. This strategy also encourages home and program managers to support new employees so their homes are selected as a preferred place to work. Homes that are consist-ently not selected by new DSPs are reviewed to see if adjustments can be made to improve the likelihood a new employee will work there. Adjustments might include modifying the pay for shifts in that home to ensure that one home or type of shift does not become chronically vacant. As an additional method for quality assurance, this "roving" superimposed workforce of new employees is used by the WM to help GoodLife assess home/program quality, management support, person-specific shadow training quality, and working conditions. This is accomplished by having DSPs complete an online survey after working a shift at an assigned home.

Recruitment, Hiring, Pay Days, and Training

Maximizing the Notice to Fill Pending and Open Positions

It is critical for staff to give notice they are terminating their position so we have as much time as possible to reduce the number of days a position is open. GoodLife offers only a few days of PTO and does not "cash-out" PTOs when employees leave, as most providers do. Instead, employees are paid $250 to $350 if they provide the WM a two-week written advance notice of their intent to leave and if they work that two-week notice period. Also, the superimposed staffing pool adds 20 to 30 *additional positions* across regions specifically to fill gaps while the agency hires and trains new employees. Finally, schedules and pay strategies are designed to limit schedule migration, which reduces delays in filling open positions.

GoodLife Recruitment

A well-designed hiring process is meaningless unless there is a strong flow of qualified talent interested in the jobs available. GoodLife employs a Recruitment Specialist whose primary job is to fill its applicant pipeline with potential talent. The Recruitment Specialist works with GoodLife's marketing team to create social media advertising, fully utilize employment search engines, advertise in newspapers and trade publications, and send eBlasts to targeted stakeholders and potential candidates. The Recruitment Specialist also implements various paid and voluntary referral programs leveraging GoodLife's network of employees, families, or advocates. Our belief, however, is that job satisfaction and stability are positively impacted for employees who work close to home (Strouse et al., 2013). Strategies to recruit specifically in neighborhoods where GoodLife has jobs are more targeted and might include posting job flyers, small mobile billboards or banners, real estate style neighborhood signage, local newsletters, community boards, neighborhood events and gatherings, and mailings to surrounding zip codes.

The GoodLife Hiring Process

GoodLife's hiring process was originally developed through research conducted with our University of Kansas partners to more efficiently hire and onboard employees (Engerman et al., 1997). GoodLife's primary hiring goals are to (a) ensure that there is an applicant-friendly process to explore job possibilities; (b) require the fewest trips possible for DSPs while we make a hiring decision; (c) shorten the latency between applying for a job to earning a wage; (d) provide realistic job previews; (e) efficiently gather all the information needed to make hiring decisions; and (f) try to match new hires to jobs that fit their skills, interests, and needs. Our overall outcome expectations are to keep our openings at or below a set number that we deem well within our capacity to fill, typically a few more than the total number of superimposed staff positions, and each month to hire the same or more positions than those vacated in the prior month.

This hiring process starts with applicants completing a short application on GoodLife's website that includes only essential information. If they meet minimum qualifications, they receive an automated notice that they will be contacted to arrange an interview. An HR Administrative Assistant calls the applicant within 24 hours, reviews the minimum qualification information, arranges the earliest time to come for an interview, and lets applicants know what documents or information to bring. Then, the HR Assistant sends an email or text messages a reminder to the candidate, logs the candidate in the applicant tracking system, and completes the appointment calendar entry for the HR Generalist who will be conducting the interview and further onboarding activities. When the applicants arrive at GoodLife, they complete a series of progressive steps that include an interview, a day program site visit to participate in a simulated realistic job preview, and a preference assessment evaluating preferred working conditions such as consumer needs, presence of pets, urban/rural locations. Following these activities, the HR Generalist may make a tentative job offer at the conclusion of the interview. If a job offer is accepted, the onboarding process begins, preferably that day or, if not, as soon as possible. During onboarding, all required information is collected, background checks are initiated, and post-offer testing such as a health screening is conducted. At the end of this process, employees receive their new employment package, their work schedule, and the location and time for new staff training.

Our University of Kansas partners and GoodLife HR staff regularly assess the performance of our hiring process, including collecting descriptive performance data and conducting surveys of new hires. The team even sends "undercover" undergraduate student applicants through the process to view it from a personal perspective. A recent review shows that GoodLife's HR staff took five to seven days to make hiring decisions and about eight to ten days before new hires would earn a wage. Applicants typically made one to two trips to complete the hiring process. These results vary across service regions and across seasons and we track these variations to adjust our strategies and goals. Notably, hiring is more difficult from November to January because people appear more reluctant to change employment during these times. We strive to ensure that the number of DSPs hired nets zero or "plus" from the number leaving during the prior month.

Pay Day

In our national quest to improve the pay for DSPs, it is ironic that most community providers pay biweekly or 26 times per year. Biweekly pay strategies essentially offer two "extra" paychecks per year. Ten months a year, however, employees are paid about 8% less pay than if pay was evenly distributed each month. Of course, the great majority of costs for hourly workers are paid monthly, such as childcare, rent, and utilities. At GoodLife, we provide weekly pay for DSPs and biweekly pay for exempt employees. Weekly pay is highly preferred by our hourly workforce (over 90% prefer it to biweekly pay) and this strategy better aligns paydays with monthly bills to maximize the functional value of compensation.

New Staff Training

GoodLife contracts with its KU partners to produce and coordinate training and oversee the shadow-training/mentoring program for new employees. Our experience is that too little training (less than a week) is insufficient, while too much training prior to working on the job may not be a good approach either because new staff, in general, can only learn so much before what they are taught needs to be applied through on-the-job experience. Thus, GoodLife provides five days of in-person, formal pre-service training for all new employees, preceded by foundational content presented via online modules. Training workshops occur twice and sometimes three times each month depending on the number of openings. In-person training includes didactic instruction with guided notes, discussion, small-group activities, and hands-on and roleplay experiences. All sessions have competency tests where trainees must meet criteria and results are entered into a cloud-based learning management software. In collaboration with its KU partners, GoodLife works hard to provide support for employees after training as well. New employees work for two shifts as extra staff to complete shadow training provided by a "certified" shadow trainer where program/home and person-specific training is completed before DSPs work independently. Each time a DSP works in a new home or program, additional person-centered shadow training is required.

In addition to this support, a few highly experienced DSPs and KU graduate students *coach* new staff on a set curriculum of on-the-job skills as they work in commonly visited program settings. For example, at least 80% of GoodLife's shift DSPs do not work overnight and work at least a few days a week in some common day services locations. This allows the "new staff" coaches the opportunity to provide on-the-job training for new staff (those with less than 60 days) as they work with persons they support. A key focus of this training is on generic skills that are useful for all employees, such as engagement, positive interpersonal interactions, effective teaching, basic care skills, use of transportation including lifts and special equipment, and other general skills. During these sessions, coaches also ask the new staff about the support they receive in-home from their supervisors or experienced DSPs. Finally, home supervisors are encouraged to communicate with this training team to relate areas of training needed for new or even seasoned employees. This process is very new and far from perfect, but the goal is to continue refining the process where concentrated training can be provided in a cost-effective manner in settings where new employees naturally gather even for short periods.

A final approach for supporting new employees is provided through GoodLife's use of its iLink Remote Support Technologies, where the Workforce Manager and KU's undergraduate and graduate students check-in "virtually" with new employees as they work in their homes. They use iLink Technologies to remotely provide support, answer questions from staff in real-time, self-direct help via intercoms connected to iLink professionals, check in to ensure that they are getting reliable shadow training on specific person-centered needs, and confirm that their in-home experience is as positive as possible.

Helping Agencies Improve Stability

GoodLife provides outreach training, consulting, and change management coaching for a growing number of service providers nationally. Our approach for helping providers is to initially focus on picking the low-hanging fruit, which we define as implementing strategies that generate the most immediate, positive results while causing the least disruption possible. In most cases, this process begins with helping agencies improve scheduling, pay, PTO, and hiring processes using many of the strategies outlined in this chapter. While we strive to make progress and create impact without requiring significant agency service design changes, small changes regarding new schedules, compensation strategies, PTO changes, and how services are provided are filled with many challenges and complexities that require experience, planning, change management, legal work, attention to detail, committed leadership, and time. Our goal is to create success with one program, one division, or one region where we can help a provider learn how to deeply review their program, understand and use our practices, use new tools, and make adjustments before moving to the next program/region. Additionally, this strategy manages support costs because the agency can increasingly independently manage future internal replications with progressively less support from GoodLife.

Specifically, our dissemination approach includes training sessions that provide an overview of various workforce strategies, agency site reviews to understand how services are provided, including deep reviews of existing staffing schedules, hiring, and training processes. Once these reviews are complete, we collaboratively construct alternative schedules, pay, PTO, and other strategies and vet our joint work with agency management and leadership. Then we run trial payrolls and design predictive models using agreed-upon assumptions to show the impact of our work. After adjustments are made, we host a series of next-step meetings where we craft pivot plans for implementation. Following this, we provide monthly coaching on implementation, make adjustments, problem solve, and provide or connect technical and legal support to help ensure success. After low-hanging fruit is harvested, we collect post-study information to review the impact and make adjustments for future replications.

Table 11.6 shows the impact of implementing changes in schedules and pay strategies for 127 homes and programs serving 604 consumers at nine agencies across five states with which we consult. These interventions do not include implementing strategies such as Professional Roommates, Professional Neighbors, Professional Families, or Professional Extended Families as these strategies generally require more extensive program design changes for agencies that can occur in future phases. As depicted, we developed schedules to increase the percentage of full-time employees, reduce the number of employees involved in care per consumer, increase pay, and offer significantly more days off. That is, three-day workweeks offer four days off while five-day workweeks offer two days off. This model increases the capacity of staff to work extra and still have multiple days off without increasing OT costs for the same or less money for all nine providers.

TABLE 11.6 Workforce impact

Demographic Data

Total Programs	9		
Total Homes Impacted	127		
Consumers Served	604		

Labor Data

	Pre	Post	Difference
Full-Time	698	833	135
Part-time	312	76	-236
Total Staff	1010	909	-101
% Full-Time Employees	69.11%	91.64%	
% Part-Time Employees	30.89%	8.36%	
Full-Time Per Consumer	1.16	1.38	
Part-Time Per Consumer	0.52	0.13	
Total Per Consumer	1.67	1.50	

Financial Data

	Pre	Post	Difference
Average Pay	$12.39	$13.60	$1.21
Average Overtime Percent	15.23%	2.56%	–12.67%
Additional Shift Capacity	0	73,164	
Total Payroll	$11,727,640	$10,972,240	–$755,399

Summary

Workforce stability is essential to providing care of the highest quality and that is more individualized and inclusive. To do this we must forge new service models that better prepare and support caregivers, managers, clinicians, and administrators. From a research perspective, we have more than enough correlational and descriptive data to identify what's likely impacting instability. We all know—or should know by now—that pay, training and early support, schedules and working conditions, challenging populations, transportation challenges, too many persons involved in care, and more are related to both service quality and staff stability. What we must have is more applied research (researcher/provider partnerships) to develop a deeper understanding of the dynamics of staff instability and validate new interventions, tools, and collective service approaches designed to actually improve important services and staff stability outcomes (President's Committee, 2017; Strouse et al., 2004, 2013). It is most critical to shine a brighter light on the plight of residential services where instability is disproportionately focused. What we need to know more about from a research perspective is exactly how to fix these challenges. This includes developing better staffing strategies, scheduling approaches, professional services, recruitment and hiring strategies, and other supports that are fully leveraged by enabling technologies so that the right support can be provided at the exact moment and place of need. To make this happen, significantly more public and private funding dollars should be focused on deeper applied research concerning strategies that can make a difference in creating new approaches for the next generation of care (President's Committee, 2017). To create a good life for people with I/DD and those DSPs who help make that possible hinges on our best efforts.

References

Bogenshutz, M. D., Hewitt, A., Nord, D., & Hepperlen, R. (2014). Direct support workforce supporting individuals with IDD: Current wages, benefits, and stability. *Intellectual and Developmental Disabilities, 52*(5), 317–329. doi: 10.1352/1934-9556-52.5.317

Braddock, D., & Mitchell, D. (1992). *Residential services and developmental disabilities in the United States: A national survey of staff compensation, turnover and related issues.* Washington, DC: American Association on Mental Retardation.

Braddock, D., Hemp, R. E., Tanis, E. S., Wu, J. & Haffer, L. (2017). *State of the states in intellectual and developmental disabilities* (11th edition). Washington, DC: American Association on Intellectual and Developmental Disabilities.

Bureau of Labor Statistics (BLS). (2020, February). USDL-20-0243. *Job Openings and Labor Turnover: December 2019.* https://www.bls.gov/news.release/archives/jolts_02 112020.htm

De Lea, B. (2019, December 23). Minimum wage to rise in these states in 2020. *Fox Business*. https://www.foxbusiness.com/money/minimum-wage-to-rise-in-these-states-in-2020

Department of Labor (DOL) (n.d.). 29 CFR § 778.203. In *Premium pay for work on Saturdays, Sundays, and other "Special Days"*. https://www.law.cornell.edu/cfr/text/29/778.203

Department of Labor (DOL) and Wage Hour Division (WHD) (2016, April 25). *Field assistance bulletin* No. 2016-1. https://www.dol.gov/sites/dolgov/files/WHD/legacy/files/fab2016_1.pdf

Diament, M. (2020, February 7). Nationally, waiting lists for waiver services growing. *Disability Scoop*. https://www.disabilityscoop.com/2020/02/07/nationally-waiting-lists-waiver-services-growing/27783/

DiGennaro Reed, F. D., & Reed, D. D. (2013). HomeLink Support Technologies at Community Living Opportunities. *Behavior Analysis in Practice*, 6(1), 80–81 doi: 10.1007/BF03391794

Engerman, J., Strouse, M., Sherman, J. A., & Sheldon, J. B. (1997). *Developing and evaluating a direct-services employee selection process for a large community-based program serving persons with developmental disabilities* [Unpublished data]. Department of Human Development and Family Life, University of Kansas.

Hewitt, A., Larson, S., Edelstein, S., Seavey, D., Hoge, M. A., & Morris, J. (2008). *A synthesis of direct service workforce demographics and challenges across intellectual/developmental disabilities, aging, physical disabilities, and behavioral health*. Minneapolis: University of Minnesota, Institute on Community Integration, Research and Training Center on Community Living.

Internal Revenue Service (IRS). (2014). *Internal revenue bulletin: 2014–4*. https://www.irs.gov/irb/2014-04_IRB#NOT-2014-7

Jarmolowicz, D. P., Reed, D. D., DiGennaro Reed, F. D., & Bickel, W. K. (2016). The behavioral and neuroeconomics of reinforcer pathologies: Implications for managerial and health decision making. *Managerial and Decision Economics, 37*, 274–293. doi:10.1002/mde.2716

Kazemi, E., Shapiro, M., & Kavner, A. (2015). Predictors of intention to turnover in behavior technicians working with individuals with autism spectrum disorder. *Research in Autism Spectrum Disorders, 17*, 106–115.

Kohn, D., & Taylor, P. (2010, December 20). *Baby boomers approach 65: Glumly*. Pew Research Center. https://www.pewsocialtrends.org/2010/12/20/baby-boomers-approach-65-glumly/

Larson, S. A., & Lakin, C. K. (1997). *A longitudinal study of turnover among newly hired residential direct support workers in small community homes serving people with developmental disabilities: Summary report*, Report 50. Minneapolis, MN: Research and Training Center on Residential Services and Community Living, Institute on Community Integration.

Larson, S. A., Lakin, K. C., & Bruininks, R. H. (1998). *Staff recruitment and retention: Study results and intervention strategies.* Washington, DC: American Association on Mental Retardation.

National Core Indicators (NCI). (2019). *National Core Indicators® 2018 staff stability survey report.* Human Services Research Institute and the National Association of State Directors of Developmental Disabilities Services, Inc. https://www.national coreindicators.org/resources/staffstability-survey/

Paraprofessional Healthcare Institute (PHI). (2011, February). Who are direct-care workers? *PHI Facts, 3,* 1–6. https://www.phinational.org/sites/phinational.org/files/ clearinghouse/PHI%20Facts%203.pdf

President's Committee for People with Intellectual Disabilities. (2017). America's direct support workforce crisis: Effects on people with intellectual disabilities, families, communities and the U.S. economy. Washington, DC: Author. https://www.acl .gov/sites/default/files/programs/2018-02/2017%20PCPID%20Full%20Report_0.PDF

Strouse, M. C., Carroll-Hernandez, T. A., Sherman, J. A., & Sheldon, J. B. (2004) Turning over turnover: The evaluation of a staff scheduling system in a community-based program for adults with developmental disabilities. *Journal of Organizational Behavior Management, 23*(2–3), 45–63. doi: 10.1300/J075v23n02_04

Strouse, M. C., Sherman, J. A., & Bowen Sheldon, J. (2013). Do good, take data, get a life, and make a meaningful difference in providing residential services! In D. D. Reed, F. D. DiGennaro Reed, & J. K. Luiselli (Eds.), *Handbook of crisis intervention for individuals with developmental disabilities* (pp. 441–465). New York: Springer.

Wine, B., Osborne, M. R., & Newcomb, E. T. (2020). On turnover in human services. *Behavior Analysis in Practice, 13*(2), 492–501. doi: 10.1007/s40617-019-00399-6

12
Restraint and Restrictive Behavior Management Practices

Peter Sturmey

This chapter reviews restraint and restrictive behavior management practices (RRBMPs) within human services organizations that serve persons with intellectual and developmental disabilities. The main sections of the chapter consider history, definitions, and rationale for RRBMPs; interventions to reduce and eliminate such procedures safely among individuals, groups, and families; and recommendations for practice and research. Much of the chapter considers evidence drawn from efficacy and effectiveness research published in multidisciplinary peer-reviewed journals.

Concern over safe restraint in asylums, private madhouses, and jails dates back to the end of the eighteenth century, in part a response to the death of a person with mental health issues that motivated the Quakers in York, Unied Kingdom, to set up the Retreat as a non-coercive mental health service. Several people were highly successful in reducing restraint in nineteenth century asylums such that care without restraint became a mental health movement for many decades (Connolly, 1856; Sturmey, 2015). Unfortunately, as institutions grew and focused on protecting society and costs of care rather than habilitation, restraint became an acceptable but largely unregulated practice.

By World War II, institutions were severely understaffed and dangerous. Groups such as Mennonites and Quakers began to document and advocate for more humane and safe care (Taylor, 2009). Several factors in the 1950's converged to promote proper care and education of individuals with disabilities, notably (a) institutional scandals in the United States, the United Kingdom, and elsewhere; (b) class action lawsuits documenting abridgment of constitutional rights and forcing states to spend more money on services; (c) growth of international disability rights legislation that eventually influenced national and regional legislation; (d) media depictions that often involved images of restraint such as *Christmas in Purgatory* (Blatt & Kaplan, 1966); and (e) legal requirements and eventual provision of education for all children with disabilities and community services for adults with disabilities in many countries. Despite these enormous changes in services and the many benefits to individuals with disabilities, their families, and society, little evidence indicates that needed reforms have reduced RRBMPs and improved safety for service recipients and caregivers. Indeed, some contemporary reports suggest that RRBMPs might be increasing in some contexts (Søndenaa et al., 2015). As well, recurrent scandals in community services in the United States and United Kingdom (Sturmey, 2015) have led some to conclude that restraint has simply moved "out of the institution, into the classroom" (Nelson, 2017).

There have been several responses to the growing concerns about RRBMPs with persons who have intellectual and developmental disabilities. In the United States, the Federal Department of Education now collects national data on restraint and seclusion, although such data are often inaccurate and incomplete (GAO, 2019). Also, the Federal Department of Education does not readily publicize their data. In some cases, investigative journalists have reconstructed and presented the data (ProPublica, 2019) and, in doing so, exposed school districts that report an unusually high rate of restraint and seclusion (Richards et al., 2019). In addition, despite changes in federal restraint regulations, states vary substantially in their response to such non-binding guidance (Gagnon et al., 2017).

There is presently no evidence that legislative approaches to manage RRBMPs are effective. For example, legislation in Norway intended to reduce restraint resulted in a substantial increase in restraint use over several years (Søndenaa et al., 2015). Some countries have now instituted national databases (Lepping et al., 2016), although again, these may be of variable and often questionable quality. A few states and countries have attempted system-wide interventions, such as Victoria, Australia (Webber et al., 2010), described more fully in a later section of the chapter.

In summary, RRBMPs have remained a widely recognized concern for over 200 years. Even with many expressions of concern, ample documentation of the problem, media coverage, and individual and class action lawsuits, there is little evidence of widespread improvement in services for individuals with disabilities. However, this chapter will show that some organizations have been able to adopt and maintain effective and ethical interventions to safely reduce RRBMPs and improve quality of life for the persons served.

Overview

It is essential to define terms related to RRBMPs but confusion abounds. Due to the vernacular use of words such as "seclusion" and "emergency," people may assume incorrectly that there is consistent and consensus terminology among professionals and the lay public. In addition, use of these terms in legislative, policy, practice, and research contexts further adds to confusion and misunderstanding. Professionals disagree, for example, as to whether emergency (*pro re nata* [PRN]) and/or routine administration of psychotropic medication constitute RRBMPs. Also, euphemistic and quasi-professional language abounds such as referring to "seclusion" as "the blue room," "the calming room," "timeout," "redirection," and "reflection time," and describing "mechanical restraint" as "postural support," a "lap lizard," or "physical therapy program." As well, restraint may be misrepresented when tying a person to a wheelchair is referred to as physical therapy for posture but is actually used as an unacceptable restrictive method to prevent self-injurious hand-biting.

It should be noted that many everyday practices are acceptable and even required by law under certain circumstances but often not recognized as restraint. Examples include car seat belts, highchairs for young children, strapping children in strollers, and stop signs. Further, we often restrict our movement by folding our arms and sitting on our hands to stop wriggling, biting our tongues to avoid saying something undesirable, and wearing splints to promote healing through immobilization and other forms of self-restraint (Skinner, 1953).

This chapter cannot provide a complete analysis of all terms related to RRBMPs. Generally, three forms of restraint can be distinguished. First, *personal restraint* is when one or more people restrict or immobilize another person's body parts. Second, *mechanical restraint* occurs when a physical device such as splints are applied to a person's body to restrict or immobilize movement And third, *chemical restraint* is administering a substance such as an antihistamine to reduce a person's motor activity. A further distinction is often made between planned and emergency restraints. Planned or programmatic restraint involves application of restraint in a predetermined fashion as described in a written protocol such as a physician's order or behavior support plan. An emergency restraint refers to the application of restraint without a predetermined criterion, such as an unanticipated crisis situation that poses immediate danger to self or others. Unfortunately, these distinctions are not always clear. For example, in an attempt to reduce RRBMPs, some organizations have prohibited programmatic restraint but approve "planned emergency restraint" as an acceptable alternative.

Beyond physical restraint, some service settings and families use environmental barriers to restrict movement. Common examples include blocking and locking exits, placing door locks out of reach of the individual, tipping modified chairs back so the person cannot move, removing shoes or tying shoelaces together, and locking bedroom doors to prevent the person from leaving. Some service settings also lock people in rooms or restrict them to spaces that are sometimes modified to prevent egress.

Yet another distinction is between locked room time-out and seclusion. Locked room time-out should be based on a functional behavioral assessment or functional analysis in which the target behavior is hypothesized to be maintained by positive reinforcement, possibly social attention or access to tangible items. The application of the locked time-out room, if done correctly, removes the reinforcer with the intent of reducing the target behavior. Typically, the duration of locked room time-out is relatively brief and there is a prespecified release criterion. Seclusion is more typically seen as an emergency procedure to protect the individual or other people. The release criterion from seclusion is often not specified operationally other than some general reference to the safety of self or others. Some service settings use seclusion extensively as a routine practice rather than for emergencies and typically do not assess function of the behaviors that lead to seclusion.

Such distinctions frequently reflect administrative, legal, and safety standards appearing in state and agency reporting requirements. Often, additional information concerning individual injuries in the form of an incident or restraint checklist must be reported. Some agencies consolidate these data across individuals, program areas, and geographical regions for the purposes of service evaluation and planning. Thus, a state agency might use such data to target certain services for program development, specialized prevention training, and intervention evaluation.

Given that society tolerates or requires so many forms of restraint, why are RRBMPs seen as problematic for individuals with disabilities or in certain contexts? One concern is that RRBMPs are often stigmatizing and lead to negative perceptions of the person restrained and often the people applying restraint. Frequently, RRBMPs are inversely related to persons interacting with the environment and receiving learning opportunities which lead to development of empirical approaches to determine the safest, least restrictive forms of restraint (LeBlanc et al., 1997). For service settings that espouse participating in the environment and learning as core values, these last two reasons should motivate initiations to reduce RRBMPs.

One reasonable purpose for implementing RRBMPs is to prevent harm to self, peers, and caregivers. Yet paradoxically, RRBMPs are commonly associated with client injuries and even deaths. However, multiple papers have reported that programs that decrease restraint use are often accompanied by large and sustained reductions in employees' compensation costs and client injuries (Sturmey, 2015). Perhaps out of concern for safety, many caretakers, union representatives, and administrators sincerely fear that attempts to reduce restraints may cause harm to service-recipients and the persons who care for them. Nevertheless, the safety of clients, peers, caregivers, and family members is one of the main incentives to reduce and eliminate RRBMPs.

Assessing and measuring safety can be problematic because some events occur infrequently such as client deaths and severe staff injuries. Hence, it is difficult to evaluate if intervention is effective. Reductions in less severe injuries and prevented injuries that could have been significant are especially difficult to measure and quantify. Some have addressed this problem by reporting worker days lost, workers compensation claims, and costs of staff surgeries rather than the absolute number of injuries.

An additional measurement problem is that the absolute number of events is not the relevant metric since this measure may simply reflect the number of clients and number of applications of a RRBMPs. For example, service-wide restraint-related injuries may increase or decrease because there are more or fewer clients in the service setting rather than an effective strategy to reduce RRBMPs. Similarly, the number of injuries might increase but reflect a reduction in more severe injuries (e.g., injuries requiring sutures dropping from three to zero per month) and a small increase in minor injuries (e.g., injuries with red marks on the skin rising from three to seven per month).

Interventions to Reduce and Eliminate RRBMPs

There are at least three types of strategies that have been used to reduce RRBMPs safely and have reasonable evidence support: namely prevention, treatment of problem behavior in individuals, and group interventions. Concerning prevention, general behavioral hygiene measures and treating the target behaviors that occasion RRBMPs are two common strategies. General behavioral hygiene refers to the desirable properties of benign environments that should be present in any ethical service setting or family. The Association for Behavior Analysis International (ABAI) *Right to Effective Treatment* statement (Van Houten et al., 1988) identified the right to a therapeutic environment, specifying "A physical and social environment that is safe, humane, and responsive to individual needs is a necessary prerequisite for effective treatment. Such an environment provides not only training, but also an acceptable living standard" (p. 111). Among three broad dimensions of an environment, individuals should have access to therapeutic services, leisure activities, and materials that are enjoyable, instructive, age-appropriate, and respect individual choices. Second, the social environment should have caregivers who are competent, responsive, and caring with high rates of positive interactions that foster enjoyment, learning, and independence. Finally, and most pertinent for consideration of RRBMPs, the environment should impose the fewest number of movement restrictions and permit access to materials consonant with individual safety and development. Mere physical location of the individual in a community setting, integrated classroom, or family does not guarantee such environmental characteristics.

The characteristics of a therapeutic environment can and should be measured. For example, classrooms and community residential and vocational services settings should have appropriate materials readily available in a physically and temporally organized manner. There should be a clear schedule that incorporates individual choice of materials, assigned staff, and sequencing of activities. Staff who are well-trained, interact frequently, behave positively, and foster independence, choice, and learning must be present. Finally, there should be administrative support that encourages implementation of best practices.

The target behaviors that most commonly occasion RRBMPs are aggression, tantrums, property destruction, self-injury (SIB), and pica. Often these behaviors occur in the context of multiple other problem behaviors. Evidence-based interventions are required to maximize individual benefit, minimize harm to the individual and caregivers, and promote efficiency (Singh, 2016; Sturmey & Didden, 2014). Didden et al. (2016) concluded that evidence-based treatment of aggression included behavioral interventions based on pre-treatment functional assessment and analysis such as extinction, differential reinforcement, functional communication training (FCT), and combinations of these procedures. They also concluded that there is little clear and replicable evidence for the use of psychotropic medication and accumulating but insufficient evidence for cognitive behavior therapy, mindfulness, and related psychological interventions. In an update of an earlier systematic review and meta-analysis of behavioral treatment of SIB (Kahng et al., 2002), Shawler et al. (2019) reported that behavioral treatment was generally very effective, with 28% of articles reporting *complete* suppression of SIB. The most common effective treatments were punishment (47%), treatment packages (38%), extinction (17%), and antecedent interventions (12%).

Hand mouthing and pica are often associated with various forms of RRBMPs including gloves, mittens, helmets, arm splints, and one-on-one staffing. These behaviors are particularly difficult to treat because they are often maintained by automatic reinforcement and it is not easy to identify and manipulate the maintaining contingencies. It is also the case that many individuals who engage in these behaviors have severe and profound cognitive disabilities, limited skills, and few functional reinforcers. Consider, too, that practitioners may not be familiar with the physical demands of effective intervention procedures. For example, Roscoe et al. (2013) evaluated a protocol of progressively intrusive interventions for 14 consecutively treated individuals. The protocol included (a) noncontingent reinforcement (NCR) which was effective with six participants; (b) NCR plus differential reinforcement of alternative behavior plus response blocking which was effective with five participants; (c) NCR plus response blocking only which was effective with two participants; and (d) NCR plus brief manual restraint which was effective with one participant. Pica that is sometimes dangerous and could be lethal has several evidence-based treatments identified as environmental enrichment, NCR, overcorrection, exchange training, and positive punishment procedures (McAdam et al., 2012; Sturmey & Williams, 2016).

Individual ABA-based treatment can also be effective in reducing restraint in high-risk populations and contexts. For example, Allen and Wallace (2013) conducted a randomized controlled trial of noncontingent escape to reduce disruptive behavior in children during dental treatment. Noncontingent escape was effective in reducing disruption and decreased the number of restraints. The number of children experiencing restraints was significantly lower in the experimental group (27%) versus the control group (45%). Research by Luiselli and colleagues with children and youth who had developmental disabilities (Luiselli et al., 2000) and brain injury (Luiselli et al., 2006) also demonstrated that ABA-based treatment which effectively reduced problem behavior also decreased frequency of physical restraint.

In addition to treating the problem behavior that occasions the use of RRBMPs, understanding the antecedent and consequent functions for both the person restrained and the person applying the restraint can inform intervention formulation. Restraint may function both as positive and negative punishers for and, perhaps surprisingly, as positive and negative reinforcers for the behavior of the person restrained. Consider that when a caretaker restrains an individual, the most obvious consequence for the implementor is that challenging behavior is terminated, at least temporarily. Further, in a classic study of the functions of restraint, Favell et al. (1978) evaluated individuals with profound intellectual disabilities who engaged in SIB and appeared to enjoy restraint. Three experiments demonstrated that access to restraint could be used to differentially reinforce the absence of SIB and increase an arbitrary response (placing a marble in a jar) suggesting that restraint functioned as a positive reinforcer. Foxx and Duphrense (1984) extended these observations in a multi-component treatment package for severe SIB in a man who asked for, looked at, and grabbed his restraints when they were removed. The treatment package consisted of (a) contingent reinforcement (access to restraint) for progressively longer periods without SIB; (b) time-out from positive reinforcement (removal of restraint contingent upon SIB); and (c) multiple restraint fading procedures for physically modifying and substituting various objects used in self-restraint. At the end of initial treatment, SIB was virtually nonexistent and these treatment effects maintained at ten-year follow-up (Foxx, 1990).

Restraints also have antecedent functions. In a Rapid Restraint Analysis (RRA), individuals are systematically exposed to differing degrees of restraint, and experimenters observe the rate of both adaptive behavior such as toy play or self-feeding and problem behavior (DeRosa et al., 2015; Deshais et al., 2015; LeBlanc et al., 1997; Wallace et al., 1999). Findings from RRA data suggest that high and low levels of restraint function as discriminative stimuli for the problem behavior. Therapists can also use these data to determine the degree of restraint that is currently safe and acceptable, and these results could be used to accelerate subsequent restraint fading protocols. Further, this analysis of the antecedent function of restraints suggests that various forms of restraint fading (e.g., restraint size or pressure) are examples of transfer of stimulus control of problem behavior. Accordingly, mechanical restraints can be replaced with non-intrusive objects such as wristbands, watches, glasses, or headwear through systematic stimulus fading and transfer of stimulus control procedures (Pace et al., 1986; Luiselli 1991a, b).

A final contribution to restraint reduction that is unique to ABA is the evaluation of procedural differences in restraint procedures. One example is evaluation of restraint release criteria. Luiselli (2008) evaluated the effects of a restraint fading protocol beginning with a 60-second fixed time (FT) restraint which was successively faded to a 7-second FT restraint in three steps. This fading protocol results in the eventual elimination of restraint. Langone et al. (2014) found that FT fading was superior to behavior-contingent release from restraint in terms of reducing the frequency and duration of restraints. A second approach comes from Luiselli et al. (2006) who evaluated procedures to identify antecedents for restraint use and found that modification of antecedents could be used to eliminate or reduce restraint.

Although practitioners commonly work with individuals, they may also be required to reduce RRBMPs safely in the context of groups of individuals in classrooms and homes. Sturmey (2015) reviewed the literature on group applications and identified 21 empirical papers, including 14 case studies and 7 experiments. The most commonly used interventions were organizational reform packages conducted in institutions and schools, staff training, monitoring, feedback, and some positive behavior support procedures. Surprisingly, there were large reductions RRBPs, fewer injuries to staff and individuals, and organizational cost savings. In some cases, these effects were maintained over a 13-year period, thus supporting several approaches to large-scale reduction in RRBMPs, which may be effective, safe, economical, and long-lasting.

Some countries have attempted to manage the use of RRBMPs at the state level as in Victoria, Australia, when legislation established and funded the office of senior practitioner to monitor and review all restrictive practices. Part of this effort was to establish a state-wide database that collected data on individuals and settings using different types of RRBMPs. Preliminary reports (Webber et al., 2010, 2011a, 2011b, 2011c) found that in a 12-month period (2008–2009), 2,102 of 23,258 service recipients (9%) experienced some form of chemical or mechanical restraint or seclusion at least once. The median number of applications per individual was approximately 12 (range 1–877) per year. Most restrictive procedures (91%) were chemical restraints used to control behavior (rather than psychiatric disorders) and approximately 9% of individuals experienced mechanical restraints. Individuals restrained were likely to be male, have intellectual disability or autism, and 15–24 years old. Government-provided services were more likely than community service organizations to use restrictive behavior management practices. The authors concluded that restrictive practices were used routinely, rather than as a last resort.

Subsequently, this research group took a number of initiatives to identify service problems and improve service quality. For example, a survey of a random sample of behavior support plans indicated that the quality of plans was generally mediocre (Webber et al., 2011a, 2011b) but that plans with greater levels of professional and technical support were often of better quality and better-quality plans were associated with reduced restrictive measures (Webber et al., 2011a, 2001b). Subsequent training improved the quality of plans, leading to beneficial changes in client mental health, less frequent problem behavior, and reductions in RRBMPs (O'Dwyer et al., 2017).

These state-wide efforts are challenged by administrative issues such as legislation not requiring data on certain forms of restraint and changes in data collection procedures such as moving from paper to online data entry. Such changes may result in poor data integrity, notwithstanding that state-wide initiatives have the potential for large-scale improvement in service quality, individual and caregiver safety, and utilization of RRBMPs.

Summary and Conclusions

Concern about RRBMPs and issues related to dignity and safety has a long and checkered history. Although successful interventions have been documented, many human services organizations are ineffective in reducing RRBMPs and ensuring individual and caregiver safety. This situation is paradoxical because there are many available solutions to reducing RRBMPs that some organizations do not adopt. Why do many service settings seem to neglect and not implement effective practices which could benefit their individuals in a manner consonant with espoused values?

One answer to the preceding question is that some organizations simply do not know what to do and/or engage in easy, palatable, but ineffective practices. Other organizations may know about effective practices but do not to engage in them because of the effort required, lack of resources, or perceived obstacles. In contrast, some organizations are able to reduce RRBMPs in response to external pressure from angry family members, negative exposure in the media, threats of defunding, and lawsuits. However, in other cases, organizations change as the result of practitioners who take on the challenge of improving services largely on their own initiative combined with organizational leadership that occasions large-scale, sustained reduction in RRBMPs. Researchers and practitioners should focus on understanding the process of how evidence-based practices are adopted or rejected by organizations as this might result in more positive individual and systems-wide effects.

The goal of practitioners, family members, and organizations should be to ensure positive and sustained client and caregiver outcomes, notably prolonged reduction and elimination of RRBMPs, enhancing the individual's quality of life, and ensuring personal safety at all times. Of course, practitioners should be competent to provide effective evidence-based practices to safely reduce RBBMPs. They should communicate with supervisors and administrators when there are concerns about competency and the need to work and consult with other professionals. Practitioners should further advance their skills through continuing education activities, seeking peer review, and keeping current with the practice and research literature.

Organizations should actively and effectively monitor systems-wide use of RRBMPs and related individual and staff safety using accurate and meaningful data. Such strategies should include performance improvement initiatives modeled on effective procedures published in the literature, comprehensive staff training, hiring supervisors and clinicians who are competent to manage RRMBPs effectively, and supporting large-scale interventions that are sustainable.

Keep in mind that system-wide issues may not support local service providers wanting to safely prevent use of RRBMPs. In illustration, many agencies responsible for providing services can avoid doing so by unloading challenging individuals to other settings or their families with impunity. Examples include placing school students out of district or into specialist segregated units. By so doing, not only do local agencies avoid having to provide technically difficult and effortful services but they may also avoid costs for expensive clients, as when a centralized state fund picks up the tab for out-of-state schooling or residential facility. Such structural problems encourage local providers to work hard to avoid serving such individuals and doing the harder work of developing local services for challenging individuals. A solution to such iatrogenic practices is to hold local services accountable for all individuals they serve by requiring them to provide effective services locally, providing adequate and effective technical support, and requiring them to fund and actively monitor expensive out-of-district services when they use them while making and implementing effective plans to repatriate out-of-district individuals to their home districts.

Relatively little attention has been given to working with families who use RRBMPs with their children, although some families do indeed do so, often out of desperation and lack of services (Elford et al., 2010). A unique study comes from Singh et al. (2018) who demonstrated that teaching controlled-breathing techniques to children with borderline intellectual disabilities and aggressive behavior reduced parental use of restraint in the family home. Future research should continue to develop this literature to understand family members' use of RRBMPs and how to support them in effective behavior management practices in the home setting.

Research has already identified many effective practices for safely reducing RRBMPs. Although such research should continue to refine our knowledge base, more work is needed to develop and evaluate methods of disseminating evidence-based practices. Such research should include both investigating the methods that might be effective, for example, comparing expert-led, top-down approaches with practitioner-led, bottom-up approaches. It would also be useful to know how many and what kinds of resources are necessary to achieve certain client and agency outcomes such as amount of time and distribution of consultations. A related question is how practitioners should work and utilize the skills and knowledge of consultants who have behavior analysis expertise within human services organizations. Lastly, researchers should develop and evaluate safety measures related to the use of RRBMPs, document successful methods of caregiver training, and assess social validity among direct and indirect treatment consumers.

References

Allen, K. D., & Wallace, D. P. (2013). Effectiveness of using noncontingent escape for general behavior management in a pediatric dental clinic. *Journal of Applied Behavior Analysis*, 46(4), 723–737.

Blatt, B., & Kaplan, F. (1966). *Christmas in purgatory*. Allen & Bacon.

Conolly, J. (1856). *The treatment of the insane without mechanical restraints*. London: Smith, Elder & Co.

DeRosa, N. M., Roane, H. S., Wilson, J. L., Novak, M. D., & Silkowski, E. L. (2015). Effects of arm-splint rigidity on self-injury and adaptive behavior. *Journal of Applied Behavior Analysis, 48*(4), 860–864.

Deshais, M. A., Fisher, A. B., Hausman, N. L., & Kahng, S. (2015). Further investigation of a rapid restraint analysis. *Journal of Applied Behavior Analysis, 48*(4), 845–859.

Didden, R., Lindsay, W. R., Lang, R., Sigafoos, J., Deb, S., Wiersma, J., ... & Lancioni, G. E. (2016). Aggressive behavior. In *Handbook of evidence-based practices in intellectual and developmental disabilities* (pp. 727–750). Springer, Cham.

Elford, H., Beail, N., & Clarke, Z. (2010). "A very fine line": Parents' experiences of using restraint with their adult son/daughter with intellectual disabilities. *Journal of Applied Research in Intellectual Disabilities, 23*(1), 75–84.

Favell, J. E., McGimsey, J. F., & Jones, M. L. (1978). The use of physical restraint in the treatment of self-injury and as positive reinforcement. *Journal of Applied Behavior Analysis, 11*(2), 225–241.

Foxx, R. M. (1990). "Harry": A ten year follow-up of the successful treatment of a self-injurious man. *Research in Developmental Disabilities, 11*(1), 67–76.

Foxx, R. M., & Dufrense, D. (1984). "Harry": The use of physical restraint as a reinforcer, timeout from restraint, and fading restraint in treating a self-injurious man. *Analysis and Intervention in Developmental Disabilities, 4*(1), 1–13.

Gagnon, D. J., Mattingly, M. J., & Connelly, V. J. (2017). The restraint and seclusion of students with a disability: Examining trends in US school districts and their policy implications. *Journal of Disability Policy Studies, 28*(2), 66–76.

General Accounting Office (2019). *Education should take immediate action to address inaccuracies in federal restraint and seclusion data*. https://www.gao.gov/products/gao-19-551r

Kahng, S., Iwata, B. A., & Lewin, A. B. (2002). Behavioral treatment of self-injury, 1964 to 2000. *American Journal of Mental Retardation, 107*(3), 212–221.

Langone, S. R., Luiselli, J. K., Galvin, D., & Hammill, J. (2014). Effects of fixed-time release fading on frequency and duration of aggression-contingent physical restraint (protective holding) in a child with autism. *Clinical Case Studies, 13*, 313–321.

LeBlanc, L. A., Piazza, C. C., & Krug, M. A. (1997). Comparing methods for maintaining the safety of a child with pica. *Research in Developmental Disabilities, 18*(3), 215–220.

Lepping, P., Masood, B., Flammer, E., & Noorthoorn, E. O. (2016). Comparison of restraint data from four countries. *Social Psychiatry and Psychiatric Epidemiology, 51*(9), 1301–1309.

Luiselli, J. K. (1991a). Evaluation of a behavioral-pharmacological intervention for the treatment of self-injury in an adult with dual sensory impairment. *Journal of Behavior Therapy & Experimental Psychiatry, 22*, 233–238.

Luiselli, J. K. (1991b). Functional assessment and treatment of self-injury in a pediatric, nursing care resident. *Behavioral Residential Treatment, 6*, 311–320.

Luiselli, J. K. (2008). Effects of fixed-time release (FTR) fading on implementation of physical restraint. *Mental Health Aspects of Developmental Disabilities, 11*(4), 127–133.

Luiselli, J. K., Kane, A., Treml, T., & Young, N. (2000). Behavioral intervention to reduce physical restraint of adolescents with developmental disabilities. *Behavioral Interventions, 15*, 317–330.

Luiselli, J. K., Pace, G. M., & Dunn, E. K. (2006). Effects of behavior-contingent and fixed-time release contingencies on frequency and duration of therapeutic restraint. *Behavior Modification, 30*(4), 442–455.

McAdam, D. B., Breidbord, J., Levine, M., & Williams, D. E. (2012). Pica. In: M. Hersen & P. Sturmey, (Eds). *Handbook of evidence-based practice in clinical psychology, Volume 1. Children and adolescents,* (pp. 303–323). Chichester: Wiley.

Nelson, L. (2017). Out of the institution, into the classroom: Legal challenges to the use of restraint and seclusion in school settings in the United States. *International Journal of Law and Psychiatry, 53*, 97–101.

O'Dwyer, C., McVilly, K. R., & Webber, L. (2017). The impact of positive behavioural support training on staff and the people they support. *International Journal of Positive Behavioural Support, 7*(2), 13–23.

Pace, G. M., Iwata, B. A., Edwards, G. L., & McCosh, K. C. (1986). Stimulus fading and transfer in the treatment of self-restraint and self-injurious behavior. *Journal of Applied Behavior Analysis, 19*(4), 381–389.

ProPublica (2019). Restraints. https://www.propublica.org/series/restraints

Richards, J. S., Cohen, J. S., & Chavez, L. (2019, December 20). The takedown. Illinois schools allows schools to physically restraint children. But workers often violated the rules in dangerous ways. *Chicago Tribune.*

Roscoe, E. M., Iwata, B. A., & Zhou, L. (2013). Assessment and treatment of chronic hand mouthing. *Journal of Applied Behavior Analysis, 46*(1), 181–198.

Shawler, L. A., Russo, S. R., Hilton, J. L., Kahng, S., Davis, C. J., & Dorsey, M. F. (2019). Behavioral treatment of self-injury: 2001 to 2016. *American Journal on Intellectual and Developmental Disabilities, 124*(5), 450–469.

Singh, N. N. (2016). *Handbook of evidence-based practices in intellectual and developmental disabilities.* New York: Springer

Singh, N. N., Lancioni, G. E., Myers, R. E., Karazsia, B. T., McPherson, C. L., Jackman, M. M., ... & Thompson, T. (2018). Effects of SOBER breathing space on aggression in children with autism spectrum disorder and collateral effects on parental use of physical restraints. *Advances in Neurodevelopmental Disorders, 2*(4), 362–374.

Skinner, B. F. (1953). *Science and human behavior.* New York: Simon & Schuster.

Søndenaa, E., Dragsten, F., & Whittington, R. (2015). Practitioner explanations for the increasing use of restraint measures in the care of people with intellectual disabilities in Norway 2000–11. *Journal of Policy and Practice in Intellectual Disabilities, 12*(1), 58–63.

Sturmey, P. (2015). *Reducing restraint and restrictive behavior management practices.* New York: Springer.

Sturmey, P., & Didden, R. (2014). *Evidence-based practice and intellectual disabilities.* Hoboken, NJ: Wiley.

Sturmey, P., & Williams, D. E. (2016). *Pica in individuals with developmental disabilities.* New York: Springer.

Taylor, S. J. (2009). *Acts of Conscience: World War II, mental institutions, and religious objectors.* New York: Syracuse University Press.

Van Houten, R., Axelrod, S., Bailey, J. S., Favell, J. E., Foxx, R. M., Iwata, B. A., & Lovaas, O. I. (1988). The right to effective behavioral treatment. *Journal of Applied Behavior Analysis, 21*(4), 381–384.

Wallace, M. D., Iwata, B. A., Zhou, L., & Goff, G. A. (1999). Rapid assessment of the effects of restraint on self-injury and adaptive behavior. *Journal of Applied Behavior Analysis, 32*(4), 525–528.

Webber, L., McVilly, K., Fester, T., & Chan, J. (2011a). Factors influencing quality of behaviour support plans and the impact of plan quality on restrictive intervention use. *International Journal of Positive Behavioural Support, 1*(1), 24–31.

Webber, L. S., McVilly, K., Fester, T., & Zazelis, T. (2011b). Assessing behaviour support plans for Australian adults with intellectual disability using the 'behavior support plan quality evaluation II'(BSP-QE II). *Journal of Intellectual and Developmental Disability, 36,* 1–5.

Webber, L. S., McVilly, K. R., & Chan, J. (2011c). Restrictive interventions for people with a disability exhibiting challenging behaviours: Analysis of a population database. *Journal of Applied Research in Intellectual Disabilities, 24*(6), 495–507.

Webber, L. S., McVilly, K. R., Stevenson, E., & Chan, J. (2010). The use of restrictive interventions in Victoria, Australia: Population data for 2007–2008. *Journal of Intellectual and Developmental Disability, 35*(3), 199–206.

PART V
Organizational Development

13
Building a Culturally and Diversity-Sensitive Workforce

Elizabeth B. Hughes Fong

Ethnic inequality and racism are key components of minority diversity in the areas of business, religion, gender, socioeconomic status, and age (George & Jones 2000). An organizational culture which fosters racism has a negative influence on the well-being of its employees, hinders the development of its marginalized individuals, makes it difficult to climb the ladder of success, limits access to economic and societal resources, and creates tension and conflict between minority and majority groups (Sintonen, 2000). Ultimately, the tensions and instabilities brought on by the toxic organizational work environment negatively impact organizational performance and profit making (Sintonen, 2000).

Several researchers have supported different theories related to the topic of diversity within the workplace. For example, van Knippenberg and Mell (2016) argued that diversity can be divided into three types: trait, state, and emergent. Trait diversity consists of gender and personality diversity. State diversity is differences in malleable characteristics, such as distributed information and preference diversity. Emergent diversity is differences in dyadic interactions and cognition. An organization likely has all three types of diversity, and individuals are required to work with those who may differ from them on any of those levels. It was originally thought that diversity was good for performance but not interpersonal relations (Williams & O'Reilly, 1998). Then in 2007, van Knippenberg and Schippers further examined diversity in the workplace and found that diversity had both positive and negative effects, which were dependent on various moderating factors. Furthermore, Guillaume et al. (2017) argued that creativity and innovation were positive for diversity, as there are open-ended tasks where diversity of ideas are valued.

As the baby boomer workforce continues to age, younger, more diverse populations of workers will take their place. The result will be considerable opportunities and challenges for organizations, one of them being that by 2030, there may not be enough younger workers to replace those workers nearing retirement (Strack et al., 2014). Therefore, it is important to understand how to attract and retain younger workers, which reflects the changing demographic of the population. Not only is the workforce diversifying ethnically, but is also becoming more demographically diverse. Millennials are seeking employment opportunities that offer them collaboration, recognition, innovation, and relationships, extremely valuable incentives for those seeking employment within human services organizations serving persons with intellectual and developmental disabilities. However, diverse ethnic workers are being asked, generally indirectly, to focus on an Anglo-capitalistic workplace and acculturate. This thinking may lead to employees being unhappy with their place of employment, and it also does not recognize diversity of the employee (Strack et al., 2014).

Sintonen (2000) argued that organizational culture is the course of action, values, norms, behaviors, symbols, crystallized knowledge, and commonly held ideas about what and how a company functions. An organization's culture can be seen through its overt behaviors (employee behavior, logo, trademark, environment), and values (Sintonen, 2000). The organizational culture is dynamic, and thus may change. The best organizations are those that are learning organizations. Organizations should be prepared to meet the growing diversity of needs by ensuring that training curricula are cultural and diverse, there are inclusive service settings, and incorporating leadership principles that value the contributions of marginalized and underrepresented groups (Sintonen, 2000).

It is important to understand cultural competence in order to know how to build a workplace which is diverse and sensitive to the needs of their workers. Many academic programs include cultural competence and multicultural training within their coursework, but most behavior analytic programs do not have a multicultural or similar course, possibly due to the past emphasis on the analysis of observable behaviors (BACB, n.d.). Furthermore, many workplaces employees are provided with limited diversity training during human resources orientation, the process of "on-boarding," and online programs such as Relias©. Apropos building a culturally and diversity-sensitive workforce, Hughes Fong et al. (2015) conducted a survey of 987 Board Certified Behavior Analysts and found that the majority of respondents reported spending less than 10% of the time working outside of their culture. The second highest among the time spent working outside of the respondent's culture was 41%–60%. Similarly, the largest number of respondents indicated that they spend 41%–60% of the time working with a different race/ethnicity. Although many respondents viewed themselves as mostly-to-somewhat competent, the majority reported to have received less than five hours of further training via webinars, seminars, workshops, in cultural training/education since receiving their degree. The second and third largest number of respondents reported receiving at least one year of experience working with culturally diverse populations, and no cultural training/education since receiving their degree. The question remains how respondents classified themselves as culturally competent when there are no adopted standards for culturally sensitive practice of behavior analysis nor what culturally sensitive practice of behavior analysis should look like. With BACB programs providing limited culturally diverse and sensitivity training, the major need within the field of behavioral analysis is: how do current practitioners gain the adequate training necessary to meet the demands of many of the diverse array of clients?

Brief History of Cultural Diversity and the American Workplace

In the early 1900s, while the workforce in the United States was diversifying due to an increase in immigrants, the importance of cultural diversity and cultural influence was overlooked (Gelfand et al., 2017). This negligence was partly due to a minimization of cultural differences and greater focus on assimilation, thus the idea of the "melting pot" in the United States (Gelfand et al., 2017). In 1906, Wundt was one of the first people to highlight the role that culture plays in understanding a person's mind and behavior (Gelfand et al., 2017). However, this work did not gain popularity and led to a focus on culture in the workplace. As time passed, very few researchers such as Garth et al. (1925) and Sánchez (1934) continued to examine the role of culture in the workplace; however, these studies concentrated on American samples and not the importance that culture plays in work, thus characterized as culture bound and culture blind (Katzell & Austin, 1992).

Gefland et al. (2017) argued that diversity increased during the mid-twentieth century, as well as the examination of culture and personality, perception, motivation, cognitions, and mental abilities. Outcomes from many of these earlier studies led to the realization that there are variabilities in cultures, and that cultural differences exist. Due to this insight gained from the cultural studies, there was greater focus on cross-cultural comparisons and cross-cultural adaptations, which led to the development of training programs to assist organizations with diverse employees (Gefland et al., 2017).

During the late twentieth century, equal opportunity laws came about and diversity management programs were rebranded as increasing the performance of women and individuals of color (Berrey, 2014). Several authors have researched how discrimination negatively affects the workforce. For example, Quinn et al. (1968) conducted research on workplace discrimination and concluded that factors other than achievement are related to promotion. Quinn et al. interviewed 139 managers and their research outcomes suggested that anti-Semitic discrimination occurred more frequently in organizations in which the employees felt a pressure to discriminate and if the managers promoted anti-Semitic attitudes.

Throughout the history of the United States, different organizations have faced legal ramifications for discriminatory behaviors. For example, in 1992, Shoney's, a family dining business, agreed to a settlement after it was charged with discrimination against Black employees (Watkins, 1993). Similar to the discrimination experienced by Jews discussed by Quinn et al. (1968), Shoney's management did not believe that Blacks should be in a position within the workplace where they would be seen by other patrons coming into the restaurant. Relevant to this case is the classic Milgram (1974) prison experiment in which the participants were obedient to authority figures even when the obedience went against human rights. Thus, while Shoney's had an unwritten policy of discrimination, the discriminatory actions of Shoney's highlights how authority figures and organizational culture can influence obedience behaviors.

After the Civil Rights Act of 1964, it might appear that race relations have become more tolerant, racial segregation is not endorsed, and negative racial statements are no longer supported. However, what were once blatant forms of prejudice were replaced with more subtle ones, such as microaggressions. For example, organizations tried to justify discriminatory practices such as "matching" a company's employees to their clientele. This idea was believed to be effective because the minority employee is more qualified due to their minority status and experiences to better understand similar needs and experiences of the clientele (Cox, 1993). During this time period, diversity management was a key focus of organizations which sought to decrease workplace inequality. In particular, high-status jobs were often demonstrated to show significant racial and gender disparities (Berrey, 2014). Women and people of color tended to be less represented in certain types of jobs (i.e., craft, management and professional), have lower pay, and be granted less autonomy. In addition, there appeared to be a "glass ceiling" that prevented advancement into high levels of organizational management due to discrimination.

In the mid 1980's, diversity management also emerged as a solution to inequalities in the workplace (Berrey, 2014). Diversity management is largely composed of personnel policies, offices, programs, trainings, mission statements, and task forces related to diversity. The motivation for diversity management came from expansions in equal opportunity law (Berrey, 2014). Within the next decade, 75% of *Fortune* 500 companies had a diversity program (Ryan et al., 2002). Berrey argued that even with the increase of diversity programs, women and people of color continue to be underrepresented, tracked, have less autonomy, marginalized in jobs, have lower-paying jobs, and relegated to lower status in the workplace in comparison to their white male counterparts. While diversity management sounds like a positive attempt at a solution to workplace inequality, in reality it minimized gender and racial boundaries (Ryan et al., 2002).

Unfortunately, workplace culture can be difficult to control. Factors such as the cultural traits of a business' staff members, clients, geographic location, and the economy are just some of the factors that impact workplace culture and are out of the hands of management (Berrey, 2014). However, management can control policies, mission statements, and other procedures. These management variables include the office culture, how staff work together, and expectations for employee behavior. Similarly, the hierarchical organization of a business, similar to a human services organization, can also set the workplace culture relative to the division of power and how information is communicated between parties. Notably, the cultural backgrounds of those who hold power within an organization impact the decision-making for the business, which can impact the organization's cultural dynamic (Berrey, 2014).

Review of Pertinent Research Literature

Recruitment

Recruitment is a dominant challenge to building a culturally and diversity-sensitive workforce. Often, minorities are hired at a lower rate than their majority counterparts, even with anti-discrimination laws and programs to promote diversity (Hofhuis et al., 2015). During recruitment and hiring, bias towards candidates whose backgrounds or worldviews do not match the organization also occurs. Those individuals who are part of a minority group suffer the consequences of not being the "norm," especially those who display a low degree of assimilation. Similarly, those minority culture individuals who appear to have assimilated to the majority culture are more likely to be hired. Those responsible for hiring tend to offer employment to individuals who they believe can complete the assigned tasks, contribute to productivity of the workplace, and enhance the social climate among employees. The social component involves assessing if the candidate would fit in well and work pleasantly with the team (Hofhuis et al., 2015). This is where bias towards those who are different from the interviewer may impact hiring decisions, as individuals are more likely to hire people more similar to themselves.

Further, interviewers frequently rely on their stereotypes when selecting candidates to interview and hire even when looking at resumes and conducting interviews. When individuals who are different enter the workplace, it can make the social environment seem less secure and psychologically threatening due to differences in interpersonal behaviors. There is a fear of productivity loss, language barriers, increased anxiety, and miscommunication when minorities are a part of the workplace. These biases, combined with the idea that a minority team member may threaten the majority's norms and values, lead to minorities being discriminated against. For example, Hofhius et al. (2015) confirmed that when a minority candidate displayed a higher level of cultural maintenance characterized by way of dressing, language use, religious habitats, recognition of their world view or norms, and interpersonal interaction style, interviewers assessed them less favorably. However, these negative assessment ratings due to cultural maintenance can be reduced by perceived diversity outcomes, specifically having a positive view on diversity and being able to see the benefits of diversity.

Microaggressions in the Workplace

With a diverse workforce, it can be assumed that there are multiple types of minorities in the population, including ability, gender, race, religion, and sexual preference, to name a few. While it has been noted that blatant expressions of discrimination have declined, the more subtle and ambiguous forms of discrimination, termed microaggressions, continue to exist (Badsford et al. (2014). In illustration, Bible and Hill (2007) argued that women are subject to a number of gender-based challenges in the workplace, including negative stereotypes and perceptions, limited mentoring and networking options, family-related issues, funding availability, and discrimination. In order to better understand discrimination against women in the workplace, Badsford et al. (2014) examined gender microaggressions using 150 undergraduate students. Perceived microaggressions and projective negative work outcomes were assessed by reading various vignettes then rating them on a Likert scale. Results indicated that women still face prejudice in the workplace and are experiencing more covert discrimination than ever. While both men and women experience workplace microaggressions, women are more attune to even subtle forms of discrimination than their male counterparts (Badsford et al., 2014).

Other Types of Diversity

Largely, this chapter has focused on the importance of diversity in terms of race and sex, but other types of diversity such as religion and ability are equally a concern. King and Franke (2017) explored the effects of religion and argued that that it is viewed negatively when expressed in the workplace. On the other hand, this research found that there were no differences if the religious expression was from a majority group (viz., Christians) or minority group (viz., Muslims). For those who choose to express their religion, it is likely that they experience negative reactions from their peers, in part because it is believed that religious identities may be viewed as controllable and disruptive (Ryan & Garner, 2019).

Similar to other types of diversity, having religious diversity means that there will be varying thoughts on issues and problem-solving. In addition, religious diversity will contribute to the overall diversity of the workplace and employees will have increased prosocial behavior and skill in working with different types of people (Héliot et al., 2020).

Pertinent to this chapter, individuals with disabilities comprise the largest minority group, yet there is a lack of awareness of disability-related issues, formal accommodation procedures and protocols, and often a hostile environment (Williams & Hagood, 2019). According to the United States Bureau of Labor and Statistics (2020), 19.3% of persons with disabilities were employed in 2019. In comparison, the employment population for individuals without a disability was 66.3% (United States Bureau of Labor Statistics, 2020). This is not a drastic change from the 19.1% of the population employed who had a disability in 2018. It is clear from the research that there is also a lack of diversity when it comes to hiring individuals with disabilities and that the need to increase diversity in the workplace is not just centered on race, sex, or religious issues.

Benefits of Having a Culturally and Diversity-Sensitive Workforce

There are benefits to having a culturally and diversity-sensitive organizational culture. For example, an anti-racist workplace increases employee productivity and enhances individuals' ability to perform their job and responsibilities (Sintonen, 2000). Since organizational culture is fluid, it is not too late to change the culture so that it is one more welcoming, accepting, and embraces diversity. However, wanting a diverse workplace and actually having a diverse workplace are two different things. In order for an organization to become more diverse several steps should be taken. First, it is important to learn and understand the culture of the organization (Sintonen, 2000). Organizational culture awareness is essential because one can learn about the unconscious patterns in its operations and functioning. In terms of reducing discrimination, it is necessary to examine the patterns and conceptions that are within the organization and how they are linked to discriminatory ideologies. The ultimate goal of the examination should focus on how discriminatory ideologies are linked to patterns and practices within the organization (Sintonen, 2000). These discriminatory practices should be identified and avoided because they may lead to a negative relationship between society and the organization. In addition, meetings and trainings should also be conducted in order to interview staff; learn about the organization, organizational culture, and employee experiences; and to obtain data as to where improvements should be made.

Furthermore, since client populations tend to be diverse, having diversity within the workplace may help the organization learn about and gain access to minority populations. Increased diversity also reduces "groupthink" and may increase the learning potential of teams, increase flexibility and creativity, improve organizational competitiveness in the market, and promote more effective decision-making (Hofhius et al., 2015).

Practice Recommendations

The following recommendations integrate general knowledge about culture and diversity in the workforce with concepts and methods emphasized in behavior analysis and organizational behavior management (OBM).

Assessment

A review of literature has found that there is currently no requirement for behavior analytic or OBM coursework to train students on cultural diversity. This could be due to the already extensive list of topics that universities are required to cover in the Behavior Analyst Certification Board (BACB) Task List. However, for those universities that are interested in addressing this need, it is important to have a clear way to assess effectiveness. After all, behavior analysis values data-based decisions; therefore, assessments in OBM aim to identify those variables which are related to employee performance issues and are intended to guide interventions (Wilder et al., 2018). With the information gained from an assessment, organization leaders can intervene on the antecedent and consequent variables that are responsible for those performance issues.

The types of assessments in OBM vary and may include historical assessments, indirect assessments, descriptive analysis, experimental analysis, or systems analysis (Wilder et al., 2018). In applying these OBM assessments to diversity, the historical assessment might include the examination of previously collected diversity information. If the goal is to increase client diversity, intake information could be examined. Furthermore, data around health care utilization and race, socioeconomic status, religion, sexual preference, or any other variable could be evaluated if an organization is seeking to understand discrimination and health service utilization.

Wilder et al. argued that an indirect assessment would seek information via interviews about environmental factors related to performance issues or process. The indirect assessment often uses an OBM questionnaire but none currently exist that specifically address issues around diversity. Therefore, it may be necessary to seek assessment questionnaires from other fields. For example, the Tool for Assessing Cultural Competence Training (TACCT) developed by the Association of American Medical Colleges assists schools in developing and evaluating cultural competence curricula to meet these requirements (Boardmanm, 2015). The TAACT is a 42-item self-administered assessment where respondents are asked to answer questions related to health disparities, community strategies, bias/stereotyping, skills specific to cross-cultural communication, use of interpreters, and self-reflection/culture of medicine (Boardmanm, 2015). Overall, the results of this assessment allow educational leaders to evaluate all components of their cultural competence curricula, identify gaps and redundancies, and make the best use of opportunities and resources. However, caution should be used because this assessment has not been validated for use in behavior analysis.

A descriptive analysis involves direct observation of the behavior of interest as well as recording of the related antecedent and consequent variables (Wilder et al., 2018). The discriminatory behaviors of leadership or employees could be defined, then an antecedent-behavior-consequence analysis could be completed to help the consultant understand what is maintaining the target behavior.

Experimental analysis occurs when the antecedent and consequent variables are manipulated (Wilder et al., 2018). For example, this might be accomplished by no longer having staff reinforce discriminatory behavior by others and seeing if there is an increase or decrease of discrimination. Conversely, increasing identified reinforcers when culturally sensitive behavior is observed could be another analysis-informed intervention.

Other Formal Assessments

Several tools are available to assess an organization's diversity and inclusion and, although not from the OBM field, offer a more concrete way to measure the diversity and inclusion of an organization. One example is the Diversity Climate Perceptions Scale (DC) developed by Mor Barak et al. (1998) to assess fairness and inclusiveness with respect to diversity in organizations and focus on human resource decisions. Items in the organizational fairness subscale cover issues related to fairness and equality within human resources and administrative policies and practices in relation to age, religion, ethnicity, and gender. On the other hand, support of diversity networks, training, and mentoring programs are assessed through the organizational inclusiveness subscale.

The Diversity Promises Scale (DP) developed by Chrobot-Mason (2003) looks at broader diversity climate issues by examining if an organization keeps its promises of having a diverse climate for its employees of color. The DP focuses on the perceptions of the respondents within the organization and whether they believe that diversity within their working environment has been honored by the organization through proper workforce representation, appreciation of minority contributions, and elimination of bias. Outcomes from DP found correlations among employees of color within different organizations when promises such as pay increases based on performance, personal problem support, and overall job security are recognized. This scale appears to have good reliability and validity, but generality is unknown because the participants were from the same organization (Chrobot-Mason, 2003).

The Organizational Diversity Needs Analysis (ODNA) developed by Dahm et al. (2009) is intended to help organizations customize diversity and inclusion awareness and skills training design. In addition, this assessment identifies gaps in skills and competencies that should be addressed and provides baseline information to measure and monitor change at many levels within the organization's structure. Once assessments are completed, the behavior analyst should move into the goal-setting phase.

Goal Setting

Goal setting is an important step in behavior change that has extensive research support (Roose & Williams, 2018). Before setting goals, it should be confirmed that the goals can be achieved and there are no conflicting goals. In addition, it should be confirmed that there is adequate commitment to achieving the goal by questioning respondents, examining if the goal matches the individual's stated goal, or directly measuring the behavior related to goal achievement after the goal has been assigned. Due to the pervasive nature of discrimination, one could argue that creating a culturally and diversity-sensitive workforce could be described as a "very difficult goal." However, the good news is that research outcomes indicate that there is a linear relationship between the level of difficulty of a goal and performance; specifically that the higher the goal, the higher the performance level (Roose & Williams, 2018). Furthermore, success is also dependent on adequate reinforcement and ensuring that the behavior is within the repertoire of the individual. Therefore, effective systems of reinforcement should be used during this phase.

Feedback is also an important component of the achievement of goals; in fact, feedback when used in conjunction with goal setting results in better performance (Roose & Williams, 2018). Feedback may be conceptualized as providing information about an individual's performance, which may allow for performance adjustments, and as the consequence and the function of the goal as the antecedent (Fellner & Sulzer-Azaroff, 1984). Therefore, feedback can increase the behavior (positive feedback) as well as decrease behavior (negative feedback). Feedback may also function as an establishing operation by increasing the value of the consequence for goal behavior (Agnew, 1997; Duncan & Bruwelheide, 1986).

Workplace Culture

Research outcomes suggest that a workplace that has positive beliefs and attitudes about diversity can decrease cultural bias (Hofhius et al., 2015). Specifically, having employees see the value in diversity has been associated with decreased diversity-related anxiety, increased intercultural contact, and an overall more positive diversity climate (Groggins & Ryan, 2013; Hofhuis et al., 2015; Shen et al., 2009; Tropp & Bianchi, 2006). Since the reduction of bias in recruitment may be difficult to remove, some researchers believe that offering incentives towards increasing diversity in the workplace or clear structures and guidelines in hiring may help to increase workplace diversity (Hofhius et al., 2015). In addition, hiring candidates based on their level of competence and diverse knowledge and experience they bring with them will help to decrease hiring biases. Promotion of the benefits of diversity within an organization and education of those benefiting factors may also help to change the mindset of individuals and promote openness to diversity within the work environment. After assessing where the need for intervention is and collecting data, one way to impact behavior is through training.

Trainings and Curricula

Cross-cultural training seeks to understand and acknowledge differences and can bring about individual changes (Schriefer, 2018). According to Dongfeng (2012), a cross-cultural training program should be comprised of four characteristics. First, there should be assistance for the training in moving from an overt and descriptive understanding to an analytic and interpretive level. Second, trainees should understand the dynamics of cross-cultural communication and adaptation. Next, trainees should be able to move from culture-general to culture-specific sensitivity where they can reflect on both their culture as well as the new culture. Finally, a training program should detail the conceptual framework in which to view and understand the new culture as well as the opportunity to develop one's own strategies for cross-cultural adjustment and communication.

There are many components which can help make a diversity training program more effective and lead to participants embracing the benefits of diversity training. Training that is four to six hours in duration tends to have a greater impact on outcomes in comparison to shorter training (Phillips et al., 2016). However, training lasting eight hours or more is not as impactful. Another finding is that training spread out over multiple weeks seems to be most effective. Finally, training that is held face to face by a trainer is also more effective than computer-based training programs. In terms of content, training which focuses on one aspect of diversity has been shown to be more effective in improving cognitive outcomes in comparison to programs that have multiple topics or programs not specific to any specific element of diversity. Training programs should also be interactive, where participants engage in task interdependence, work with others, and implement active learning methods (e.g., role-playing, discussion, games). Opportunities for mentorship and goal setting should also be offered. As well, it is important for managers to attend diversity trainings, as it is more impactful when management is directly involved in educating employees on diversity goals (Phillips et al., 2016).

However, just because an organization provides diversity training does not mean that the attendees will transfer the knowledge, skills, and attitudes they learned to practice. Instead, there should be a clear link between the organization's diversity training, mission, and culture to performance (Cunningham, 2012). Consider, too, that training is not enough to change the biases of others. Therefore, in addition to offering training, opportunities for reflection, discussion, and awareness-raising should be continued in the spirit of cooperative learning (Noon, 2018). In effect, although comprehensive training can improve the effects of certain diversity programs, employers have to pair training with contingencies that support change (Dobbin & Kalev, 2018)

Yet another opportunity for diversity training is through professional continuing education. Continuing education is a requirement for Board Certified Behavior Analysts and learning objectives must be included in a continuing education event that is behavior-analytic in nature, addresses the practice, science, and methodology of behavior analysis, and is conducted by a qualified instructor. Continuing education events must be designed for certified individuals, extend beyond the content areas on the task list or relate directly to the profession of behavior analysis, and be accurate, up to date, and consistent with current best practices (BACB Learning CE, 2020). The field of behavior analysis and OBM would be enhanced by increasing continuing education training opportunities devoted to improving cultural and diversity sensitivity in the workplace.

Research Directions

While this chapter has reviewed social sciences and medical research concerned with culture and diversity in the workforce, similar inquiry in behavior analysis and OBM is lacking. Some objectives of behavior analysis and OBM research within human services organizations for persons with IDD are to align standardized assessments of diversity with indirect and descriptive assessment methods commonly conducted by behavioral practitioners and consultants. As noted previously, such assessment is not only essential for outcome evaluation but also informs organizational-change interventions and systems initiatives that address a culture of diversity sensitivity and the needs of minorities and underrepresented groups.

Another research priority is to evaluate the effects of different training approaches on cultural and diversity sensitivity among employees. Process variables such as the content, duration, and requirements of training are likely to affect learning and performance outcomes in multiple ways. Component analyses of training programs is another research objective that can guide decisions about the most effective procedures for widespread application in the workforce. Thankfully, the vast behavior analysis training literature provides many options for empirically evaluating the effects of diversity training across several domains (Shapiro & Kazemi, 2017).

Lastly, social validity research will help evaluate the perceptions of employees who participate in diversity training programs by having them rate acceptance and approval of training goals, methods, and results (Wolf, 1978). Social validation ranks high as a priority within behavior analysis and, accordingly, should be an integral component of organizational research devoted to cultural and diversity sensitivity. The persons responsible for formulating and implementing diversity training programs as well as administrative leaders should also be targeted in social validity research.

References

Agnew, J. L. (1997). The establishing operation in organizational behavior management. *Journal of Organizational Behavior Management*, 18(1), 7–19. doi:10.1300/J075v18n01_02

Basford, T. E., Offermann, L. R., & Behrend, T. S. (2014). Do you see what I see? Perceptions of gender microaggressions in the workplace. *Psychology of Women Quarterly*, 38(3), 340–349.

Behavior Analysis Certification Board (n.d.). About behavior analysis. Retrieved from: https://www.bacb.com/about-behavior-analysis/

Behavior Analysis Certification Board (2020). Learning ce event checklist. Retrieved from: https://www.bacb.com/wp-content/uploads/2020/05/ACE-Provider-Handbook_201112.pdf

Berrey, E. (2014). Breaking glass ceilings, ignoring dirty floors: The culture and class bias of diversity management. *American Behavioral Scientist, 58*(2), 347–370.

Bible, D., & Hill, K. L. (2007). Discrimination: Women in business. *Journal of Organizational Culture, Communication and Conflict, 11*(1), 65–76.

Chrobot-Mason, D. L. (2003). Keeping the promise: Psychological contract violations for minority employees. *Journal of Managerial Psychology, 18*, 22–45.

Cox, T., Jr. (1993). *Cultural diversity in organizations: Theory, research, and practice.* San Francisco: Berrett–Koehler.

Cunningham, G. B. (2012). Diversity training in intercollegiate athletics. *Journal of Sport Management, 26*(5), 391–403.

Dahm, M. J., Willems, E. P., Ivancevich, J. M., & Graves, D. E. (2009). Development of an organizational diversity needs analysis (ODNA) Instrument. *Journal of Applied Social Psychology, 39*, 2, 283–318.

Dobbin, F., & Kalev, A. (2018). Why doesn't diversity training work? The challenge for industry and academia. *Anthropology Now, 10*(2), 48–55.

Dongfeng, L. (2012). Culture shock and its implications for cross-cultural training and culture. *Cross-Cultural Communication, 8*(4), pp. 70–74.

Duncan, P. K., & Bruwelheide, L. R. (1986). Feedback: Use and possible behavioral functions. *Journal of Organizational Behavior Management, 7*(3–4), 91–114. doi:10.1300/J075v07n03_06

Fellner, D. J., & Sulzer-Azaroff, B. (1984). A behavioral analysis of goal setting. *Journal of Organizational Behavior Management, 6*(1), 33–51. doi:10.1300/J075v06n01_03

Fong, E. H., Jarmuz-Smith, S., Dogan, R., Serna, R., & Woolery, K. (2015). *The Behavior Analyst and Cultural Competency.* Rev EDUCCap (Research Electronic Data Capture).

Garth, T.R., Serafini, T.J., & Dutton, D. (1925). The intelligence of full blood Indians. *Journal of Applied Psychology, 9*, pp. 382–89.

Gelfand, M. J., Aycan, Z., Erez, M., & Leung, K. (2017). Cross-cultural industrial organizational psychology and organizational behavior: A hundred-year journey. *Journal of Applied Psychology, 102*(3), 514

George, J. M., & Jones, G. R. (2000). The role of time in theory and theory building. *Journal of management 26*(4), 657–684.

Groggins, A., & Ryan, A. M. (2013). Embracing uniqueness: The underpinnings of a positive climate for diversity. *Journal of Occupational and Organizational Psychology, 86*, 264–282. doi:10.1111/joop.12008

Guillaume, Y. R., Dawson, J. F., Otaye-Ebede, L., Woods, S. A., & West, M. A. (2017). Harnessing demographic differences in organizations: What moderates the effects of workplace diversity? *Journal of Organizational Behavior, 38*(2), 276–303.

Héliot, Y., Gleibs, I. H., Coyle, A., Rousseau, D. M., & Rojon, C. (2020). Religious identity in the workplace: A systematic review, research agenda, and practical implications. *Human Resource Management, 59*(2), 153–173.

Hofhuis, J., van der Zee, K. I., & Otten, S. (2015). Measuring employee perception on the effects of cultural diversity at work: Development of the benefits and threats of diversity scale. *Quality & Quantity, 49,* 177–201. doi:10.1007/s11135-013-9981-7

Katzell, R. A., & Austin, J. T. (1992). From then to now: The development of industrial-organizational psychology in the United States. *Journal of Applied Psychology, 77*(6), 803.

King, J. E., & Franke, G. R. (2017). Faith bias or religious expression: The real religious diversity challenge?. *Journal of Management, Spirituality & Religion, 14*(1), 81–99.

Mor Barak, M. E., Cherin, D. A., & Berkman, S. (1998). Organizational and personal dimensions in diversity climate. *Journal of Applied Behavioral Science, 34,* 82–104.

Noon, M. (2018). Pointless diversity training: Unconscious bias, new racism and agency. *Work, Employment and Society, 32*(1), 198–209.

Phillips, B. N., Deiches, J., Morrison, B., Chan, F., & Bezyak, J. L. (2016). Disability diversity training in the workplace: Systematic review and future directions. *Journal of Occupational Rehabilitation, 26*(3), 264–275.

Quinn, R. P., Tabor, J. M., & Gordon, L. K. (1968). *The decision to discriminate: A study of executive selection.* Ann Arbor, MI: Institute for Social Research.

Roose, K. M., & Williams, W. L. (2018). An evaluation of the effects of very difficult goals. *Journal of Organizational Behavior Management, 38*(1), 18–48.

Ryan, A., & Gardner, D. (2019). Religious harassment and bullying in the workplace. *Dignity and Inclusion at Work.* Singapore: Springer.

Ryan, J., Hawdon, J., & Branick, A. (2002). The political economy of diversity: Diversity programs in fortune 500 companies. *Sociological Research Online, 7*(1), 26–40.

Sánchez, G. I. (1934). Bilingualism and mental measures. A word of caution. *Journal of Applied Psychology, 18*(6), 765.

Schneider, S. (2018). Supporting a better appreciation of socio-cultural pre-conceptions in environmental education.

Shapiro, M., & Kazemi, E. (2017). A review of training strategies to teach individuals implementation of behavioral interventions. *Journal of Organizational Behavior Management, 37*(1), 32–62. doi: 10.1080/01608061.2016.1267066

Shen, J., Chanda, A., D'Netto, B., & Monga, M. (2009). Managing diversity through human resource management: An international perspective and conceptual framework. *International Journal of Human Resource Management, 20,* 235–251. doi:10.1080/09585190802670

Sintonen, T. (2000). Racism and business ethics. *EJBO-Electronic Journal of Business Ethics and Organization Studies.*

Strack, R., Baier, J., Marchingo, M., &Sharda, S. (2014). *The global workforce crisis: $10 trillion at risk.* Boston, MA: Boston Consulting Group.

Tropp, L., & Bianchi, R. (2006). Valuing diversity and interest in intergroup contact. *Journal of Social Issues, 62,* 533–551. doi: 10.1111/j.1540-4560.2006.00472.x

United States Bureau of Labor Statistics. (2020). *Persons with a Disability: Labor Force Characteristics −2019* [PDF file]. Retrieved from https://www.bls.gov/news.release/di sabl.nr0.htm

Van Knippenberg, D., & Mell, J. N. (2016). Past, present, and potential future of team diversity research: From compositional diversity to emergent diversity. *Organizational Behavior and Human Decision Processes, 136,* 135–145.

Van Knippenberg, D., & Schippers, M. C. (2007). Work group diversity. *Annual Review of Psychology, 58,* 515–541.

Watkins, S. (1993, October 18). Racism du jour at Shoney's. *The Nation.*

Wilder, D. A., Lipschultz, J. L., King, A., Driscoll, S., & Sigurdsson, S. (2018). An analysis of the commonality and type of pre intervention assessment procedures in the Journal of Organizational Behavior Management (2000–2015). *Journal of Organizational Behavior Management, 38*(1), 5–17.

Williams, K. Y., & O'Reilly III, C. A. (1998). Demography and diversity in organizations: A review of 40 years of research. *Research in Organizational Behavior, 20,* 77–140.

Williams, T., & Hagood, A. (2019). Disability, the silent D in diversity. *Library Trends, 67*(3), 487–496.

Wolf, M. M. (1978). Social validity: The case for subjective measurement or how applied behavior analysis is finding its heart. *Journal of Applied Behavior Analysis, 11,* 203–214.

14
Organizational Ethics

Joy S. Pollard, Shawn P. Quigley, and Steve Woolf

The historical significance of Watson's (1913) proclamation of behavior as the primary focus of psychology has had considerable influence on the science of behavior analysis. The scientific community and knowledge of determinants of behavior have continued to expand, with Skinner (1938, 1953) and colleagues' pioneering experimentation and initial demonstrations of application (e.g., Ayllon & Michael, 1959; Fuller, 1949). In 1968, Baer, Wolf, and Risley outlined tenets extending the science into application for improvement of socially significant behavior. The work of Lovass and colleagues (1987) demonstrated the power of the implementation science of behavior analysis to make a socially meaningful change in the lives of children and families affected by Autism Spectrum Disorder (ASD). Application of the laws and principles have further yielded robust outcomes for various socially important needs (e.g., Carr & Nosik, 2017). These historical factors led to the development of a professional practice domain of behavior analysis, and in 1998, the Behavior Analyst Certification Board (BACB) was founded to develop professional behavior analytic credentials (Carr & Nosik).

The field has continued to mature over the last decade and the number of Board Certified Behavior Analysts (BCBA®) have grown over 110% (BACB, 2019). According to the BACB's jobs report (2019), there has been an increased demand for BCBAs® in almost every US state, with an 800% increase in job advertisements over the last seven years. Trump and Ayers (2019) suggest that the rapid growth rates of BCBAs® are related to the Autism Spectrum Disorder (ASD) treatment legislation across the nation. All 50 states now mandate that commercial health care insurers cover Applied Behavior Analysis (ABA) as a medically necessary treatment to ameliorate the symptoms associated with ASD. In addition, over 20 states currently cover ABA treatment for ASD through Medicaid. Furthermore, the bellwether states of Massachusetts and California have created mandates where any child with a mental health diagnosis is eligible to receive services from an appropriately credentialed applied behavior analyst. The increasing prevalence rates of ASD have also been instrumental to the growth of the field, with rates increasing from 1 in 58 to 1 in 40 (Kogan et al., 2018). The Centers for Disease Control and Prevention's (CDC) Autism and Developmental Monitoring (ADDM) Network hypothesizes the increased ASD prevalence rates are due to greater exposure to high-risk factors such as environmental toxins and expanded public awareness identifying ASD symptoms (CDC, 2019).

Given the increasing prevalence of ASD, treatment models that include multiple provider levels for delivering behavior analytic services for individuals with ASD have emerged. Treatment is typically delivered in a 1:1 setting and might be classified as focused (i.e., 10–25 hours per week) or comprehensive (i.e., 30–40 hours per week; CASP, 2020). ABA treatment varies by dosage and by service-delivery model, although a tiered model is typical (CASP). Under this model, the direct hours are most frequently provided by a paraprofessional (e.g., behavior technician) who is overseen by a professional with at least a master's degree (e.g., BCBA®). The intensive supports and tiered nature of the treatment model require multiple professionals to support one client. This is further complicated given treatment may continue for multiple years, sometimes throughout the lifespan. Additionally, according to Peacock et al. (2012), comorbid conditions might require additional non-behavior analytic resource allocation (e.g., professional time, money) to meet individual needs. It is unfortunate that despite the increasing growth rates of BCBAs® across the country, only about 40% of families affected by ASD receive ABA-based treatment (Xu et al., 2019).

The combination of ASDs' high prevalence, shortage of providers, nationwide treatment mandates, and other factors set the occasion for robust business opportunities for autism treatment providers and investors. Indeed, the ASD ABA treatment market was valued at $1.87 billion in 2017 in the US growing at 3.9% annually. With the ASD market valuation expected to increase to $2.23 billion by 2022 (Research and Markets, 2017) private equity investment has increased in this sector. In fact, the ASD market currently has the highest valuations in the healthcare industry (Provident, 2018). Provident, an investment banking firm that specializes in merger and acquisitions, anticipates the ASD sector will continue to experience elevated valuations as private equity continues to builds traction.

The short history of the professional practice of behavior analysis (i.e., since the first professional credential in 1998; Carr & Nosik, 2017), the high number of new BCBAs® entering the marketplace, family demand for ABA services, the dosage and treatment model, as well as favorable revenue business conditions set the occasion for numerous ethical challenges for such a young field. As described by Graber and O'Brien (2019), reimbursement rates and practices (e.g., hourly billing versus single event billing), differing levels of care for individuals (e.g., consult, home-based, intensive clinic-based), and professional expertise in service delivery may create ethical no-win situations. These types of situations are affected by the leadership, and thereby the values of the organization. For example, a neophyte behavior analyst committed to improving the lives of those served with little understanding of business management and a non-provider with a business degree will likely arrive at different solutions when balancing quality service with financial stability. Additional challenges arise with the entrance of investment firms who are consolidating smaller behavior analytic organizations to capitalize upon investment opportunities (e.g., Provident, 2018). Balancing competing contingencies of providing quality care, while also reporting to investors who may not have direct knowledge of best practice ABA treatment, can be not only challenging but also create ethical distress among the providers rendering care within the organization. As such, it is important for our field to engage in open dialogue about the ethical dilemmas that may arise and how to promote high-quality, ethically sound ABA treatment within the evolving landscape of applied behavior analysis treatment.

To this end, the purpose of this chapter is to focus on organizational ethics as it refers to the ethical issues from an administrative or management perspective within a healthcare organization, rather than addressing ethical issues purely related to clinical practice (Lovitky & Ahern, 1999; Suhonen et al., 2011). Organizational leadership should be well-versed in how to thoughtfully approach and create an ethical environment for clinical practice (Ko et al., 2017; Rosenberg & Schwartz, 2019). We will provide an overview of the ethical constraints healthcare organizations typically encounter and offer solutions for creating an ethical clinical climate. The discussion is influenced by business ethics literature, organizational behavior management (OBM; Malott, 2003), and tiered support systems (e.g., Walker et al., 1996). In offering solutions, we do not purport the suggestions are exhaustive nor complete. Each situation requires analysis of contextual variables, philosophical variables guiding right and wrong, and selecting contingencies (e.g., professional ethics code; company policy and procedure), which are beyond the scope of this chapter. Our recommendations across organizational and professional levels are intended to help readers create an environment where such an analysis will occur.

Ethics, OBM, and Multi-Tiered Systems

Ethics in its simplest form is about defining what is the right thing and acting in a manner that coincides with the side of the right (Boone, 2017). Similarly, Brodhead et al. (2018) define ethical behavior as, "the emission of behavior in compliance / coordination with the verbally stated rules and behavior-analytic cultural practices guiding provider behavior that are espoused by the BACB Code." These definitions emphasize the need for defining what is right and the expected behaviors that may follow. However, as discussed below, these definitions and expectations are not as readily available as behavior analysts might hope for.

Brodhead et al. (2018) provide three criteria for ethical dilemmas: 1) A choice between incompatible behaviors; 2) each choice is congruent with an ethical code; and 3) the chosen action satisfies one aspect of the code and violates a different aspect. Graber and O'Brien (2019) provide a similar definition and introduce the concept of ethically permissible choice. Specifically, in an ethical dilemma, one of the choices might be the ethically best choice when compared to other choice options. While these ethical dilemmas are often discussed at the level of the individual professional, the institutional structure needs to be considered and how it relates to the ethical dilemma (Graber & O'Brien, 2019). Defining ethics and the contingencies of ethical behavior can, and should be, discussed at multiple levels such as macrosystems, organizational systems, and performer-level systems.

Malott (2003) discusses the total performance system (TPS; see also Diener et al., 2009), as a tool for analyzing how behavioral systems within an organization interact to select behavior over time. The basic components of the TPS are mission, product, customers, customer feedback, product creation, product creation feedback, resources, and competition. These components are analyzed to determine behavioral contingencies (i.e., relationship between a behavior and a consequence), interlocking contingencies (i.e., components of two different behavioral contingencies that interact), and metacontingencies (i.e., interaction of interlocking contingencies that produces a product in demand). Based upon this foundation, Malott states organizational change is assessed and changed at macro, organizational, process, task, behaviorial, and management levels. In order to build an ethical organization, analysis of behavioral contingencies, interlocking contingencies, and metacontingencies must occur.

Similar to the TPS model, educators have proposed a multi-tiered system approach when evaluating socially important behaviors in school settings. Walker and colleagues (1996) stated increased levels of lethal and non-lethal violence could be addressed via assessment and intervention at multiple levels within a school system. Recognizing the school as a complex system, the authors proposed four interactive systems: schoolwide system, specific setting system, classroom system, and individual system. In line with Malott (2003), understanding the organizational structure and interaction of contingencies within schools allows educators to develop appropriate supports to prevent unacceptable behavior (e.g., bullying) by teaching acceptable behavior and responding to unacceptable behavior. The multi-tiered model adds an emphasis of preventing unwanted behavior through teaching expected behavior, providing targeted teaching in response to early identified misbehavior, and individualized assessment and response to continued misbehavior (Scheuermann & Hall, 2016). Throughout this chapter, ethical behavior is discussed in the context of the organizational structure as opposed to the individual employee. Other behavior analytic professionals have also suggested the need to approach applied ethics from an organizational perspective (Brodhead et al., 2018; Brodhead & Higbee, 2012).

Organizational Ethics

Organizational mission, vision, and core philosophies are the defining framework for expected organizational culture. The stated culture and corresponding behaviors should permeate all aspects of the business and clinical operations within an organization. The organizational culture formulates the ethical environment or "climate" of the "individual perceptions of the organization that influences attitudes and behavior and serves as a frame of reference for employee behavior" (Olson, 1995; p. 90). The ethical climate of an organization also serves as a guide to provide employees with a sense of what is valued by the organization, how people work together to maintain organizational values, and how business and clinical practices should be conducted within the organization. The impact of a weak ethical culture within an organization leads to many concerns across an organization. Notably, there is often lack of congruence between clinical ethics and organizational ethical values as it relates to patient care (Hart, 2005; Suhonen et al., 2011). Given that behavior analytic services are relatively new to the healthcare marketplace, behavior analytic agencies have no standard or little experience in the development or creation of ethical values and culture. Considering the variables currently affecting the young behavioral industry (e.g., new CPT codes, scarce BCBAs, negotiating insurance regulation, and patient demand), it is especially timely to assess the ABA business culture during its nascent state.

The decisions of organizational leadership can subsequently impact clinical practice with wide-ranging implications for patient care and outcomes, as well as provider satisfaction, burnout, and turnover that can have further implications for the organization's financial health (Ambrose et al., 2008; Broadhead & Higbee, 2012; Gabel, 2013; Suhonen et al., 2011). Whereas the majority of continuing education and literature in ethical behavior-analytic services has focused on ethical behavior of the individual provider, organizational ethics in healthcare is primarily concerned with the ethical implications of decisions implemented by organizational leaders and the subsequent impact on clinical practice (Suhonen et al., 2011). For example, the *Professional and Ethical*

Compliance Code for Behavior Analysts is specifically directed towards the individual provider as the governing board may only enforce violations for certificants (BACB, 2014). As such, behavior analysts are traditionally guided to resolve ethical issues as they arise, within the context of their individual practice and healthcare organization (Broadhead et al., 2018). However, organizations have an ethical responsibility to conduct all aspects of business and clinical operations with a high level of ethically sound practices (Graber & O'Brien, 2019).

One practice that might strengthen organizational responsibility for ethical behavior is organizational accreditation. Much like individual professional licenses and certifications demonstrate a minimum competency to practice, define a practice area, and provide a context for enforcement of standards, organizational accreditation may achieve similar results. The Joint Commission is a nonprofit entity that has been accrediting healthcare organizations since 1951 to "improve healthcare for the public" (see https://www.jointcommission.org for more information). Similarly, accreditation of behavior analytic organizations has recently begun (see https://bhcoe.org for more information). Although the outcomes of organizational accreditation are complicated and difficult to measure (e.g., Devkaran & O'Farrell, 2015), behavior analytic providers should attend to this emerging practice as it can impact organizational practices such as funding (i.e., some funders will not reimburse if not accredited).

Organizational Ethical Dilemmas

Ethical dilemmas emerge in the governance and management of behavioral health organizations, especially as it relates to the competing contingencies within the organizational context of stakeholder needs and values (Griffith, 1995). Healthcare organizational ethics encompasses a broad range of areas and may include (a) resource allocation and priority setting; (b) safeguarding an ethically high standard of clinical care; (c) safeguarding justice and access to care; (d) strategic planning and value setting; (e) business development and healthcare service conduct; and (f) safeguarding the integrity of healthcare billing (Suhonen et al., 2011). Based on the complexities of the broader healthcare systems the organizations work within, it is vital that organizations actively engage patients, providers, and other stakeholders to ensure congruence with ethical principles across organizational practices.

Resource Allocation and Priority Setting

The healthcare systems in which organizations function can impact the clinical care patients receive (Graber & O'Brien, 2019). Resource allocation within the broader scope of the federal and state healthcare systems, as well as within healthcare organizations could lead to ethical dilemmas and impede a provider's ability to provide treatment aligned with the standards of care (Nelson et al., 2007; Suhonen et al., 2011). Funder-driven clinical practice guidelines and restricted billable units for treatment may create a context where only a portion of the provided treatment is reimbursed. This qualification may in turn lead to alterations in the assessment and treatment choices that are based on fiscal constraints that reduce clinical standards or quality of care (Graber & O'Brien, 2019; Sortedahl, 2018). For example, an untimed procedural code used for behavioral assessments (e.g., H0031 and H0032) may not cover the actual cost of a functional behavioral assessment with caregiver interviews, behavioral observations, and experimental evaluations (e.g., Carr & Wilder, 2003; O'Neill et al., 2015). Similarly, some healthcare payers may not reimburse the simultaneous billing of the BCBA® and behavior technician, resulting in some ABA based agencies to reduce necessary case supervision. Additionally, most payers do not provide funding for behavior analysts to coordinate services with other professionals involved in the patient's care.

Organizational ethical dilemmas may also arise due to limited personnel resources (Nelson et al., 2009). A barrier frequently encountered by behavior analytic organizations is the severe provider shortage across all certification levels (BCBAs®, BCaBAs®, and RBTs®; Grindle et al., 2009; Montes et al., 2009). This impediment may lead to misalignment with ethical prioritizations of the healthcare organization and practicing providers (Broadhead et al., 2018). For example, organizations may encourage registered behavioral technicians (RBTs) to begin treatment with a client prior to meeting all clinical competencies or billing for a provider under another provider while awaiting credentialing. As such, it is important for organizational leaders to engage in active dialogue with professional organizations and public policy committees to address policies that may impact ethically sound behavior analytic healthcare and work collaboratively to remediate these issues (Graber & O'Brien, 2019). For example, behavior analytic agencies that hire a new BCBA staff must wait for the professional to be credentialed by the healthcare company prior to billing for services, which may take up to six months. During this interim non-credentialed period, the agency may need to carry the BCBA's salary for an overall short-term financial loss. To mitigate these financial losses, some agencies may have a new staff supervise a case under the billing of an established BCBA; however, this may not be an option under all health insurance contracts.

Funding priorities may also differ across organizations with respect to financial budgeting for quality assurance programs, continuing education for providers, and administrative team members. The training requirements of behavior technicians are often directly dictated by the ABA healthcare organizations. The staff personnel standards required by many healthcare providers are designed to meet a one-time credentialing standard. Few healthcare providers have requirements for continuing education or ongoing training of BCBA or behavior technician staff. A common practice for many behavioral organizations is to provide continuing education opportunities for behavior analyst level providers; however, it may be prudent to allocate resources for direct care staff ongoing educational initiatives. The technician credential indicates a minimum competency level has been achieved and ongoing education and supervision aligned with BACB best practice guidelines is recommended.

Further, in other medical disciplines, technician-level training is provided by colleges, universities, and/or vocational schools, whereas ABA healthcare organizations may provide all classroom training internally. Even when training is provided through a third party, the structure of the technician credential may require the providers within an organization to complete competency evaluations. This structure may foster ethical challenges for providers as the needs of the healthcare organization may not align with the individual provider's values. For example, staffing shortages have been found to result in difficult ethical prioritizations for healthcare organizations and reduced standards or quality of care (Cooper et al., 2004; Suhonen et al., 2011). Quality of training may differ across organizations based on available resources. Smaller organizations may be more limited in available resources and may not, for example, have training departments available to assist with advanced training and development of technicians. Further, many small organizations have limited human resource departments and many administrative responsibilities such as interviews, training, credentialing, and insurance authorizations may be delegated to the providers. This situation increases the organizational risk of ethical and compliance violations, as providers often do not often have the appropriate human resource and insurance training to oversee these critical systems, particularly when managing a clinical caseload.

Safeguarding an Ethically High Standard of Clinical Care

Based on organizational needs to maintain financial stability under current reimbursement structures (Graber & O'Brien, 2019), a common structure is to enforce a minimum quota for providers to bill clinical services in order to cover the costs of the provider's full-time salary and benefits, as well as business-related overheads (e.g., billing departments, office space, therapeutic materials, technology). However, it is important that organizations are cautious when setting salaries and billable quota expectations. In the current landscape of severe provider shortages, organizations may be pressured to offer high salaries to attract talent.

If the billable quota is not clinically feasible for a provider to achieve within a standard salaried position (e.g., requiring a billable quota of 36 hours per week when the provider is traveling two hours or more per day to client homes), the organization might foster billing abuse and fraud (Loria, 2018). Organizations may mitigate this risk by structuring clinical positions that are realistic and feasible for clinicians to render high-quality care, such as providing sufficient indirect clinical planning time that may be non-billable. Given BCBA provider shortages, organizations may consider incorporating telehealth delivered care to patients when covered under the patient's health plan (Boisvert et al., 2010; Ferguson et al., 2019). Under this model, providers may leverage technology to render a percentage of clinical direction that allows providers to render more frequent and/or higher dosage of clinical management per client. This service deliver structure meets organizational needs and may assist with resolving ethical concerns regarding quality of care.

Another area of risk for organizations may be a common profit-sharing structure that is implemented to reinforce employees who render services above the required billable quota (Gunderman & Hubbard 2005). The performance-based structure may have ethical implications on patient care if quality indicators are not incorporated. One method in which organizations can ensure high-quality care is delivered is to require certain quality metrics are met before the provider is able to access incentive pay. Examples include regularly occurring quality assurance programs for treatment reviews, ongoing RBT treatment fidelity measures, meeting established case supervision ratios, successful completion of session notes, and acquiring patient outcome data as well as RBT and parent satisfaction measures (Graber & O'Brien, 2019). By incorporating clinical quality indicators, organizations can establish an ethical environment, in which clinicians are reinforced for working above billable quotas only when they are providing high-quality care. Further, by incorporating provider quality assurance (QA) audits on clinical treatment and documentation, organizations may reduce risk by demonstrating corporate compliance policies are in place to reduce inappropriate billing activities (Lovitky & Ahern, 1999).

Safeguarding Justice and Access to Care

Concerns that practice standards have yet to be established with patient triage and care prioritization have been raised when determining patient access to care (Jecker & Berg, 1992). Some healthcare systems may have established priorities for patient care and may provide guidelines requiring providers to triage and prioritize specific patient populations or age groups (New Mexico Human Services Department, 2019). Additional ethical implications of organizational practices with case triage may arise when determining which patients should receive care first (Tonnessen et al., 2011). For example, some organizations may prioritize patients with specific healthcare funders who reimburse at a higher rate or those clients who would likely benefit from a comprehensive treatment program due to the financial benefits. Leading a healthcare organization requires careful balance of quality clinical care and managing business operations to ensure financial stability of the organization. Misalignment may occur when organizational leadership is not balanced with clinical leadership and has unintended consequences on patient care, provider satisfaction, and long-term organizational goals. Fortunately, healthcare managers across all departments and levels of an organization play can play an integral role in developing and sustaining an ethical climate (Cooper et al., 2002; Suhonen et al., 2011).

Strategic Planning and Value Setting

A values-driven leadership can promote ethically sound ABA healthcare by supporting a strong ethical organizational culture. Due to the rapidly changing landscape of ABA services, providers encounter challenges with providing consistently high-quality and ethically sound care to patients due to the demands of the organization and healthcare funders (Aiken et al., 2001). Healthcare leaders who are Board Certified Behavior Analysts also have an ethical responsibility to support the healthcare organization in developing an ethically responsible climate as strategic planning goals for the organization are developed. In light of legislation mandating coverage of ABA treatment for ASD across the United States, there has been significant growth and consolidation of behavior analytic agencies within the private sector. Behavior analysts are held to a high standard within our professional ethical code of compliance, in which we "do not implement contingencies that would cause others to engage in fraudulent, illegal, or unethical conduct" (BACB, 2014).

Organizational leadership decisions on clinical structure development during rapid growth cycles have ethical implications on clinical practice. Organizational leaders must balance the needs of clients and private equity investors, which increases the stress leaders experience when organizational policies and procedures conflict with their own personal values (Dellve & Wikstrom, 2009). By promoting a positive ethical environment, organizational leaders can increase employee morale, improve employees' commitment to an organizational commitment, and enhance job satisfaction, when those values and strategic planning initiatives are thoughtfully aligned with the field's ethical codes of conduct (Shirey, 2005).

Business Development and Healthcare Service Conduct

The unique landscape of ABA treatment and field creates challenges in promoting ethically sound ABA healthcare. Due to provider capacity issues, organizations may be motivated to quickly hire new clinicians and technicians in order to meet the needs of families requiring care. For example, direct care is typically rendered by an entry-level technician, most of whom are working as a part-time employee, partly due to the 1:1 and intensive nature of services. Whereas in other disciplines, a child may be removed from school for a once per week hour-long appointment, the intensity of ABA treatment does not allow for extensive school absences. Therefore, the highest demand during after-school hours often leads to part-time work and a high rate of employee turnover. These circumstances may create ethical dilemmas as interview and onboarding processes are expedited and steps may be overlooked. Analysts commonly report receiving offers of employment without speaking to a representative from a company or interviewing for the position. Providers also may be urged to complete competency exams as quickly as possible, potentially before a technician has met all desired competencies.

Organizational needs may be at odds with providing quality care aligned with best practice guidelines as it relates to clinical management of cases. By creating a heavy caseload requirement, with extensive travel time, organizations may be fostering an ethical climate in which lower quality of care is being provided that is at odds with provider values, creates moral distress, and further impacts provider burnout. Organizations may address these matters by creating standards related to the ongoing supervision and training of employees that are aligned with the standards of care in the field and ensuring leadership implements the organizational standards consistently.

Safeguard the Integrity of Healthcare Billing

Organizational conduct within the context of healthcare service billing raises ethical considerations for developing internal policies and processes. Organizational leaders may consider having a compliance officer or selected individual who is responsible for understanding state and federal law, as well as funding policies to ensure compliance (Broadhead & Higbee, 2012; Lovitky & Ahern, 1999; Rudman et al., 2009). This individual may conduct ongoing training for all employees and create an audit process to monitor compliance and reduce risk. Common areas of risk include: (a) providers failing to accurately or sufficiently document services rendered; (b) use of incorrect procedural codes (e.g., billing group services as 1:1 services); (c) moving billing of services to different day and/or time; (d) billing for services in an incorrect setting; and (e) billing under alternative provider (Ikono et al., 2019; Rudman et al., 2009). For example, unless explicitly stated by the healthcare funder, an organization that routinely bills newly employed providers under a "supervising" provider while they are awaiting credentialing is engaged in billing fraud. Organizations may mitigate these concerns by carefully developing policies and procedures for onboarding new providers. An organization may identify the typical credentialing timeline and offer postdated offer letters to account for this timeline. This strategy also has the added benefit of allowing the provider to give adequate notice to their current employer and properly transition care, which sets the tone of the organization's clinical integrity. Oversight through regular internal audits of documentation and billing is also a critical component for an organization to foster an ethical billing culture and provide opportunities for continued education and training (Lovitky & Ahern, 1999).

Strategies for Promoting an Ethical Climate

Below, we provide suggestions for developing an organizational climate that prevents and responds to ethical needs. As described above, the focus of the recommendations is organizational practices at multiple tiers. The suggestions are visually represented in Figure 14.1.

Organizational Ethics Assessments

Healthcare organizations may consider evaluating the ethical climate of their organization by gathering feedback from all stakeholders using standardized and validated instruments (Stolt et al., 2018). For example, the Ethics Environment Questionnaire, Corley's Morale Distress Scale, and Moral Sensitivity Questionnaire, are self-reporting Likert-scale questionnaires that can easily be administered within an organization (Corley et al., 2001; Lützén et al., 1997; McDaniel, 1997). Using the results of such measures, organizations can develop a comprehensive strategy for improving their ethical climate, including (a) strengthening organizational policies and procedures; (b) implementing targeted training initiatives; (c) developing ethics and compliance committees; and (d) using technology to provide quality and compliance oversight to monitor the maintenance of an ethical climate of their organization. Additionally, as presented in subsequent sections of the chapter, more direct observations of behavior to monitor the ethical culture and inform organization practices are warranted.

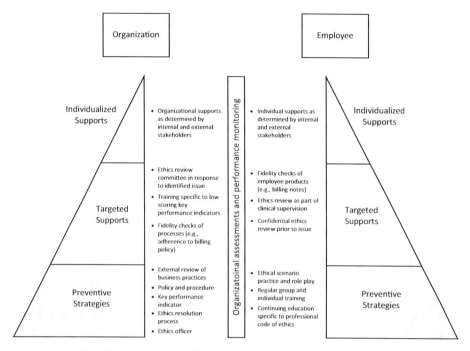

FIGURE 14.1 Visual representation of ethical supports at the organizational and individual level.

Organizational Policies and Procedures

Organizations may consider investing resources into the development of comprehensive policies and procedures around commonly encountered ethical situations with specific populations and service settings in which care is rendered. By outlining policies and providing information to families and providers alike, organizations can mitigate risk and expedite processes for resolving ethical concerns through improved communication with families about policies, including the rationale for each policy. For example, parents requesting last-minute community support that more closely resembles respite or custodial services may benefit from clarification of the criteria for accessing medically necessary ABA care. Alternatively, healthcare organizations rendering services in a home-based setting may implement policies addressing client's falling asleep during sessions to ensure technician level providers are not inappropriately billing a funder for treatment that was not rendered. As described by Bailey and Burch (2017), one policy should be a declaration of practices. Smaller organizations with limited resources may leverage organizational policies and resources from professional organizations, such as the Association for Professional Behavior Analysts (APBA) or Council for Autism Service Providers (CASP), to bolster their compliance programs. Due to the changing landscape of ABA services, it is important that organizational leaders confer with professional organizations and public policy committees to address policies that may impact ethically sound behavior analytic healthcare (Graber & O'Brien, 2019). Organizational policies are the foundation of setting employee and family expectations, creating structure to teach behavior correlated with the policies, and to ultimately prevent ethical dilemmas and violations across the organization.

Ethics Committee

Consultation on ethical concerns can enhance clinical care and patient communication (McGee et al., 2001). Ethics committees may be comprised of a multidisciplinary board. Given the broad scope of the committee, representatives should have knowledge of clinical practice, ethical philosophy and codes, legal matters, procedural codes and billing practices, and cultural considerations. This expertise is often not possessed by a single individual and organizations may therefore establish their own ethics committee (see Cox, 2020 for further details). Financial commitment to such a committee is a concern and organizations may consider filling some roles of the committee by members of existing organizational departments (e.g., training department, human resource department; Lee et al., 2018; Niemira et al., 1989). Based on the goals and size of the committee, the committee provides support in many ways (Rasoal et al., 2017).

In line with a multitiered approach, the committee should first support prevention of ethical issues. In addition to policy development, the committee should actively teach expectations of ethical behavior. The committee should define metrics of ethical behavior and monitor those metrics, which in turn guides development of future policies and training. Second, the committee should more actively support processes with additional ethics risk. For example, billing practices present risk of unethical behavior. The committee might develop billing monitoring tools and conduct fidelity checks of billing practices. Additionally, many states have regulations regarding particular treatment procedures that may infringe upon individual rights. The ethics committees may provide guidance through individual case reviews utilizing such treatments to ensure right infringement is minimized. Lastly, the committee should play an integral role in responding to possible ethics violations.

Ethics Education

Ethics in healthcare and behavior analytic treatment can be systematically enhanced through targeted training and consultation initiatives (Stolt et al., 2018). Researchers have also demonstrated increased ethical empowerment through training initiatives, which led to reduced morale distress (Suhonen et al., 2011). Studies evaluating interventions to improve ethical knowledge and performance report that a didactic-only model was not effective in improving ethical competence (Stolt et al., 2018). Rather, a multi-modal approach in which participants were able to reflect and engage in meaningful dialogue with others was most effective (Stolt et al., 2018). Accordingly, organizations therefore may consider implementing a comprehensive ethical training program that is embedded across all organizational systems, departments, and provider levels to promote ethical practices (Broadhead & Higbee, 2012; Rudman et al., 2009).

Training can be broken into the areas of ethical philosophies, ethics codes, and applied ethics. Training about ethical philosophies (see Boone, 2017 for an excellent resource) creates a forum for discussing various approaches to defining right and wrong. Such training also allows the organization to define and develop an ethical philosophy statement that outlines the guiding factors for policies, procedures, and action. The training further provides a context for teaching professionals how to discuss ethical concerns from multiple perspectives, engage in problem-solving, and being good colleagues.

Most behavior analytic organizations will employ professionals with specific ethics codes. Training specific to these codes should be provided to ensure compliance. Consideration should be given to developing training applying the codes to organizational structure, practices, and context (e.g., see Graber & O'Brien, 2019 for an example of unique organizational structures, practices, and context that might require individualized training). Lastly, training specific to applying the ethical philosophy and ethics code within the organization should be provided. The focus of this training is teaching employees a decision-making process for ethical dilemmas. No matter how good policies and procedure are, employees will face many choices about ethical and unethical behavior. In this regard, Bailey and Burch (2017) present a decision-making model for dilemma resolution, and Sush and Najdowksi (2019) offer a ready-to-use workbook for practicing ethical decision-making.

The above areas need not be addressed solely in stand-alone trainings. Although some employees will likely require focused training and practice (e.g., initial acquisition of a decision-making model), much ethical training can occur on-the-job or with simple additions to existing meetings. For example, monthly department meetings can be enhanced with five- to ten- minute reviews of ethical scenarios and discussion. Clinical supervision can be enhanced with discussion of ethical codes related to current client needs or organizational practices. A key factor in conducting these ongoing trainings is a strong leadership group. Targeted training for supervisors and managers across all departments on how to promote an ethical work environment and mediate these training opportunities is needed. Additionally, targeted trainings for families might be warranted, perhaps in the context of quarterly parent gatherings, company social events, and progress review meetings. These trainings serve as refreshers to policies and procedures the family agreed to upon service initiation and may prevent drift from those agreements.

Organizations may also tailor ethics training based on their business model, internal ethics reports, and parent surveys. The ethical dilemmas encountered by a behavior analyst working in a client's home or community are very different compared to a behavior analyst rendering care in a clinical setting. For example, The Defense Health Agency (DHA) reported that it improperly paid for Autism-Related Services to Selected Companies. The DHA improperly paid $1.9 million of the total $3.1 million paid to the five companies for ABA services performed in 2015. An examination of the DHA suggested that many individual billing sessions failed to properly document the activities that occurred during the one-to-one ABA-based treatment sessions. Given this situation, agencies would find it beneficial to train staff on appropriate billing practices and documentation. These trainings should be followed with a strong OBM system to provide feedback on the session note quality and retraining when required.

A final consideration of when developing ethics training, regardless of modality, is the distinction between teaching how to behave in every possible situation versus a decision-making process. Given the complexities of behavior analytic treatment and healthcare, providers must develop a sophisticated knowledge of how to identify ethical dilemmas, evaluate resolutions, and resolve the dilemma (Knapp et al., 2013). Guidelines from professional organizations, including the BACB, commonly incorporate "modifiers" (e.g., "reasonable" and "appropriate") into the ethical code to provide guidance but allow clinicians sufficient judgment to approach ethical problem-solving (Knapp et al., 2013; Rosenberg & Schwartz, 2019).

An extension of the above-mentioned department meeting training options is incorporation of ethical dialogue within clinical review practices and/or a clinical review meeting that focuses only upon ethical considerations. More specifically, as part of the clinical review, professionals are trained to state variables that might create conflict between treatment and codes, policies, or regulations as a means of prevention and proactive responses. For example, the professional might identify that a family member has made repeated statements about needing more "discipline" in response to challenging behavior and has difficulty implementing "fluffy interventions" based in "bribery." The focus of the discussion would be identification of potential conflicts with professional codes (e.g., use of punishment and least restrictive procedures), policy and procedures (e.g., skill development as a means to reduce challenging behavior), funder regulations (e.g., prohibition of time-out, response cost) and what actions are needed now and in the future. As stated by Rosenberg and Schwartz (2019), using a structured, systematic method for evaluating ethical dilemmas and engaging in thoughtful discourse with other professional behavior analysts may improve ethical fitness.

Organizational Ethics Monitoring

Malott (2003) and Scheuermann and Hall (2016) emphasized outcome data of the system is integral for assessing effect of changes. Organizational leaders should create a multiple modality reporting process and specify the process for responding to reported concerns expeditiously. Multiple modalities may reduce response effort for reporting and may improve rate of employees' consistently reporting potential ethical violations. Frequent reminders and well-posted/disseminated bulletins about reporting options to ensure employees are frequently reminded of the available options are an important component. Reporting options may include (a) an anonymous reporting mechanism in which employees are able to raise concerns about possible ethical misconduct without fear of repercussion (Lovitky & Ahern, 1999); (b) database for supervisors to enter data regarding policy violations; and (c) data analysis of required reporting variables (e.g., funder defined neglect or abuse). It may also be beneficial to have multiple avenues of reporting, including phone, email, and written responses, all of which might include a process for anonymity. For example, behavioral agencies may establish a toll-free ethics hotline. The ethics hotline can be easily set up and made available to both clients and staff to report ethical concerns. Typically, agencies provide the ethics hotline number to families in their start of care documents and to all staff during new employee orientation. The agency should continually remind staff and family of the toll-free number via newsletters, website, and training. Individuals who call the ethics hotline may report potential ethical concerns anonymously to the organization's chief compliance officer. All ethics complaints should follow an internal review policy with findings reporting to the executive team.

Many applications of a tiered model within schools use office disciplinary referrals and the information contained therein to evaluate preventive and responsive strategies (e.g., Crone et al., 2015). The referrals contain information about the violated rule, location, time of day, grade, and other variables that can be analyzed for trends and needed interventions. An organizational ethics corollary might be tracking failure to comply with funder regulations, policy and procedure violations, and professional ethics code violations. Types of violations, locations of violations (e.g., departments, community versus clinic), and training level for employees (e.g., paraprofessionals versus professional; clinical staff versus nonclinical) are a few areas that can be analyzed to guide preventive interventions in response to trends. A document of this sort would need to be individualized given state regulations, funder requirements, and internal policies and procedures.

Lastly, data collected are only useful if analyzed and acted upon. The organization should state how the data are analyzed, acceptable levels of performance, and typical responses to needs of employees. Analysis of collected data should occur frequently enough to identify organizational and professional issues while risk is minimal. We suggest a monthly review of outcomes measures by key leadership is the minimal period needed for review, analysis, and decision about needed action. Key leadership is defined as individuals who have the ability to alter organizational policy and practices and leverage potentially needed resources. It should also include employees familiar with the day-to-day processes to not overlook important variables contributing or not contributing to the situation.

Conclusion

Many behavior analytic organizations have struggled within the growing marketplace, which increases the risk of ethical dilemmas. As the behavior analytic field grows, continued conversations on the organizational impact of ethical care and the impact on patient outcomes are warranted. The strategies discussed above are largely based on organizational ethics research within the practice of medicine, but can be applied to behavioral health organizations.

Providers are working within state and federally managed healthcare systems, as well as within organizational contexts that may have competing contingencies impacting care. We provided some examples of competing contingencies that may impact care, discussed these contingencies across multiple organizational levels, and proposed organizational and individual strategies of resolution. As Graber and O'Brien (2019) indicated, it is important to evaluate ethical needs at the individual and organizational levels. Although only the professionals are bound by an ethics code, we hope our discussion will encourage organizational leaders to create organizational systems to support professionals encountering ethical dilemmas. Our field may benefit from standards that promote ethical conduct organization-wide and regulate organizational conduct to ensure ethical care. It is vital that leaders systematically evaluate the ethical climate within their organization, actively respond to ethical dilemmas, and engage in proactive strategies to reduce the risk of ethical misconduct that impacts patient outcomes and provider satisfaction. Further, research is needed in the area of organizational ethics as it applies to OBM and behavior analytic practices, assessment, care provider training, and intervention maintenance.

References

Aiken, L. H., Clarke, S. P., Sloane, D. M., Sochalski, J. A., Busse, R., Clarke, H., *et al.* (2001). Nurses' reports on hospital care in five countries. *Health Affairs, 20,* 43–53. DOI: 10.1377/hlthaff.20.3.43

Ambrose, M. L., Arnaud, A., & Schminke, M. (2008). Individual moral development and ethical climate: The influence of person-organization fit on job attitudes. *Journal of Business Ethics, 77,* 323–333. DOI: 10.1007/s10551-007-9352-1.

Ayllon, T., & Michael, J. (1959). The psychiatric nurse as a behavioral engineer. *Journal of the Experimental Analysis of Behavior, 2,* 323–334.

Baer, D. M., Wolf, M. M., & Risley, T. R. (1968). Some current dimensions of applied behavior analysis. *Journal of Applied Behavior Analysis, 1*(1), 91–97. DOI: 10.1901/jaba.1968.1-91

Bailey, J. S., & Burch, M. R. (2017). *Ethics for behavior analysts* (3rd ed.). New York: Routledge. ISBN: 978-1-138-94919-5.

Behavior Analyst Certification Board. (2014). *Professional and ethical compliance code for behavior analysts.* Littleton, CO: Author. Retrieved from http://BACB.com/ethics-code/

Behavior Analyst Certification Board (2019). *US employment demand for behavior analysts: 2010–2018.* Littleton, CO: Author. Retrieved from https://www.bacb.com/team-view/us-employment-demand-for-behavior-analysts-2010-2017/

Boisvert, M., Lang, R., Andrianopoulos, M., & Boscardin, M. L. (2010). Telepractice in the assessment and treatment of individuals with autism spectrum disorders: A systematic review. *Developmental Neurorehabilitation, 13*(6), 423–432. DOI: 10.3109/17518423.2010.499889

Boone, B. (2017). *Ethics 101: From altruism and utilitarianism to bioethics and political ethics, an exploration of the concepts of right and wrong.* Avon, MA: Adams Media. ISBN: 9781507204931

Brodhead, M., Cox, D., & Quigley, S. (2018). *Practical ethics for effective treatment of autism spectrum disorder.* Cambridge, MA: Academic Press. ISBN: 978-0-12-814098-7.

Brodhead, M. T., & Higbee, T. S. (2012). Teaching and maintaining ethical behavior in a professional organization. *Behavior Analysis in Practice, 5*(2), 82–88. DOI:10.1007/BF03391827

Brodhead, M. T., Quigley, S. P., & Cox, D. J. (2018). How to identify ethical practices in organizations prior to employment. *Behavior Analysis in Practice, 11*, 165–173. DOI: 10.1007/s40617-018-0235-y

Carr, J. E., & Nosik, M. R. (2017). Professional credentialing of practicing behavior analysts. *Policy Insights from the Behavioral and Brain Sciences, 4*(1), 3–8. DOI: 10.1177/2372732216685861

Carr, J. E., & Wilder, D. A. (2003). *Functional assessment and intervention* (2nd ed.). Homewood, IL: High Tide Press.

Center for Disease Control and Prevention. (2019). Research on autism spectrum disorder. Retrieved from https://www.cdc.gov/ncbddd/autism/research.html#RiskFactors

Cooper, R. W., Frank, G. L., Gouty, C. A., & Hansen, M. C. (2002). Key ethical issues encountered in healthcare organizations: Perceptions of nurse executives. *Journal of Nursing Administration, 32*(6), 331–337.

Cooper R. W., Frank G. L., Hansen M. M., & Gouty C. A. (2004). Key ethical issues encountered in healthcare organizations: The perceptions of staff nurses and nurse leaders. *Journal of Nursing Administration, 34*(3): 149–56.

Corley, M. C., Elswick, R. K., Gorman, M., & Clor, T. (2001). Development and evaluation of a moral distress scale. *Journal of Advanced Nursing, 33*(2), 250–256.

Council for Autism Service Providers (CASP) (2020). *Applied behavior analysis treatment of autism spectrum disorders: Practice guidelines for healthcare funders and managers (Second Edition).* Retrieved https://casproviders.org/asd-guidelines/

Cox, D. J. (2020). A guide to establishing ethics committees in behavioral health settings. *Behavior Analysis in Practice, 13*(4), 939–949.

Crone, D. A., Hawken, L. S., & Horner, R. H. (2015). *Building positive behavior support systems in schools: Functional behavior assessment* (2nd ed.). New York: Guilford Press.

Dellve, L., & Wikström E. (2009) Managing complex workplace stress in health care organizations: Leaders' perceived legitimacy conflicts. *Journal of Nursing Management, 17*(8), 931–941. DOI: 10.1097/NHL.0b013e31818ede46

Devkaran, S., & O'Farrell, P. N. (2015). The impact of hospital accreditation on quality measures: An interrupted time series analysis. *BMC Health Services Research, 15*, 137–151. DOI: 10.1186/s12913-015-0784-5

Diener, L. H., McGee, H. M., & Miguel, C. F. (2009). An integrated approach for conducting a behavioral systems analysis. *Journal of Organizational Behavior Management, 29*(2), 108–135. DOI: 10.1080/01608060902874534

Ferguson, J., Craig, E. A., & Dounavi, K. (2019). Telehealth as a model for providing behaviour analytic interventions to individuals with autism spectrum disorder: A systematic review. *Journal of Autism and Developmental Disorders, 49*(2), 582–616. DOI: 10.1007/s10803-018-3724-5

Fuller, P. R. (1949). Operant conditioning of a vegetative organism. *American Journal of Psychology, 62,* 587–590.

Gabel, S. (2013). Demoralization in health professional practice: Development, amelioration, and implications for continuing education. *Journal of Continuing Education in the Health Professions, 33,* 118–126. DOI: 10.1002/chp.21175

Graber, A., & O'Brien, M. (2019). The promise of accountable care organizations: "The code," reimbursement, and an ethical no-win situation for behavior analysts. *Behavior Analysis in Practice, 12,* 247–254. doi.org/10.1007/s40617-018-0209-0

Griffith, J. R. (1995). *The Well-Managed Health Care Organization* (3rd ed.). Ann Arbor, MI: AUPHA Press/Health Administration Press. ISBN: 978-1567930344.

Grindle, C. F., Kovshoff, H., Hastings, R. P., & Remington, B. (2009). Parents' experiences of home-based applied behavior analysis programs for young children with autism. *Journal of Autism and Developmental Disorders, 39*(1), 42–56. DOI:10.1007/s10803-008-0597-z

Gunderman, R. B., & Hubbard, M. A. (2005). The wages of healing: Ethical issues in the compensation of physicians. *Medical Science Monitor, 11*(2), SR5–SR10.

Hart, S. E. (2005). Hospital ethical climates and registered nurses' turnover intentions. *Journal of Nursing Scholarship, 37*(2), 173–177. DOI: 10.1111/j.1547-5069.2005.0 0030.x

Ikono, R., Iroju, O., Olaleke, J., & Oyegoke, T. (2019). Meta-analysis of fraud, waste and abuse detection methods in healthcare. *Nigerian Journal of Technology, 38*(2), 490–502.

Jecker, N. S., & Berg, A. O. (1992). Allocating medical resources in rural America: Alternative perceptions of justice. *Social Science & Medicine, 34*(5), 467–474. DOI: https://doi.org/10.1016/0277-9536(92)90201-Z

Knapp, S., Handelsman, M. M., Gottlieb, M. C., & VandeCreek, L. D. (2013). The dark side of professional ethics. *Professional Psychology: Research and Practice, 44*(6), 371.

Ko, C., Ma, J., Bartnik, R., Haney, M. H., & Kang, M. (2017). Ethical leadership: An integrative review and future research agenda. *Ethics & Behavior, 28*(2), 104–132. DOI: 10.1080/10508422.2017.1318069

Kogan, M. D., Vladutiu, C. J., Schieve, L. A., Ghandour, R. M., Blumberg, S. J., Zablotsky, B., ... & Lu, M. C. (2018). The prevalence of parent-reported autism spectrum disorder among US children. *Pediatrics, 142*(6), e20174161. https://doi.org /10.1542/peds.2017-4161

Lee, G. T., Williams, D. E., Simmons, J., & Johnson-Patagoc, K. (2018). The right to effective treatment for people with developmental disabilities and severe problem behaviors. *Behavior Analysis: Research and Practice, 18*(4), 436.

Loria, K. (2018). Why is there a problem with upcoding and overbilling? Medical Economics, Retrieved October 14th, 2019 from: https://www.medicaleconomics.com/health-law-and-policy/why-there-problem-upcoding-and-overbilling

Lovitky, J. A., & Ahern, J. (1999). Designing compliance programs that foster ethical behavior. *Healthcare Financial Management, 53*(3), 38–43.

Lützén, K., Evertzon, M., & Nordin, C. (1997). Moral sensitivity in psychiatric practice. *Nursing Ethics, 4*(6), 472–482.

Malott, M. (2003). *Paradox of organizational change: Engineering organizations with behavioral systems analysis.* Oakland, CA: Context Press. ISBN: 978-1878978424.

McDaniel, C. (1997). Development and psychometric properties of the Ethics Environment Questionnaire. *Medical Care, 35*(9), 901–914.

McGee, G., Spanogle, J. P., Caplan, A. L., & Asch, D. A. (2001). A national study of ethics committees. *American Journal of Bioethics, 1*(4), 60–64.

Montes, G., Halterman, J., & Magyar, C. (2009). Access to and satisfaction with school and community health services for US children with ASD. *Pediatrics, 124,* S407–S413. DOI: 10.1542/peds.2009-1255L

Nelson, W., Pomerantz, A., Howard, K., & Bushy, A. (2007). A proposed rural healthcare ethics agenda. *Journal of Medical Ethics, 33*(3), 136–139. DOI:10.1136/jme.2006.015966.

Nelson, W., Rosenberg, M. C., Weiss, J., & Goodrich, M. (2009). New Hampshire critical access hospitals: CEOs' report on ethical challenges. *Journal of Healthcare Management, 54*(4): 273–283. DOI: 10.1097/00115514-200907000-00009

New Mexico Human Services Department. (2019). Provider health policy and billing manual for providers treating medicaid beneficiaries. Retrieved October 14th, 2019 from: https://www.hsd.state.nm.us/providers/behavioral-health-policy-and-billing-manual/

Niemira, D. A., Orr, R. D., & Culver, C. M. (1989). Ethics committees in small hospitals. *Journal of Rural Health, 5,* 19–32. DOI: 10.1111/j.1748-0361.1989.tb01067.x

Olson, L. (1995). Ethical climate in health care organizations. *International Nursing Review, 42*(3), 85–90.

O'Neill, R. E., Albin, R. W., Storey, K., Horner, R. H., & Sprague, J. R. (2015). *Functional assessment and program development for problem behavior* (3rd ed.). Stamford, CT: Cengage Learning.

Peacock, G., Amendah, D., Ouyang, L., & Grosse, S. (2012). Autism spectrum disorders and health care expenditures: The effects of co-occurring conditions. *Journal of Developmental and Behavioral Pediatrics. 33,* 2–8.

Provident. (2018). Investment & consolidation in autism. *Provident Perspective, Quarterly,* 1–13.

Rasoal, D., Skovdahl, K., Gifford, M., & Kihlgren, A. (2017). Clinical ethics support for healthcare personnel: An integrative literature review. *HEC Forum, 29*(4), 313–346.

Research and Markets. (2017). Autism: Pipeline insights. Retrieved from https://www .researchandmarkets.com/research/lvtkj6/the_u_s_autism?w=4

Rosenberg, N. E., & Schwartz, I. S. (2019). *Behavior Analysis in Practice, 12*(2), 473–482. https://doi.org/10.1007/s40617-018-00287-5

Rudman, W. J., Eberhardt, J. S., Pierce, W., & Hart-Hester, S. (2009). Healthcare fraud and abuse. *Perspectives in Health Information Management, 6*(Fall).

Scheuermann, B. K., & Hall, J. A. (2016). *Positive behavioral supports for the classroom* (3rd ed). New York: Pearson.

Shirey, M. R. (2005). Ethical climate in nursing practice: The leader's role. *JONA'S Healthcare Law, Ethics, and Regulation, 7*(2), 59–67.

Skinner, B. F. (1938). *The behavior of organisms: An experimental analysis.* New York: Appleton-Century.

Skinner, B. F. (1953). *Science and human behavior.* New York: Macmillan.

Sortedahl, C., Mottern, N., & Campagna, V. (2018). Case managers on the front lines of ethical dilemmas. *Professional Case Management, 23*(1), 4–9. DOI: 10.1097/ NCM.0000000000000264

Stolt, M., Leino-Kilpi, H., Ruokonen, M., Repo, H., & Suhonen, R. (2018). Ethics interventions for healthcare professionals and students: A systematic review. *Nursing Ethics, 25*(2), 133–152. DOI: 10.1177/0969733017700237

Suhonen, R., Stolt, M., Virtanen, H., & Leino-Kilpi, H. (2011). Organizational ethics: A literature review. *Nursing Ethics, 18,* 285–303. DOI: 10.1177/0969733011401123

Sush, D. J., & Najdowski, A. C. (2019). *A workbook of ethical case scenarios in applied behavior analysis.* San Diego, CA: Academic Press. ISBN: 978-0-12-815893-7

Tønnessen, S., Nortvedt, P., & Førde, R. (2011). Rationing home-based nursing care: Professional ethical implications. *Nursing Ethics, 18*(3), 386–396. DOI: https://doi .org/10.1177/0969733011398099.

Trump, C. E., & Ayres, K. M. (2019). Autism, insurance, and discrimination: The effect of an autism diagnosis on behavior-analytic services. *Behavior Analysis in Practice,* https://doi.org/10.1007/s40617-018-00327-0

Walker, H. M., Horner, R. H., Sugai, G., Bullis, M., Sprague, J. R., Bricker, D., *et al.* (1996). Integrated approaches to preventing antisocial behavior patterns among school-age children and youth. *Journal of Emotional and Behavioral Disorders, 4,* 194–209.

Watson, J. B. (1913). Psychology as the behaviorist views it. *Psychological Review, 20,* 158–177. DOI:10.1037/h0074428.

Xu, G., Strathearn, L., Liu, B., O'Brien, M., Kopelman, T. G., Zhu, J., *et al.* (2019). Prevalence and treatment patterns of autism spectrum disorder in the United States, 2016. JAMA *Pediatrics,* 173(2), 153–159. DOI:10.1001/jamapediatrics.2018.4208

15
Advancing OBM Practice and Research

Florence D. DiGennaro Reed, Azure J. Pellegrino,
Abigail L. Blackman, Tyler G. Erath, Sandra A. Ruby,
Matt J. Harbison, and Helena Maguire

This book is a treasure trove of information to help practitioners and organizational leaders improve services for individuals with intellectual and developmental disabilities (IDD) by applying organizational behavior management (OBM) practices. Readers have access to state-of-the-art techniques based on empirically sound research in a variety of areas, including assessment and evaluation; training, supervision, and performance improvement; systems interventions; and organizational development. The purpose of this chapter is to present recommendations for advancing OBM practice and research within IDD service settings. We accomplish this aim by sharing practical strategies for strengthening the IDD workforce and building its capacity to conduct OBM-related activities or other systems-level initiatives. We also summarize other ways to advance OBM practice and research through peer review, the use of performance scorecards, and strategic planning. An important caveat is that organizational leaders must endorse these initiatives and make a commitment to ensuring the activities sustain (i.e., institutionalization; Sigurdsson & Austin, 2006). Ideally, individual practices are tied to a behavioral systems approach, which bakes the practices into the framework of the organization (Malott, 2003).

Strengthening IDD Workforce Skills

Organizational leaders have at their disposal a variety of research-supported procedures to train and support staff with the goal of achieving high levels of performance or strengthening the skills of their workforce. As described in this book, these procedures include performance-based pay (Chapter 3), behavioral skills training (Chapter 5), best-practice supervision and ongoing mentoring (Chapter 8), and employee-level preference assessments (Chapter 9), among others. Ongoing professional development of staff may also include participating in journal clubs, and research and writing groups. These development opportunities can flexibly accommodate needed areas of growth to strengthen the skills of the IDD workforce at all levels. For example, practitioners addressing clinical needs could participate in a journal club that reviews and discusses empirical articles on those very topics. The readings and focused discussion for administrators and management-level staff, however, might emphasize OBM research and how to apply those practices given resource constraints and unique features of the workplace. Recognizing that behavior-analytic research evaluating the effects of these professional development opportunities is virtually nonexistent, below we describe potential benefits, challenges, and guidelines for establishing these opportunities.

Journal Club

A journal club involves a group of people who gather regularly to discuss an article published in a journal (Bauer, 2015; Carr & Briggs, 2010). Journal clubs have historically involved a discussion leader who presents an article without requiring other members to read it, which produces a less-engaged experience as the "discussion" reverts to a more traditional lecture. Because this approach involves a passive learning process, experts recommend an interactive journal club format (Rosenthal & Rosenthal, 2017). According to Rosenthal and Rosenthal (2017), an interactive journal club adopts a structured approach for discussion that "directs participants to process information, share interpretations with peers, reflect on the information's relevance, and reflect on their own knowledge and gaps of understanding" (p. 2). Although an interactive journal club emphasizes active participation instead of passive listening, in our view, it would be difficult to foster an engaged discussion if members have not read the article.

Journal clubs present several advantages that make them appealing to organizations. First, they offer a time- and cost-efficient way to foster professional development (Parsons & Reid, 2011), which organizations may prefer over expensive conferences and workshops, particularly given resource constraints. Another advantage is they help ensure practitioners and administrators stay abreast of the scholarly literature (Carr & Briggs, 2010; Novak et al., 2019) and research-supported practices (Normand, 2008). Third, if a journal club flexibly targets areas of needed growth of its members, it has the potential to teach members about recommended evidence-based clinical (e.g., Szucs et al., 2017) and OBM practice, which in turn may enhance the quality of services provided to individuals with IDD. Unfortunately, to the best of our knowledge, there is no research documenting this potentially beneficial effect. Parsons and Reid

(2011) evaluated the effects of a monthly reading group on educator knowledge of reading topics (e.g., evidence-based practices, autism characteristics, seizures). Using a multiple-baseline design, the researchers documented improvements on both multiple-choice and short-answer quizzes along with high intervention acceptability. However, the study did not measure the effects on actual workplace performance or service quality over long periods. A final advantage is that participation in journal clubs can serve as a mechanism for obtaining continuing education units for certified or licensed behavior analysts if the organization has an authorized continuing education program through the Behavior Analyst Certification Board.®

Despite these potential benefits, organizational leaders must address possible challenges when attempting to incorporate a journal club into their clinical or management operations. First, someone must assume responsibility for coordinating the journal club even though discussion leaders will presumably change over time. Although planning activities are not necessarily time-intensive, particularly when members become accustomed to the expectations, an organization must take into account the added responsibility when considering this activity. Relatedly, organizational leaders must determine how to integrate journal clubs into existing systems, which requires added response effort. Will the journal club involve an additional gathering or be incorporated into an already recurring meeting? Who should attend the journal club and at what frequency? Will there be different journal clubs given employees' responsibilities? These are only some of the decisions organizational leaders must make when planning for this professional development opportunity.

Another challenge is determining how to address situations in which group members are not prepared for discussion (e.g., have not read the article, regularly miss journal club meetings). A lack of preparation or failure to participate may prevent members from experiencing the above-described potential benefits. Moreover, this situation could get uncomfortable if the coordinator or discussion leader is a direct report of the unprepared colleague. Thus, determining consequences for a lack of participation and preparation before the agency launches the journal club is highly recommended. We also encourage organizational leaders to allow members to use work time to prepare for the gathering. Finally, members may lack the prerequisite skills to critically analyze articles or discuss potential implications for adopting discussed practices. If this situation arises, the coordinator could offer supplemental training and guidance to affected members, but this would require additional, valuable time and effort.

Parsons and Reid (2011) offer several helpful guidelines for arranging journal club meetings. They recommend obtaining approval from organizational leaders to ensure upper-level support. In addition, Parsons and Reid encourage members

TABLE 15.1 Potential questions to prepare for a journal club gathering

Questions
What is the rationale for the study? What previous research justifies the study purpose?
What is the research question?
Who are the participants?
What are the independent and dependent variables? How did the researchers measure these variables?
What is the research design?
What procedures did participants experience? What did the researchers do?
What were the findings?
Do the findings answer the research question?
What other variables could explain the findings (rather than the independent variable)?
What are the implications for the real world?
What are the implications for future research?
What other limitations might exist?

to conduct groups in a structured manner. Varied approaches exist (e.g., Parsons & Reid, 2011; Rosenthal & Rosenthal, 2017) and members should modify these approaches over time to ensure they benefit from the experience. In Table 15.1 we offer recommended questions to help members prepare for the article discussion. These recommendations are loosely based on our experience and both failed and successful attempts to create journal clubs across settings. Finally, Parsons and Reid (2011) encourage organizations to offer continuing education units, solicit member input on topics of interest, and incorporate other rewarding features (e.g., offering refreshments at gatherings, providing tangible reinforcers for participating) to foster high acceptability.

Research Group

Another way to strengthen the skills of the IDD workforce and advance OBM practice and research is to organize a research group within the organization. A research group involves a group of people who meet to pursue a line of research, which could include subgroups focused on specific projects or a larger group of all interested employees. For example, practitioners with clinical responsibilities may form a group that pursues applied research on the assessment and treatment of problem behavior. Supervisory staff could evaluate the effects of supervision and performance management in their own programmatic line of research. Organizational leaders could embark on research that tackles systems-level interventions. Numerous configurations are possible to strategically advance both OBM practice and research.

Forming one or more research groups offers several advantages to the organization. Perhaps the most important advantage of conducting applied research is that it permits practitioners to determine if their programs and change initiatives are producing desired change (LeBlanc et al., 2018). Research should inform organizational practices to improve outcomes, thereby increasing the value to the organization and the likelihood organizational leaders will commit the necessary financial and personnel resources to sustain these practices. Second, permitting interested employees to participate in a research group can teach valuable skills necessary for conducting high-quality applied research. Moreover, conducting research may also enhance clinical and management skills such as skills in visual analysis, baseline logic, data-based decision-making, and ruling out threats to internal validity. Another advantage is that embracing the scientific method through applied research activities fosters skepticism and critical thinking, which is particularly relevant in autism service delivery where pseudoscience is common (McDonald & DiGennaro Reed, 2018). Fourth, presumably the research group's activities are informed by discussions taking place at journal club gatherings, which could permit formal evaluation of change initiatives. Another advantage is that researchers can disseminate their findings at local, regional, and national conferences and in peer-reviewed journals. These dissemination activities contribute to the scientific literature and have the added benefit of enhancing the reputation of the organization and the researchers (Luiselli, 2017). Finally, establishing a line or multiples lines of research could lead to the pursuit of foundation grants or other extramural funding, which helps mitigate the costs of the initiatives or services provided.

Organizational leaders should be aware of several challenges to establishing research groups. First, research groups require coordination and effort. The necessary expertise, time, and project management skills required to effectively and ethically establish a research group are considerable. Thus, the organization must be prepared to invest personnel, financial, and other resources to accomplish this goal. Another challenge is the ambiguity surrounding what activities constitute research. Organizations must also ensure they have a research review committee with established procedures that protect research participants and agency employees. LeBlanc et al. (2018) provide a helpful summary of the important distinctions regarding the activities that constitute research as well as guidance for establishing a research review committee. Researchers and organizational leaders must resolve both challenges before launching applied research.

If organizations plan to invest in coordinating and maintaining a research group, the activities of the group should be an inherent part of the organizational mission or vision. Additionally, organizational leaders should establish research as an expectation in the job duties of relevant employees and evaluate the behavior of those employees accordingly. It is important that employees do not relegate research to tasks they will accomplish only if they have time. If organizational leaders do not address this issue in the early planning stages, it is likely research will simply be an isolated event and not a coordinated endeavor. Several resources provide recommendations for coordinating a research group (e.g., Anderson, 2015; Gil, 2014). In general, guidelines include (a) fostering a positive, trusting, and supportive culture; (b) establishing clear goals; (c) clarifying the roles of team members; (d) meeting regularly with a planned agenda; (e) rewarding success and acknowledging contributions, and (f) engaging good mentors. Unfortunately, there is limited research evaluating the effects of research groups on research productivity or other outcome measures. Love et al. (2013) evaluated the effects of a modified behavioral skills training package on practitioner knowledge and performance (e.g., measuring behavior, assessing reliability, developing data sheets). The researchers found statistically significant improvements on tests of knowledge, high performance on homework assignments, high social validity, and increases in research involvement at a one-year follow-up. These findings offer preliminary support for the potential benefits of training employees on research-related activities.

Writing Group

Another way to strengthen the skills of the IDD workforce and advance OBM practice and research is to organize a writing group within the organization. A writing group involves a group of people who meet to pursue the goal of writing for publication. Although there may be opportunities to write in the absence of disseminating research, these opportunities are likely rare. Thus, the activities of the writing group will probably stem from the contributions and outputs of the research group.

Organizing a writing group has several advantages. First, many people find writing to be a challenging task, particularly if they are new to the activity and unfamiliar with scientific prose. A writing group can serve as a mechanism to teach the behavior of writing and educate interested members on the publication process. Second, the writing group can establish goals for writing and hold members accountable for reaching these goals. In our laboratory, for example, we post writing graphs each week at the start of lab meeting. Although they vary in the behavior being measured, the graphs align with each member's goals and writing commitments. These graphs, and the conversations they evoke (e.g., praise for meeting goals, brainstorming reasons for and solutions to low productivity), ensure members are held accountable to the goals they set. Collectively, goal setting and accountability help foster productivity.

Although there are several advantages, writing groups also face challenges. Like the previously described workforce strengthening opportunities, establishing and maintaining a writing group requires resources. Thus, before embarking on this activity, interested employees should ensure they have organizational support to invest personnel resources and time to writing. A second challenge involves ensuring the group adopts research-supported practices related to goal setting and shaping writing behavior. Failure to do so may result in inadvertently setting stretch goals that are difficult to achieve, periods of extinction early in the writing process, and possible punishment for writing. Unfortunately, existing research focuses on student and faculty productivity (e.g., Kozar & Lum, 2013; Lassig et al., 2009); presently, we do not know if those procedures generalize to the writing behavior of practitioners or administrators working in applied settings. Finally, some writers have argued that writing groups are a wasted effort in part because it is difficult to give peers honest feedback about their writing, particularly if one has not mastered the art of writing (Nash, 2015).

Luiselli (2010; 2017) provides excellent resources for effective writing we have found useful for our own work. For example, Luiselli (2010) offers guidance for enhancing the performance of human services professionals interested in writing for publication. After identifying common obstacles, Luiselli presents a plan to build initial writing repertoires, including (a) scheduling writing time; (b) establishing writing objectives; and (c) developing writing tactics. He then shares helpful information about manuscript submission and responding to editorial reviews. Luiselli (2017) builds upon this guidance; both papers should be the starting point for any writing group as they are relevant and appropriate. Rockquemore (2010) describes different types of writing groups, which organizations might consider given the recent shift to remote work due to the COVID-19 pandemic and the varied and unique needs of employees who may be interested in participating in a writing group. Finally, UNC Chapel Hill has an excellent writing group starter kit that organizations could adapt to help launch a writing group (see https://writingcenter.unc.edu/tips-and-tools/writing-groups/writing-group-starter-kit/).

Peer Review

Peer review is another method to advance OBM research and practice. Within this chapter, we refer to peer review as "routine evaluation of practice standards that will produce the highest quality of habilitative care" (Luiselli & Russo, 2005, p. 470). In other words, peer review refers to the analysis of an organization's activities to ensure its alignment with recommended or best practices (Luiselli, 2013). The organization's activities included in peer review could range from individual client treatment programming to staff management practices depending on the size and needs of the organization.

Internal Peer Review

Peer review can involve individuals within or outside of the organization. Internal peer review involves individuals who work within the organization conducting ongoing review. Given the nature of the items generally analyzed in peer review, internal members should have expert knowledge in at least one of the following: (a) up-to-date best practices documented in the research literature; (b) federal and state disability law; (c) billing and finance; and (d) OBM. Specialists in related fields (e.g., psychologists, speech and language pathologists) should also be part of planning if the organization provides services in these fields.

Conducting internal peer review has several advantages. First, the review process can occur routinely and often (Luiselli & Russo, 2005). Rather than recruiting and scheduling individuals or companies outside of the organization to conduct a review, internal reviewers can dedicate routine meetings specifically for peer review. Another potential advantage is that because the internal reviewers work for the organization, there may be establishing operations in place to identify areas for improvement and implement recommended changes. For example, an internal reviewer who had recently attended a workshop on effective supervision of entry-level staff may be interested in reviewing existing supervisory practices and implementing recommended changes. The nature of the internal reviewers' jobs within the organization can also ensure frequent contact between the reviewers and staff members who are implementing the recommendations. A final benefit of internal peer review is there is no additional direct monetary cost to the organization compared to external review. However, there must be an additional time commitment assigned to the internal reviewers for the peer review process, which can be viewed as a related organizational cost.

Internal peer review also has disadvantages. First, the existing professional relationships between reviewers and staff may impede rather than promote recommended practices. That is, staff members could be resistant to implementing the internal reviewers' recommendations due to features of their existing professional relationship; for example, if the organization has a history of implementing but not sustaining previous recommendations or has not solicited feedback from staff members. To address this issue, we advise internal reviewers to follow the guidelines described within the Supervision and Mentoring chapter of this book to mitigate potential issues with adoption of new practices and communication. Another potential disadvantage is that reviewers may find it challenging to be objective with the peer review process (Luiselli & Russo, 2005). Although internal peer review may facilitate understanding the contingencies and history of the organization, it can also potentially lead to bias when reviewing. For example, reviewers may be tempted to maintain practices they implemented previously despite data demonstrating their ineffectiveness. Including individuals from different areas of the organization to review products within peer review may mitigate this issue. Finally, the potential for conflict between peer review duties and other job duties can be a disadvantage. If an internal reviewer's job responsibilities do not include peer review duties—including meeting with other reviewers, implementing procedures, and following up with staff—these duties may be overshadowed by competing non-reviewer priorities within the organization. If peer review duties are deferred, the review process can become more reactive than proactive, leading to organizational practices that are changed to avoid penalty rather than to promote best practices. We recommend regular, routine meetings, or sections of meetings dedicated to peer review only.

External Peer Review

External peer review involves a review conducted by one or more reviewers not affiliated with the organization who have expertise in the field or specific areas under review (Luiselli & Russo, 2005). External peer review typically involves an on-site visit consisting of reviewers examining work products, viewing processes, and meeting with key stakeholders, followed by submitting their findings and suggestions in a report for the organization. External reviewers are usually available for follow-up questions about the suggestions provided. Like internal peer review, there are no distinct rules regarding the frequency of external peer review. In our experience, some organizations arrange for it annually, some biannually, and some only when they introduce a new practice.

External peer review has several advantages compared to internal peer review. Because the reviewer does not work for the organization, the process can limit bias toward existing practices or procedures. Additionally, recruiting an external reviewer can bring unique expertise in an area that the organization would like to develop, especially if the organization's administration has limited experience in that area. External reviewers can also be helpful if an organization consistently meets goals within the internal peer review process but would like more nuanced, qualitative information in a specific area. The reviewer could examine various data summaries and observe the practices of interest and note staff behaviors to maintain and change.

Disadvantages of external peer review mainly lie in its arrangement. It can be difficult to find professionals who are both experts in the area of interest and available to provide a review. Scheduling external reviews may also be difficult for key members of the organization. An external review usually involves full days of reviewing data, observing practices, and interviewing key stakeholders, compared to regular, shorter periods of time dedicated to these activities within internal peer review. Ensuring that key members of the organization have time to meet with an external reviewer is also necessary. Finally, there are monetary costs for the external reviewer. Minimally, the organization assumes responsibility for the external reviewer's travel and boarding, and compensation for the reviewer's time is common practice.

Organizations may instead reciprocate by providing external peer review to the reviewer's organization on a topic in which they are experts rather than monetary compensation. For example, one organization may recruit external peer review from an expert in the assessment and treatment of problem behavior and provide external peer review on behavior acquisition programming for the reviewer's organization in return. The organization may also employ internal peer review for most of their practices and recruit external review for specialized areas as needed.

Commission on Accreditation of Rehabilitation Facilities

The Commission on Accreditation of Rehabilitation Facilities (CARF), founded in 1966, is a nonprofit accreditation body that specializes in standards for quality services across a range of international health and human services providers, including behavioral health. Its stated mission is "to promote the quality, value, and optimal outcomes of services through a consultative accreditation process and continuous improvement services that center on enhancing the lives of persons served" (CARF, n.d.). Because a third party provides an accreditation report of findings, the CARF accreditation process can serve as a type of external peer review and shape organizational practices. The accreditation process includes a provider's self-examination of its program(s), a site visit by CARF-approved practitioners, a written report of strengths and areas of improvement prepared by CARF, possible accreditation, and a quality improvement plan developed by the provider, if necessary. In addition to ensuring services are in accordance with service delivery standards as determined by content experts, benefits of CARF accreditation include differentiation from other providers, compliance with funder requirements, and generation of press.

Measures

Peer review minimally includes four measures requiring data-based assessment of (a) outcome measures of consumers, (b) process-variables, (c) social validity, and (d) sentinel events (Luiselli & Russo, 2005). We describe each of these next with illustrative examples relevant to the IDD service setting. Assessment of outcome measures of consumers entails a review of data on consumers' progress. For smaller organizations, this review can include assessment scores and changes from previous assessments, behavior acquisition outcomes (e.g., progress toward individualized program goals), or behavior reduction outcomes (e.g., percent change of problem behavior from the last month). Larger organizations can scale up these measures to aggregate data of consumer outcomes. For example, a larger organization may wish to calculate the number of consumers who have shifted to less restrictive settings or the number of consumers who have met a target of 80% problem behavior reduction within their behavior plans. Peer review also includes assessment of process variables (i.e., practices implemented in the organization). These process variable measurements can range from the number of times a specific procedure is used with clients to how often staff members meet for team meetings or article discussions. Social validity measures are a third area of measurement included in peer review. This area of measurement is where other stakeholders are particularly important, including staff members and family opinions in satisfaction surveys. For larger organizations, including organization-wide and site- or program-specific data is helpful to note possible trends within and across programs. Finally, peer review includes sentinel events, or unanticipated events resulting in injury. Examples of sentinel events include the number of times consumers or staff members experienced an injury or the number of times an emergency procedure was used. Sentinel event measures may be emphasized in organizations that include assessment and treatment of severe problem behavior. Nevertheless, the health and safety of consumers and staff members are important measures to review, improve, and maintain in all IDD settings.

Markers of a Successful Peer Review Process

Ensuring best practices are upheld requires an iterative peer review process, as the field continually disseminates the best available evidence for recommended practices in IDD service settings. In addition, as the mission and goals of an organization evolve, so too must the peer review process. Luiselli and Russo (2005) describe four markers of a successful peer review process. First, a successful peer review process includes purposeful direction and resource allocation. This direction includes short- and long-term plans for each area of focus (e.g., sentinel event reduction as the short-term focus and consumer outcome measure improvement as the long-term goal). Next, a successful peer review process assigns time and specific tasks to the reviewers to contribute to the peer review. Although it may appear that the duties of an individual would automatically include tasks to contribute to peer review by virtue of their position within an organization, tasks such as preparing data presentation for review and conducting additional analyses require time and resources. Third, a successful peer review process involves regular meetings with review of products. This activity is more frequent for internal peer review than external peer review. Of importance is that time is allocated to proactively and regularly present and discuss peer review data rather than reactively calling an impromptu meeting when an isolated incident occurs and focusing only on one subset of the review. A successful peer review process also involves frequent contact between the reviewers and staff members. The foci of peer review should not be a secret to the staff members. Rather, organizations should strive to ensure transparent communication between the reviewers and direct support staff. Not only does this transparent communication help develop rapport between groups, but it is also a way to receive valuable staff feedback.

A final marker of a successful peer review is multi-measure evaluation (Luiselli & Russo, 2005). What is measured—in addition to the four areas described earlier—can be based on the mission of the organization, if new programs are put in place (e.g., a residential program has been added to day habilitation services), and the population served, among others. Quantitative and qualitative measures each have their place in peer review. For example, quantitative measures on staff member satisfaction within a Likert-type scale can be helpful to understand with which areas staff are most and least satisfied. Allowing for qualitative measures, such as staff members listing suggestions to make their experience in the workplace more enjoyable, can be equally if not more informative in assessing current climate, practices to continue, and changes that can be implemented within an organization.

Performance Scorecards

Another way to advance OBM practice and research is with performance scorecards (also referred to as a performance matrix; hereafter referred to as a scorecard). This portion of the chapter will outline what scorecards are and how organizations may use them as a form of continuous quality improvement or a source of feedback.

A performance scorecard is an organizational tool to measure staff performance (Abernathy, 1996; Daniels & Bailey, 2014). Scorecards are one way for organizations to link staff performance to objective benchmarks or standards within and across areas. Scorecards allow organizations to summarize behavioral data to determine the degree to which staff performance aligns with desired outcomes. Often organizations adopt scorecards to provide staff with feedback on their performance in comparison to their previous performance or a set standard (Abernathy, 2014).

There are numerous ways to design scorecards (see Abernathy, 1996; 2014; Daniels & Bailey, 2014). Figure 15.1 displays several popular components often included in scorecards. Within most scorecards a variety of behavioral measures (i.e., performance measures; Abernathy, 1996) are included, as depicted in the far-left column of the figure. We provide an example involving billable hours, given that this measure is often critical for fiscal viability of an organization. Organizations should operationally define each performance measure to meet the criteria for a comprehensive behavioral definition (i.e., objective, clear, complete, and accurate; Cooper et al., 2019). In our example, we define billable hours as the number of hours submitted to an insurance agency for reimbursement each month. According to Abernathy, each performance measure should also be linked to a scale and assigned a weight. Scales establish the minimally acceptable performance level and the targeted goal. Traditionally, scales are created along a continuum and based on baseline levels of performance which potentially permits employees to create goals for improvement (Abernathy, 1996). Other variations include Likert-type scales (e.g., scales with a rating of 1–5, where 1 may represent poor performance and 5 may represent excellent performance) and behaviorally anchored rating scales (Daniels & Bailey, 2014). Measurement weighting prioritizes which performance measures are of higher organizational significance. Weights should sum to 100% across all performance measures. The extent to which staff have control over the performance measure is also an important variable to consider when assigning measurement weights. Finally, to obtain the overall score, the value earned on the scale is multiplied by the weight for each performance measure (as depicted in the far-right column of the figure).

Scorecards should be developed to fit the needs of the organization (Tagg, 2020). Figure 15.2 depicts one variation of a scorecard we have used to measure

Behavioral Measure	Operational Definition	Scale	Weight	Score
Billable hours	*Number of hours submitted to an insurance agency for reimbursement each month*	*1 (poor performance) – 5 (excellent performance*	*25%*	*(Scale value x weight)*

FIGURE 15.1 An example of the components commonly included within scorecards

Measure category	Measure title	Methodology	Frequency	Threshold	Department	Staff responsible
Finance	Billable hours	Enter the total # of hours billed for that behavior analyst	Monthly	Green – 80 or more Yellow – 65-80 Red – 64 or less	Finance	(name)

FIGURE 15.2 A variation of a scorecard

performance. The scorecard includes information regarding the performance measure (i.e., measure category, measure title, methodology), measurement frequency, the criteria to determine whether the measure has been met (i.e., threshold), and who is responsible for summarizing the measurement information (i.e., department and staff responsible). This scorecard differs from the scorecard displayed in Figure 15.1 in that we omitted the scale and weight. Instead, we have adopted a stoplight color coding approach where green, yellow, and red indicate performance at or above criterion, close to criterion, or below criterion, respectively. The color coding provides staff with the opportunity to quickly analyze overall performance (i.e., assess quality at-a-glance), as well as performance within and across measurement domains.

Use of scorecards in a sustainable manner requires that organizations provide employees with the appropriate training, supports, and resources to meet objectives established in the scorecards. Moreover, scorecards should cascade up into organizational dashboards informing organizational leaders where to focus resources to improve outcomes. Too often leaders assume performance is only related to **employee** performance and mistakenly neglect addressing an organization's **environment** to support employee behavior for high-quality outcomes (Malott, 2003).

Organizations may use scorecards as a measure of quality assurance and link results to pay. For example, Szabo et al. (2012) incorporated scorecards into a service review procedure to enhance direct support staff and consumer behavior on pinpointed measures within a community-based disability organization. Results indicated that, at the team level, the addition of the scorecards improved performance of both staff and supervisors to better meet desired clinical performance objectives. Further, Griffin et al. (2019) assessed the effects of scorecards on improving clinicians' behavior within behavior-analytic clinics and the added effects of linking the scorecard to a lottery. Results indicated moderate performance improvements with the implementation of scorecards and further improvements with the addition of the lottery system. Based on our review of the human services literature, there are no empirical recommendations regarding the number of items or domains that should be included within a scorecard or the benefits of linking them to pay.

Scorecards for Quality Improvement

Organizations may use scorecards to facilitate high-quality service delivery. Thus, as a performance management tool, organizational leaders must thoughtfully decide which performance measures would be most appropriate to include within scorecards. One issue to consider is whether the performance measures are leading or lagging measures. Leading measures quantify *current* (i.e., in close temporal proximity) behaviors or activities (DiGennaro Reed et al., 2018; Rodriguez et al., 2016). These measures differ from lagging measures, which quantify *past* behaviors or activities. Performance measures on a scorecard should be leading measures, as much as possible, to aid in performance improvements.

It may be beneficial for organizations to incorporate accreditation standards or performance indicators as a component that helps to certify quality assurance (smartsheet.com, n.d.). The national core indicators® (NCI®) are a collection of performance and outcome measures used to evaluate service quality across a variety of domains (NCI®, n.d.) and may be of interest to human service organizations. Founded in 1997 with seven US states as part of the collaboration, NCI® has since expanded to now include service providers across 46 states, each of which provides data on the performance for programs providing services to individuals with IDD. The purpose of this collaboration in general, and the performance indicators in particular, is threefold: to (a) provide a mechanism for tracking performance over time; (b) create a national database that allows for data comparisons across states; and (c) create national standards that can be used as benchmarks—at both the national and state levels—and to inform policy.

The primary modality through which these national core indicators are currently measured is through surveys (i.e., self-report) conducted in person with various stakeholders that are impacted by service provision. Family surveys (e.g., adult family survey, family/guardian survey, child family survey) are conducted using questionnaires sent via mail, and staff stability surveys are conducted using questionnaires sent via email (NCI®, n.d.). With regard to the types of data collected and analyzed, outcome measures have been collapsed into several indicator categories that can broadly be classified as individual (e.g., health, welfare, and rights; community inclusion; self-determination) or organizational (e.g., staff stability, systems-level performance) indicators. Additionally, each of these indicator domains can be broken down into more specific measures that evaluate a particular topic or area (for more information, see nationalcoreind icators.org). Given their reliance on self-report, these data must be interpreted with some degree of caution. Thus, organizations may benefit from also incorporating other evaluative services (i.e., CARF) to further enhance the robustness of performance measures on quality assurance.

Scorecards as Feedback

Scorecards may be used to provide feedback to individual staff and organizational leaders. During the initial scorecard design process, organizational leaders may seek stakeholder input to ensure they have captured relevant aspects of the job and outlined achievable measures (Tagg, 2020). Once the scorecard is developed, leaders may schedule a recurring meeting to present performance data with relevant staff and discuss barriers to achieving desired performance levels. During this time, chronically low-performing measures may flag an area requiring improvement, which may trigger an assessment and subsequent function-based (i.e., indicated) intervention. Organizations may then use the scorecards to evaluate the effectiveness of interventions to improve performance within the flagged areas. Scorecards should not be static (smartsheet.com; Tagg, 2020); therefore, performance measures can change as frequently as necessary and should be part of an iterative process to meet the needs of the organization.

Strategic Planning

A final way to advance OBM practice and research is through a strategic planning process. Strategic planning refers to "a deliberative, disciplined effort to produce fundamental decisions and actions that shape and guide what an organization (or other entity) is, what it does, and why" (Bryson et al., 2018, p. 317). It entails deliberate and purposeful analysis of common goals along with identifying the decision points and actions to achieve those results. Although effortful, this approach is advantageous because of its technicality and specificity. Strategic planning can also be conceptualized as a process that guides an organization toward its mission by defining objectives (McHatton et al., 2011). The process involves assessment, goal setting, analysis, and action planning conducted at regular intervals (Pasha et al., 2018).

Strategic planning has been used successfully in a variety of settings, including nonprofit (McHatton et al., 2011), governmental (Poister, 2010), transit (Pasha et al., 2018), and professional (O'Neil & Willis, 2005) organizations. Benefits to strategic planning include an organization's ability to create and achieve defined goals, plan for its mission and vision, satisfy stakeholders (McHatton et al., 2011), and ensure flexibility within a changing environment. A meta-analysis by George et al. (2019) revealed a positive and significant relation between the strategic planning process and organizational performance.

Preparation

Figure 15.3 illustrates recommended practices for strategic planning. First, an organization must prepare for this process. We recommend organization leaders make *a priori* determinations regarding meeting attendees, the person who facilitates the planning process, and the meeting location and duration. To determine who should attend the meeting, George et al. (2019) suggest incorporating

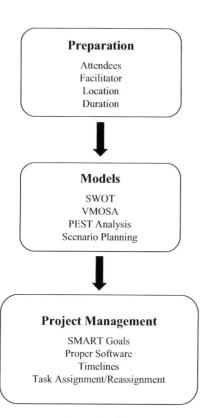

FIGURE 15.3 Strategic planning process

cross-organizational stakeholders who can make competent decisions regarding systems and practices. We caution against involving only one department if attendees will make decisions that impact the entire organization.[1] Stakeholders representing different departments (e.g., clinical services, staff training, finance) should attend to permit well-rounded insight and ensure any subsequent plan aligns with the organization's mission and vision.

Other necessary preparations include the meeting's facilitator, location, and duration. Organizations may ask an existing employee to lead the meeting or hire an external facilitator. There are advantages and disadvantages to both options. An internal facilitator could provide insight into the organization's systems but may not have experience with creating a strategic plan and may infuse their preferences or biases into an otherwise objective planning process. An external facilitator provides insight into the planning process but can be costly. With respect to location, organizations may schedule the meeting at the organization's office building or arrange it at an off-site location. Influences on this decision are likely cost, the group's size, and whether participants will be distracted by competing responsibilities if they remain on site. In our experience, the strategic planning process typically takes hours, so we recommend planning for at least a half-day meeting.

Strategic Planning Models

One of the most important considerations for the strategic planning process is determining which model the organization will adopt. Several unique models exist that accomplish different objectives. We list four models in Figure 15.3, including SWOT (strengths, weaknesses, opportunities, and threats) analysis (Renault, n.d.), VMOSA (vision, mission, objectives, strategies, and action plans) analysis (Nagy & Fawcett, n.d.), PEST (political, economic, sociocultural, technological) analysis (Barbra et al., 2017; Sammut-Bonnici & Galea, 2015), and scenario planning (Azalia & Steil, 2017; Steil & Gibbons-Carr, 2005). Space constraints prevent us from elaborating on each of these models. We encourage organizations to carefully review each model's aims and select one that best aligns with the outcomes they hope to achieve at the conclusion of the strategic planning process.

Project Management

After the strategic planning meeting, the project management phase begins. Project management involves "the application of processes, methods, skills, knowledge and experience to achieve specific project objectives" (Association for Project Management, n.d.). It ensures the organization's activities remain aligned with the goals developed through the strategic planning process by developing action plans, using SMART (specific, measurable, achievable, relevant, and time-bound) goals, and adopting an effective task management system. Action plans delegate task responsibilities and due dates or timelines to individuals. One person should be responsible for task delegation. SMART goals help clarify expectations, reducing the probability of confusion or miscommunication. An effective task management system helps all stakeholders track their action plans, goals, and deadlines, which may help inform daily decision-making. As an added benefit, accurate and up-to-date timelines tell leaders if goals need correction or clarification or if goals are complete and should be celebrated.

Accountability is an essential piece to accomplishing organizational goals, which a task management system can foster. Accountability occurs when staff report ongoing progress toward strategic planning goals, sufficient software is adopted to track progress, and goals remain flexible. One way to ensure staff remain informed about progress is to provide frequent updates on both individual and organizational progress. A reporting system needs to be tailored to the organization. This system can take several forms and reporting frequency can vary. For example, a progress update or accomplishment can be a written message (e.g., e-updates) or be communicated verbally (e.g., team meetings or generating committees) to the individual(s) responsible for keeping track of updates. Regardless of the communication platform, all updates should be documented for later reference or to communicate to those who may have been absent from the discussion. Software commonly used for project management include Trello, Smartsheet, or Excel spreadsheets, which may help foster organizational results and reporting accuracy. Even when reports are up to date, plans and goals will likely require reassessment and adjustment due to a fluctuating environment. We recommend reinitiating the strategic planning and project management process at regular intervals (e.g., every three to five years) to foster continuous quality improvement.

Summary

This chapter provided recommendations for advancing OBM practice and research within IDD service settings by sharing practical strategies for strengthening the IDD workforce and describing peer review, the use of performance scorecards, and strategic planning within a behavioral systems approach. Behavior-analytic research in these areas is limited or nonexistent; thus, we encourage readers to evaluate the effects of these strategies on organizational performance. Unfortunately, we were unable to cover the many ways OBM practice and research could be advanced within human service settings. We hope these recommendations serve as a helpful starting point for organizations to tackle the important yet challenging task of advancing OBM practice and research within their own walls.

Note

1 Individual departments may conduct strategic planning for their unit, which has benefits. We describe an organizational-level strategic planning process in this chapter.

References

Abernathy, W. B. (1996). *The sin of wages: Where the conventional pay system has led us, and how to find a way out.* Atlanta, GA: Performance Management Publications.

Abernathy, W. B. (2014). Beyond the skinner box: The design and management of organization-wide performance systems. *Journal of Organizational Behavior Management, 34*(4), 235–254. doi:10.1080/01608061.2014.973631

Anderson, S. D. (2015). Advice for running a successful research team. *Nurse Researcher, 23*(2), 36–40. doi:10.7748/nr.23.2.36.s8

Association for Project Management (n.d.). *What is project management.* Retrieved from https://www.apm.org.uk/resources/what-is-project-management/

Azalia, J. C. L., & Stein, W. C. (2017). Strategic planning and scenario planning in public institutions: The case study of pacific alliance. *FIIB Business Review, 6*(3), 26–37. Retrieved from http://www2.lib.ku.edu/login?url=https://searchhttp://-pr oquest-com.www2.lib.ku.edu/docview/1968399809?accountid=14556

Barbra, C., Cortis, D., Perotte, R., Sammut, C., & Vella, A. (2017). The European insurance industry: A PEST analysis. *International Journal of Financial Studies, 5*(2), 14. doi:10.3390/ijfs5020014

Bauer, L. (2015, March 30). 5 tips for journal club first-timers. *I Am Intramural Blog.* Retrieved from https://irp.nih.gov/blog/post/2015/03/5-tips-for-journal-club-first-timers

Bryson, J. M., Hamilton Edwards, L., & Van Slyke, D. M. (2018). Getting strategic about strategic planning research. *Public Management Review, 20*(3), 317–339. doi:1 0.1080/14719037.2017.1285111

Carr, J. E., & Briggs, A. M. (2010). Strategies for making regular contact with the scholarly literature. *Behavior Analysis in Practice, 3*(2), 12–18. doi:10.1007/BF03391760

Commission on Accreditation of Rehabilitation Facilities (n.d.) Retrieved from http://www.carf.org/About/Mission/

Cooper, J. O., Heron, T. W., & Heward, W. L. (2019). *Applied Behavior Analysis* (3rd ed.). Upper Saddle River, NJ: Pearson.

Daniels, A. C., & Bailey, J. S. (2014). *Performance management: Changing behavior that drives organizational effectiveness.* Atlanta, GA: Aubrey Daniels International, Inc.

DiGennaro Reed, F. D., Novak, M. D., Erath, T. G., Brand, D., & Henley, A. J. (2018). Pinpointing and measuring employee behavior. In B. Wine & J. Pritchard (Eds.), *Organizational behavior management: The essentials* (pp. 143–168). Orlando, FL: Hedgehog.

George, B., Monster, J., & Walker, R. M. (2019). Does strategic planning improve organizational performance? A meta-analysis. *Public Administration Review, 79*(6), 810–819. doi:10.1111/puar.13104

Gil, Y. (2014). Ten simple rules for starting a research group. *AI Matters, 1*(2), 4–10. doi:10.1145/2685328.2685330

Griffin, M., Gravina, N. E., Matey, N., Pritchard, J., & Wine, B. (2019). Using scorecards and a lottery to improve performance of behavior technicians in two autism treatment clinics. *Journal of Organizational Behavior Management, 39*(3–4), 280–292. doi:10.1080/01608061.2019.1632241

Kozar, O., & Lum, J. F. (2013). Factors likely to impact of the effectiveness of research writing groups for off-campus doctoral students. *Journal of Academic Language & Learning, 7*(2), A-132–A-149.

Lassig, C. J., Lincoln, M. E., Dillon, L. H., Diezmann, C. M., Fox, J., & Neofa, Z. (2009). Writing together, learning together: The value and effectiveness of a research writing group for doctoral students. Paper presented at the Meeting of the Australian Association for Research in Education. http://www.aare.edu.au/data/publications/2009/las091458.pdf

LeBlanc, L. A., Nosik, M. R., & Petursdottir, A. (2018). Establishing consumer protections for research in human service agencies. *Behavior Analysis in Practice, 11*, 445–455. doi:10.1007/s40617-018-0206-3

Love, J. R., Carr, J. E., LeBlanc, L. A., & Kisamore, A. N. (2013). Training behavioral research methods to staff in an early and intensive behavioral intervention setting: A program description and preliminary evaluation. *Education and Treatment of Children, 3*(1), 139–160. doi:10.1353/etc.2013.0003

Luiselli, J. K. (2010). Writing for publication: A performance enhancement guide for the human services professional. *Behavior Modification, 34*(5), 459–473. doi:10.1177/0145445510383529

Luiselli, J. K. (2013). Peer review. In D. D. Reed, F. D. DiGennaro Reed, & J. K. Luiselli (Eds.), *Handbook of crisis intervention and developmental disabilities* (pp. 27–28). New York, NY: Springer. doi:10.1007/978-1-4614-6531-7_3

Luiselli, J. K. (2017). Practice dissemination: Writing for publication. In J. K. Luiselli (Ed.), *Applied behavior analysis advanced guidebook: A manual for professional practice* (pp. 325–347). Cambridge, MA: Elsevier. doi:10.1016/B978-0-12-811122-2.00014-0

Luiselli, J. K., & Russo, D. C. (2005). Clinical peer review: Description of a comprehensive model in behavioral healthcare. *Behavior Modification, 29*(3), 470–487. doi:10.1177/0145445504273279

Malott, M. E. (2003). *Paradox of organizational change: Engineering organizations with behavioral systems analysis.* Reno, NV: Context Press.

McDonald, M. E., & DiGennaro Reed, F. D. (2018). Autism spectrum disorders: Distinguishing science and pseudoscience. In J. Naglieri, S. Ozonoff, & S. Goldstein, (Eds.) *Assessment of autism spectrum disorders* (415–441). New York: Guilford Press.

McHatton, P. A., Bradshaw, W., Gallagher, P. A., & Reeves, R. (2011). Results from a strategic planning process: Benefits for a nonprofit organization. *Nonprofit Management & Leadership, 22*(2), 233–249. doi:10.1002/nml.20051

Nagy, J., & Fawcett, S. B. (n.d.). Section 1. An overview of strategic planning or "VMOSA" (vision, mission, objectives, strategies, and action plans). *Community Tool Box.* Retrieved from https://ctb.ku.edu/en/table-of-contents/structure/strategic-planning/vmosa/main

Nash, J. (2015, June 25). The 4 hidden dangers of writing groups. *Jane Friedman.* Retrieved from https://www.janefriedman.com/dangers-of-writing-groups/

National Core Indicators. (n.d.). Retrieved from https://www.nationalcoreindicators.org/

Normand, M. P. (2008). Science, skepticism, and applied behavior analysis. *Behavior Analysis in Practice, 1*(2), 42–49. doi:10.1007/BF03391727

Novak, M. D., DiGennaro Reed, F. D., Erath, T. G., Blackman, A. L., Ruby, S. A., & Pellegrino, A. J. (2019). Evidence-based performance management. Applying behavioral science to support practitioners. *Perspectives on Behavior Science, 4,* 955–972. doi:10.1007/s40614-019-00232-z

O'Neil, S. L., & Willis, C. L. (2005). Challenges for professional organization: Lessons from the past. *Delta Pi Epsilon Journal, 47*(3), 143–153.

Parsons, M. B., & Reid, D. H. (2011). Reading groups: A practical means of enhancing professional knowledge among human service practitioners. *Behavior Analysis in Practice, 4*(2), 53–60. doi:10.1007/BF03391784

Pasha, O. Q., Poister, T. H., & Edwards, L. H. (2018). Mutual relationship of strategic stances and formulation methods, and their impacts on performance in public local transit agencies. *Administration & Society, 50*(6), 884–910. doi:10.1177/0095399715587524

Poister, T. H. (2010). The future of strategic planning in the public sector: Linking strategic management and performance. *Public Administration Review, 70*(1), 246–254. doi:10.1111/j.1540-6210.2010.02284.x

Renault, V. (n.d.). Section 14. SWOT analysis: Strengths, weaknesses, opportunities, and threats. *Community Tool Box.* Retrieved from https://ctb.ku.edu/en/table-of-contents/assessment/assessing-community-needs-and-resources/swot-analysis/main

Rockquemore, K. A. (2010). Shut up and write. *Inside Higher Ed.* Retrieved from https://www.insidehighered.com/advice/2010/06/14/shut-and-write

Rodriguez, M., Sundberg, D., & Biagi, S. (2016). *OBM applied: A practical guide to implementing organizational behavior management.* Melbourne, FL: ABA Technologies, Inc.

Rosenthal, J., & Rosenthal, K. S. (2017). Interactive journal club: Teaching an old dog new tricks. *Journal of Medical Education and Curricular Development, 4,* 1–6. doi:10.1177/2382120517719710

Sammut-Bonnici, T., & Galea, D. (2015). PEST analysis. In Sir C. L. Cooper (Ed.), *Wiley encyclopedia of management* (Volume 12). John Wiley and Sons, Ltd. https://doi.org/10.1002/9781118785317.weom120113

Sigurdsson, S. O., & Austin, J. (2006). Institutionalization and response maintenance in organizational behavior management. *Journal of Organizational Behavior Management, 26*(4), 41–77. https://doi.org/10.1300/J075v26n04_03

Smartsheet (n.d.). *The right balanced scorecard for you: Examples, samples, and templates.* Retrieved from https://www.smartsheet.com/balanced-scorecard-examples-and-templates

Steil, G., & Gibbons-Carr, M. (2005). Large group scenario planning: Scenario planning with the whole system in the room. *Journal of Applied Behavioral Science, 41*(1), 15–29. doi:10.1177/0021886304272888

Szabo, T. G., Williams, W. L., Rafacz, S. D., Newsome, W., & Lydon, C. A. (2012). Evaluation of the service review model with performance scorecards. *Journal of Organizational Behavior Management, 32*(4), 274–296. doi:10.1080/01608061.2012.729408

Szucs, K. A., Benson, J. D., & Haneman, B. (2017). Using a guided journal club as a teaching strategy to enhance learning skills for evidence-based practice. *Occupational Therapy in Health Care*, *31*(2), 143–149. doi:10.1080/07380577.2016.1 278296

Tagg, B. (2020, January 13). Scorecard do's and don'ts with Shannon Biagi of CMO (No. 52) [audio podcast]. *The Business of Behavior*. Retrieved from https://thebusinesso fbehavior.com/session-52-scorecard-dos-and-donts-with-shannon-biagi-of-cmo/

Index

Page numbers in **bold** denote tables, those in *italic* denote figures.